T. Th 4:10-4:40 room 303 A.

M. W. F. 1:30-1:40 303

prob. 231 all

232 1

232

p. 4 p. 36

p. 37 all

9:16

212 1

all prob.

251

296, 297 no. 4, 5, 6

Friday morning June 6, 8:30 A.M.

252   7

254-5   (a)   Parts that have answers
2, 3
5

6
7
11
12

258   all right
read P. 257

Read th. end

Prob.   83
2   4
1, 3,   #, 9, 11, 13

the rest of prob.
decide what type of surface they
represent

7, 8, 12,

3, 4   P.283

ANALYTIC GEOMETRY

ANALYTIC GEOMETRY

BY

CHARLES H. SISAM

PROFESSOR OF MATHEMATICS
COLORADO COLLEGE

NEW YORK
HENRY HOLT AND COMPANY

PREFACE

This textbook has been written with the actual needs and desires of the teachers of analytic geometry constantly in mind. It is primarily intended for a course of three semester hours but it includes ample, carefully selected material for a five hour course. The text has been arranged to facilitate a selection of material with a minimum of inconvenience. The essentials of the first six chapters constitute what is customarily considered to be the basic course in plane analytic geometry. To this should be added as much of the remaining subject matter as time permits. The starred articles may be omitted without interrupting the continuity of the text. As far as is practicable, these articles have been put near the ends of chapters.

The course in analytic geometry has several major objectives, each of which has been fully considered in the preparation of this text. It should follow in a natural way from the student's previous work in mathematics, which it is expected to unify; it must acquaint the student with the methods, the spirit, and the essential facts of analytic geometry; and it should stress the particular types of geometric reasoning that the student will encounter most frequently in his later work. It is for this last reason that a number of devices helpful in the drawing of graphs have been emphasized in chapters eight and ten and their usefulness has been illustrated by applying them to several higher plane curves that the student is likely to meet in subsequent courses.

The exercises are sufficiently numerous and have been graded so that a selection may be made to fit the needs of students of varying ability. In particular, it is hoped that the Selected Exercises at the ends of certain chapters will be found to be stimulating and challenging by distinctly superior students. Answers have been given to approximately one third of the exercises. These have been selected with the purpose of enabling the student to assure himself of the correctness of his methods and to encourage accuracy in his computations.

In preparing this text, the author has received helpful suggestions from so many sources that it is plainly impossible to acknowledge all of them. He is especially indebted, however, to Professor Ralph Beatley, of Harvard University; Professor E. R. Hedrick, of the University of California; Professors A. J. Kempner and C. A. Hutchinson, of the University of Colorado; Professor E. B. Lytle, of the University of Illinois; Professor Virgil Snyder, of Cornell University; and Miss Martha Belschner, of Colorado College, for valuable constructive criticisms of the text.

C. H. S.

CONTENTS

PLANE ANALYTIC GEOMETRY

CHAPTER I. COÖRDINATES AND GRAPHS

CHAPTER II. FUNDAMENTAL DEFINITIONS AND THEOREMS

POLAR COÖRDINATES

CHAPTER III. THE LINE

CHAPTER XI. TANGENTS, NORMALS, DIAMETERS, POLES, AND POLARS

CHAPTER XII. EMPIRICAL EQUATIONS

SOLID ANALYTIC GEOMETRY

CHAPTER XIII. FUNDAMENTAL DEFINITIONS AND THEOREMS

INTRODUCTION

In this introduction, we have gathered together, for reference, a number of definitions, theorems, and formulas from algebra, geometry, and trigonometry. A thorough knowledge of these facts will be most helpful to the student in the study of analytic geometry.

1. Quadratic Equations. The roots of the quadratic equation

$$ax^2 + bx + c = 0, \qquad (a \neq 0)$$

are

$$x_1 = \frac{-b + \sqrt{b^2 - 4ac}}{2a} \quad \text{and} \quad x_2 = \frac{-b - \sqrt{b^2 - 4ac}}{2a}.$$

If a, b, and c are real numbers, these roots are

real and unequal if $\qquad b^2 - 4ac > 0$,

real and equal if $\qquad b^2 - 4ac = 0$,

imaginary and unequal if $\qquad b^2 - 4ac < 0$.

2. Determinants. The symbol

$$\begin{vmatrix} a_1 & b_1 \\ a_2 & b_2 \end{vmatrix} \qquad (1)$$

is used to denote the quantity

$$a_1 b_2 - a_2 b_1.$$

The symbol (1) is called a **determinant of the second order** and the numbers a_1, a_2, b_1, b_2 are its **elements**.

Similarly, the name **determinant of the third order** is given to the expression

$$\begin{vmatrix} a_1 & b_1 & c_1 \\ a_2 & b_2 & c_2 \\ a_3 & b_3 & c_3 \end{vmatrix}$$

Its value may be found from the formula

$$a_1 \begin{vmatrix} b_2 & c_2 \\ b_3 & c_3 \end{vmatrix} - a_2 \begin{vmatrix} b_1 & c_1 \\ b_3 & c_3 \end{vmatrix} + a_3 \begin{vmatrix} b_1 & c_1 \\ b_2 & c_2 \end{vmatrix} =$$

$$a_1 b_2 c_3 + a_2 b_3 c_1 + a_3 b_1 c_2 - a_1 b_3 c_2 - a_2 b_1 c_3 - a_3 b_2 c_1.$$

Determinants of higher orders may be written, and their values found, in a similar way.

3. Linear Equations. The solution of two simultaneous equations of the first degree

$$a_1 x + b_1 y = c_1,$$
$$a_2 x + b_2 y = c_2,$$

may be written in the form

$$x = \frac{\begin{vmatrix} c_1 & b_1 \\ c_2 & b_2 \end{vmatrix}}{\begin{vmatrix} a_1 & b_1 \\ a_2 & b_2 \end{vmatrix}}, \qquad y = \frac{\begin{vmatrix} a_1 & c_1 \\ a_2 & c_2 \end{vmatrix}}{\begin{vmatrix} a_1 & b_1 \\ a_2 & b_2 \end{vmatrix}}, \qquad (2)$$

provided that the determinant occurring in the denominators is not equal to zero.

If the determinant appearing in the denominators is equal to zero, and if the numerators are not both zero, the given linear equations have no simultaneous solution.

If all three of the determinants appearing in (2) are equal to zero but a_1 and b_1 are not both zero, then every solution of the first of the given equations is a solution of the second also.

In particular, the simultaneous equations

$$a_1 x + b_1 y = 0,$$
$$a_2 x + b_2 y = 0,$$

have obviously the solution $x = 0$, $y = 0$. They will have solutions other than x and y both zero if, and only if,

$$\begin{vmatrix} a_1 & b_1 \\ a_2 & b_2 \end{vmatrix} = 0. \qquad (3)$$

Formulas similar to (2) and (3) may be obtained for three, four, or any larger number of variables.

4. Logarithms. If N, x, and a are three numbers (a positive and not equal to unity) that satisfy the equation

$$N = a^x,$$

then the exponent, x, is called the *logarithm of N to the base a* and we may write the above equation in the equivalent form

$$x = \log_a N.$$

The following properties of logarithms are important.

$$\log_a (MN) = \log_a M + \log_a N, \qquad \log_a \left(\frac{M}{N}\right) = \log_a M - \log_a N,$$

$$\log_a M^p = p \log_a M, \qquad\qquad \log_a M = \frac{\log_b M}{\log_b a},$$

$$\log_a \left(\frac{1}{M}\right) = - \log_a M, \qquad\qquad \log_a a = 1.$$

5. Loci. Graphs. In many problems of analytic geometry, it is necessary to locate all those points (and no others) that satisfy a given geometric condition. The assemblage of all such points is called the **locus** of a point that satisfies the given condition.

The student is already familiar with a considerable number of loci. For example, it is shown in plane geometry that

The locus of a point at a given distance a from a given point C is a circle with center at C and radius a.

The locus of a point equidistant from two given points A and B is the line perpendicular to the segment joining A and B and passing through its middle point.

The locus of a point equidistant from two given intersecting lines is the two lines that bisect the two pairs of vertical angles formed by the given lines.

If the given geometric condition is defined by an equation, the locus of a point that satisfies the given condition is called the *graph of the equation.*

6. Half-lines. Angles. The part of a straight line that extends indefinitely in one direction from a fixed point on it is called a **half-line** (or **ray**). The fixed point is called the **end point** of the half-line.

An angle *IO T* is thought of as generated by the rotation of a half-line about its end point *O* from the position *OI* to the

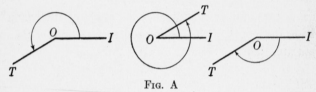

position *OT*. The point *O* is the **vertex**, the half-line *OI* is the **initial side**, and *OT* is the **terminal side** of the angle.

The rotation may include one or more complete revolutions, as is indicated in the second figure, and it may be in the clockwise or counter-clockwise direction. An angle is *positive* if the generating half-line rotates counter-clockwise and *negative* in the contrary case.

7. Radian Measure. In elementary mathematics, angles are usually measured in degrees, minutes, and seconds but in advanced mathematics it is customary to express them in **ra-**

dian (or **circular**) **measure.** In this system, the unit angle is the **radian** which is defined as an angle such that, if placed at the center of a circle, it will intercept an arc equal in length to the radius of the circle.

To determine the relation between degrees and radians, we notice that, in an angle of

half a revolution, there are 180°. There are also π radians since the length of the semi-circumference is π times the radius. Hence

$$\pi \text{ radians} = 180°$$

$$1 \text{ radian} = \left(\frac{180}{\pi}\right)° = 57° \ 17' \ 45'', \text{ approximately.}$$

$$1° = \left(\frac{\pi}{180}\right) \text{ radians} = 0.01745 \text{ radians, approximately.}$$

In practice, the word *radian* is usually omitted in stating the size of an angle in radian measure. Thus, an angle $\frac{\pi}{2}$ is a right angle, an angle $\frac{\pi}{3}$ is one of 60°, etc.

If θ is the number of radians in an angle at the center of a circle, a, the length of the radius, and s, the length of the intercepted arc, then

$$s = a\theta.$$

8. Trigonometric Functions. In order to define the trigonometric functions of a given angle θ ($= XOP$) we may place the angle so that its initial side (Art. 6) is horizontal and extends

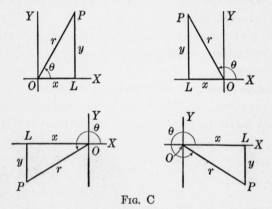

Fig. C

to the right from the vertex O. Choose any point P on the terminal side and drop a perpendicular PL from P to the initial side (or to the initial side produced).

Denote by r the length of the segment OP, which we shall always consider as positive. The length of the segment OL is denoted by x and is positive if L is to the right of O and negative if it is to the left. The length of LP, which is denoted by y, is positive if P lies above the initial line and negative if P is below.

We now define the trigonometric functions of the given angle θ as follows

$$\sin \theta = \frac{y}{r} \qquad\qquad \csc \theta = \frac{r}{y}$$

$$\cos \theta = \frac{x}{r} \qquad\qquad \sec \theta = \frac{r}{x}$$

$$\tan \theta = \frac{y}{x} \qquad\qquad \operatorname{ctn} \theta = \frac{x}{y}.$$

9. Trigonometric Identities. The above six functions are connected by the following relations

$$\csc \theta = \frac{1}{\sin \theta} \qquad\qquad \sin^2 \theta + \cos^2 \theta = 1$$

$$\sec \theta = \frac{1}{\cos \theta} \qquad\qquad \sec^2 \theta - \tan^2 \theta = 1$$

$$\operatorname{ctn} \theta = \frac{1}{\tan \theta} \qquad\qquad \csc^2 \theta - \operatorname{ctn}^2 \theta = 1$$

$$\tan \theta = \frac{\sin \theta}{\cos \theta} \qquad\qquad \operatorname{ctn} \theta = \frac{\cos \theta}{\sin \theta}.$$

10. Reduction Formulas.

$$\sin (90° - \theta) = \cos \theta \qquad \sin (90° + \theta) = \cos \theta$$
$$\cos (90° - \theta) = \sin \theta \qquad \cos (90° + \theta) = - \sin \theta$$
$$\tan (90° - \theta) = \operatorname{ctn} \theta \qquad \tan (90° + \theta) = - \operatorname{ctn} \theta$$
$$\sin (- \theta) = - \sin \theta \qquad \sin (180° - \theta) = \sin \theta$$
$$\cos (- \theta) = \cos \theta \qquad \cos (180° - \theta) = - \cos \theta$$
$$\tan (- \theta) = - \tan \theta \qquad \tan (180° - \theta) = - \tan \theta.$$

11. Formulas for the Sum and Difference of Two Angles.

$$\sin (\theta + \phi) = \sin \theta \cos \phi + \cos \theta \sin \phi$$
$$\sin (\theta - \phi) = \sin \theta \cos \phi - \cos \theta \sin \phi$$
$$\cos (\theta + \phi) = \cos \theta \cos \phi - \sin \theta \sin \phi$$
$$\cos (\theta - \phi) = \cos \theta \cos \phi + \sin \theta \sin \phi.$$

$$\tan (\theta + \phi) = \frac{\tan \theta + \tan \phi}{1 - \tan \theta \tan \phi}$$

$$\tan (\theta - \phi) = \frac{\tan \theta - \tan \phi}{1 + \tan \theta \tan \phi}.$$

12. Formulas for the Double and Half Angle.

$$\sin 2\theta = 2 \sin \theta \cos \theta$$
$$\cos 2\theta = \cos^2 \theta - \sin^2 \theta = 1 - 2 \sin^2 \theta = 2 \cos^2 \theta - 1$$
$$\tan 2\theta = \frac{2 \tan \theta}{1 - \tan^2 \theta}$$
$$\sin \frac{\theta}{2} = \pm \sqrt{\frac{1 - \cos \theta}{2}} \qquad \cos \frac{\theta}{2} = \pm \sqrt{\frac{1 + \cos \theta}{2}}$$
$$\tan \frac{\theta}{2} = \pm \sqrt{\frac{1 - \cos \theta}{1 + \cos \theta}} = \frac{1 - \cos \theta}{\sin \theta} = \frac{\sin \theta}{1 + \cos \theta}.$$

13. Triangle Formulas.

If we denote the lengths of the sides of a triangle by a, b, and c, and the magnitudes of the opposite angles by α, β, and γ, respectively, then

$$\frac{\sin \alpha}{a} = \frac{\sin \beta}{b} = \frac{\sin \gamma}{c}. \qquad \text{Law of Sines}$$
$$a^2 = b^2 + c^2 - 2bc \cos \alpha. \qquad \text{Law of Cosines}$$

14. The Greek Alphabet.

Letters	Names	Letters	Names	Letters	Names
A α	Alpha	I ι	Iota	P ρ	Rho
B β	Beta	K κ	Kappa	Σ σ	Sigma
Γ γ	Gamma	Λ λ	Lambda	T τ	Tau
Δ δ	Delta	M μ	Mu	Υ υ	Upsilon
E ϵ	Epsilon	N ν	Nu	Φ ϕ	Phi
Z ζ	Zeta	Ξ ξ	Xi	X χ	Chi
H η	Eta	O o	Omicron	Ψ ψ	Psi
Θ θ	Theta	Π π	Pi	Ω ω	Omega

PLANE ANALYTIC GEOMETRY

CHAPTER I

COÖRDINATES AND GRAPHS

1. Introduction. Analytic Geometry is a subject wherein algebra, geometry, and trigonometry are studied together in such a way that each is helpful in simplifying and clarifying the solution of problems arising in the others. It is largely for this reason that the concepts and methods of analytic geometry are constantly made use of in more advanced branches of mathematics. The student should, accordingly, throughout the course, emphasize this useful concept of the interrelations between subjects which is so important in the applications of analytic geometry.

The invention of analytic geometry is usually attributed to René Descartes, a French mathematician and philosopher, whose *La Géométrie*, which appeared in 1637, was the source from which the mathematical world learned the value of the methods of analytic geometry. Because of this work of Descartes, analytic geometry is sometimes called "Cartesian geometry."

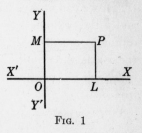

Fig. 1

2. Rectangular Coördinates. Let there be given two lines $X'X$ and $Y'Y$ (Fig. 1) which are perpendicular to each other and intersect at a point O. These two lines are called the **coördinate axes**; $X'X$ is the **x-axis** and $Y'Y$, the **y-axis**. The point O is the **origin**. Distances on the x-axis are considered positive if measured from left to right and negative if measured in the opposite direction. Similarly, distances on the y-axis are positive if measured up-

3

ward and negative if measured downward. This convention as to signs may be expressed briefly by saying that the x-axis is "directed to the right" and that the y-axis is "directed upward."

Let P be any point in the plane of the coördinate axes. From P drop perpendiculars to the x- and y-axes and denote the feet of these perpendiculars by L and M, respectively. The length of the segment OL, measured from O to L and taken with its proper sign, is denoted by x and is called the x-coördinate, or abscissa, of P. Similarly, the segment measured from O to M and taken with its proper sign is denoted by y and is called the y-coördinate, or ordinate, of P. The two numbers x and y are the coördinates of P and are written thus: (x, y).

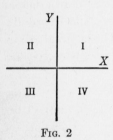

FIG. 2

The coördinated axes divide the plane into four parts, called quadrants, which are numbered (conforming to the usage familiar from trigonometry) as in the adjoining figure (Fig. 2).

3. Plotting Points. If we have given a pair of real numbers * (x, y), we can always find a point P for which x is the abscissa and y the ordinate. Suppose, for example, that the given coordinates are $(3, -2)$. We first determine L by laying off on the x-axis three units to the right from O and then locate P by laying off, on a parallel to the y-axis, two units downward from L.

When a point P is located in this way by means of its co-

---

* If either of the numbers x or y is imaginary, the corresponding point P cannot be plotted by the methods used in this course. When we are drawing graphs of equations (as in Art. 4), we shall often obtain solutions of the given equation for which at least one of the coördinates x or y is imaginary. Such a solution does not determine a point on the required graph. Geometric interpretations of these imaginary solutions will be found in advanced courses in analytic geometry, but they lie beyond the scope of this book.

ordinates, it is said to be **plotted.** Thus, in Fig. 3, we have plotted the points that have the coördinates $(3, -2)$, $(4, 3)$, $(-2, 2)$, and $(-1, -3)$.

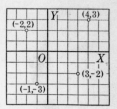

Whenever it is necessary to plot points, time can be saved, and greater accuracy secured, by using coördinate paper; that is, paper that is ruled with equally spaced

Fig. 3

lines parallel to the coördinate axes. Correctly drawn figures greatly simplify the work in analytic geometry and frequently suggest the method for solving problems. The habitual use of coördinate paper is the most convenient aid in constructing accurate figures.

EXERCISES

1. Plot the points: $(2, 4)$, $(-1, 6)$, $(-4, -3)$, $(4, -5)$, $(3, 0)$, and $(0, -4)$.

2. Plot the points: $(3, -5)$, $(1, 4)$, $(-2, -6)$, $(-3, 1)$, $(0, 2)$, and $(-5, 0)$.

3. Draw the triangle which has the following points as vertices:
(a) $(4, 1)$, $(-2, 5)$, $(-4, -2)$
(b) $(3, -1)$, $(2, 4)$, $(-1, 2)$.

4. Draw the triangle and find its area, given that its vertices are:
(a) $(-1, -2)$, $(5, -2)$, $(1, 4)$
(b) $(1, -2)$, $(4, 0)$, $(1, 3)$.

5. Draw the rectangle and find its area, given that its vertices are $(-2, -3)$, $(4, -3)$, $(4, 1)$, and $(-2, 1)$.

6. Three vertices of a rectangle are $(-1, 2)$, $(3, 2)$, and $(-1, 5)$. Draw the rectangle and find the coördinates of the fourth vertex.

7. Find the length of the hypotenuse of the right triangle whose vertices are $(2, 1)$, $(4, 1)$, and $(4, 6)$.

8. Find the coördinates of the midpoint of the segment joining the origin to the point $(6, 2)$.

9. The center of a square is at the origin and its sides are parallel to the coördinate axes. If the length of the side of the square is 10, find the coördinates of the vertices.

10. In what quadrant does a point lie if both of its coördinates are positive? if both are negative?

11. What is the ordinate of any point that lies on the x-axis? What is the abscissa, if it lies on the y-axis?

12. Draw a line through $(2, 4)$ perpendicular to the x-axis. Show that the abscissas of all points on this line are equal and find this common value.

13. What is the locus of a point for which the abscissa is 3? for which the ordinate is -2?

14. What is the locus of a point for which $x = y$? for which $x + y = 0$?

15. Two vertices of an equilateral triangle are $(0, 0)$ and $(2, 0)$. The third vertex lies in the first quadrant. Find its coördinates.

16. In Fig. 1, show that $MP = x$ and $LP = y$. Hence state a second definition of the coördinates of P.

4. Functions and their Graphs. If, in a given problem, two quantities x and y are so related that, when a value is assigned to x, then one or more values of y are determined, we say that **y is a function of x** in the given problem.

In most problems in mathematics, y is defined as a function of x by means of some equation connecting x and y. Thus, any one of the following equations defines y as a function of x:

$$y = x^2 + 5, \quad y = \sin x, \quad 3x + 7y - 2 = 0, \quad x^3 + y^3 = 8.$$

The statement, "y is a function of x," is often written in one of the following forms:

$$y = f(x), \text{ or } y = F(x), \text{ or } y = \phi(x), \text{ etc.}$$

If y is a known function of x, it is an important problem of analytic geometry to find the graph of the function, that is, to find the locus of a point whose abscissa is x and whose ordinate is the value of y determined by the given function for that value of x. In particular, if y is defined as a function of x by means of an equation, such as any one of those mentioned above, then the required graph is also called the *graph of the given equation*.

Some methods for drawing approximately the graphs of given equations will be illustrated by means of the following examples.

Example 1. Draw the graph of the equation $2x + y - 4 = 0$.

We first solve the given equation for one of the variables. In this case, it is easier to solve for y. We find

$$y = 4 - 2x.$$

We now assign to x an arbitrary set of values, substitute each of these in the above equation, determine the resulting values of y, and make a table of the corresponding pairs of values, as follows:

x	-2	-1	0	1	2	3	4
y	8	6	4	2	0	-2	-4

The result of plotting on coördinate paper the pairs of values of x and y from this table is shown in Fig. 4a. A smooth curve drawn through these points represents the required graph (Fig. 4b).

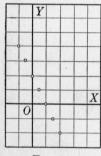

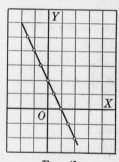

FIG. 4a   FIG. 4b

It is seen from the figure that the graph of $x + 2y - 4 = 0$ is a line.* It belongs, in fact, to the class of equations of the form

$$Ax + By + C = 0,$$

which, as we shall show in Chapter III, are the equations of lines.

---

* We shall use the word *line*, throughout, to mean a straight line.

Example 2. Draw the graph of $y = x^2 + 2x - 3$.

By tabulating the values of y corresponding to integer values of x from -4 to $+2$, we have

x	-4	-3	-2	-1	0	1	2
y	5	0	-3	-4	-3	0	5

The graph of the given equation (Fig. 5) is represented by plotting these points and drawing a smooth curve through them.

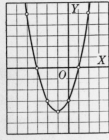

Fig. 5

The graph of the above equation is called a *parabola*, a curve we shall study more fully in Chapter V.

Notice that the abscissas of the points of intersection of this graph with the x-axis are the roots of the quadratic equation $x^2 + 2x - 3 = 0$. Similarly, if the roots of any given quadratic equation,

$$ax^2 + bx + c = 0,$$

are real, one can find them approximately by drawing the graph of

$$y = ax^2 + bx + c,$$

and measuring the abscissas of the points of intersection of the graph with the x-axis.

Example 3. Draw the graph of $x^2 + y^2 = 25$.

By solving the given equation for y, we obtain *

$$y = \pm\sqrt{25 - x^2}.$$

For a given value of x, there are thus two values of y, as shown by the following table:

x	-5	-4	-3	-2	-1	0	1	2	3	4	5
$y = \sqrt{25 - x^2}$	0	3	4	$\sqrt{21}$	$2\sqrt{6}$	5	$2\sqrt{6}$	$\sqrt{21}$	4	3	0
$y = -\sqrt{25 - x^2}$	0	-3	-3	$-\sqrt{21}$	$-2\sqrt{6}$	-5	$-2\sqrt{6}$	$-\sqrt{21}$	-4	-3	0

The graph is a circle (Fig. 6) with center at the origin and radius 5.

---

* By the symbol $\sqrt{\ }$, unless preceded by a sign, we shall always mean the *positive* square root of the quantity under the radical.

In this example, if we had assigned
to x values greater than $+ 5$, or less
than $- 5$, the values of y defined by
the equation would have been imaginary, so that no corresponding points
could have been plotted. This is because the graph, in this case, does not
extend more than five units from the
y-axis.

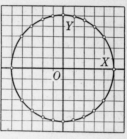

Fig. 6

5. Symmetry. Two points (x, y) and $(x, - y)$, whose x-
coördinates are equal and whose y-coördinates differ only in
sign, are said to be *symmetric* with respect to the x-axis. Similarly, the points (x, y) and $(- x, y)$ are symmetric with respect
to the y-axis.

We have seen, in example 3 of the preceding article, that if
(x, y) is any point on the graph of the given equation then its
symmetric point $(x, - y)$ with respect to the x-axis also lies on the
graph. This circle is thus an illustration of a curve that satisfies
the following definition: *any curve possessing the property that
the symmetric point, with respect to the x-axis, of every point on
it also lies on the curve is said to be symmetric with respect to
the x-axis.*

Similarly, a curve is *symmetric with respect to the y-axis*, if the
symmetric point with respect to the y-axis of every point on
it also lies on the curve. It will be seen from Fig. 6 that
the circle $x^2 + y^2 = 25$ is also symmetric with respect to the
y-axis.

It can be shown that: *if there are no odd powers of y in an
equation, its graph is symmetric with respect to the x-axis and, if
the equation is free of odd powers of x, then the graph is symmetric
with respect to the y-axis.*

Considerations of symmetry are very helpful in drawing the
graphs of given equations. If, for example, the part of the curve
that lies above the x-axis has been drawn, and if the graph is

known to be symmetric with respect to the x-axis, then we can locate as many points as we please on the lower half by choosing points on the part already drawn and plotting their symmetrical points with respect to the x-axis. Similarly, if the curve is symmetric with respect to the y-axis, we first draw the part of it to the right of the y-axis, then locate points on it to the left of the y-axis by symmetry.

EXERCISES

Draw on coördinate paper the graphs of the following equations. State which of the graphs are symmetric with respect to the x-axis and which with respect to the y-axis.

1. $x + y + 3 = 0$ **2.** $x - y + 6 = 0$

3. $\dfrac{x}{2} + \dfrac{y}{3} = 1$ **4.** $\dfrac{x}{3} - \dfrac{y}{5} = 1$

5. $y = 4x - 5$ **6.** $y = 2x + 1$

7. $y = 2$ **8.** $x = -4$

9. $y = 3x^2 + 2x - 1$ **10.** $y = 2x^2 - 3x + 2$

11. $x^2 + y^2 = 4$ **12.** $x^2 + y^2 = 36$

13. $x^2 + y^2 - 4y + 3 = 0$ **14.** $y^2 = 4x.$

15. Show algebraically that the graphs of the equations in Ex. 10 and 13 do not intersect the x-axis.

16. The formula for changing from Centigrade to Fahrenheit thermometer readings is $F = \frac{9}{5}C + 32$. Exhibit this formula graphically and explain the meaning of the intersections with the coördinate axes.

With the aid of the table on page 293, draw the graphs of the following curves when the angle varies from $-\pi$ to π.

17. $y = \sin x$ **18.** $y = \cos x$

19. $y = \tan x$ **20.** $y = \cos^{-1} x.$

6. Intersections of Graphs. The graphs of the two equations,

$$5x - 3y = 1,$$
$$3x + 2y = 12,$$

are seen, from the figure, to be two lines that intersect in some point P_1. It is required to find the coördinates of this point.

Let (x_1, y_1) be the coördinates of P_1. Since this point lies on the first line, its coördinates satisfy the equation of this line, that is

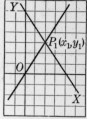

$$5x_1 - 3y_1 = 1;$$

and since it lies on the second line, we have similarly,

$$3x_1 + 2y_1 = 12.$$

FIG. 7

To find the coördinates of P_1, we, accordingly, solve these two equations as simultaneous. We find

$$x_1 = 2, \quad y_1 = 3,$$

that is, the required intersection is the point $(2, 3)$. This result should be checked by measuring the coördinates of the point of intersection in the figure.

By precisely similar reasoning we find in general that: *to determine the coördinates of the points of intersection of the graphs of any two equations, solve the two equations as simultaneous.*

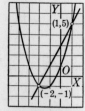

FIG. 8

The solutions, if there are any, for which x and y are both real, are the coördinates of the points common to the two graphs.

This method of determining the points of intersection of two curves is illustrated by the following examples. The results may be checked, approximately, by measuring the coördinates of the points of intersection of the graphs.

Example 1. Find the points of intersection of the graphs of the equations $y = 2x + 3$ and $y = x^2 + 3x + 1$.

If we substitute the value of y from the first equation in the second, we have

$$2x + 3 = x^2 + 3x + 1 \quad \text{or} \quad x^2 + x - 2 = 0,$$

from which $x = 1$ or -2. These two numbers are the *abscissas of the required points of intersection.*

To find the corresponding ordinates, we substitute these values of x successively in the first of the given equations and compute the value of y. The resulting simultaneous solutions of the two equations, which are the coördinates of the intersections of the two graphs, are $(1, 5)$ and $(-2, -1)$.

Example 2. Determine the intersections of the graphs of the equations $x - 2y + 2 = 0$ and $x^2 + 4y^2 = 100$.

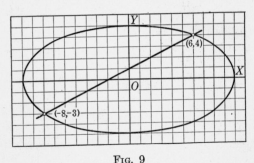

FIG. 9

If we substitute the value of x from the first equation in the second, and simplify, we obtain

$$y^2 - y - 12 = 0.$$

The roots of this equation, $y = 4$ and $y = -3$, are the ordinates of the required points of intersection.

If we substitute these values of y successively in the first of the given equations and solve for x, we find that the required intersections are $(6, 4)$ and $(-8, -3)$.

If we had substituted one of the values of y, as $y = 4$, in the second of the given equations, instead of the first, and solved for x, we would have obtained $x = 6$ and $x = -6$. One of these values of x is correct for the abscissa of a point of intersection but the other is not. The reason for this extraneous value of x, when we attempt to complete the solution in this way, may be seen from the figure. There are two points, $(6, 4)$ and $(-6, 4)$, on the graph of $x^2 + 4y^2 = 100$ that have the ordinate $y = 4$. Only the first of these points lies on the line $x - 2y + 2 = 0$.

Example 3.   Find the intersections of the graphs of the equations $x + y = 10$ and $x^2 + y^2 = 16$.

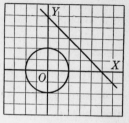

From the figure, we see that the graphs of these two equations do not intersect. To determine this fact algebraically, we solve the two equations as simultaneous and obtain $(5 + \sqrt{-17}, 5 - \sqrt{-17})$ and $(5 - \sqrt{-17}, 5 + \sqrt{-17})$ as the simul-

Fig. 10

taneous solutions. As these values of x and y are imaginary, the corresponding points cannot be plotted and the curves do not intersect.

EXERCISES

Solve the following pairs of equations algebraically and check your results by solving graphically:

1. $x + 3y = 5$
$\quad 3x - y = 5$

2. $7x - 2y = 4$
$\quad 3x + y = 11$

3. $3x - 2y = 5$
$\quad x + 4y = 4$

4. $2x + 3y + 4 = 0$
$\quad 5x - 2y - 9 = 0$

5. $3x + 13y = 2$
$\quad 7x + 5y = 9$

6. $11x + 7y = 6$
$\quad 5x + 13y = 4$

7. $2y = x^2 + 7x - 14$
$\quad y = 3x - 1$

8. $y = 2x^2 - 3x - 1$
$\quad y = 4x - 7$

9. $x^2 + y^2 = 20$
$\quad x = 3y - 10$

10. $x^2 + y^2 = 10$
$\quad x - 2y + 5 = 0$

11. $x^2 + y^2 = 5$
$\quad xy = 2$

12. $x^2 + y^2 = 25$
$\quad x^2 + 2y^2 = 34.$

Draw the graphs of the following pairs of equations and show algebraically that the curves do not intersect.

13. $y^2 = 4x$
$\quad y = x + 2$

14. $x^2 + y^2 = 4$
$\quad y^2 = 2x - 11.$

15. Find a temperature at which the Centigrade and Fahrenheit thermometer readings are equal, given that the relation connecting them is $F = \frac{9}{5}C + 32$.

CHAPTER II

FUNDAMENTAL DEFINITIONS AND THEOREMS

7. Directed Line Segments. One important distinction between elementary geometry and analytic geometry is that, in the latter, constant use is made of directed line segments. This concept is used in trigonometry in defining the signs of the trigonometric functions (Introd., Art. 8) and we have encountered it in this course in the definitions of the coördinates of a point; but we shall use it frequently, from now on, for segments not beginning at the origin and on lines lying anywhere in the plane.

If a line segment with end points A and B (Fig. 11) is thought of as generated by a point which traverses the line in a definite

FIG. 11

direction, either from A to B or from B to A, it is called a **directed line segment** for which the direction is that in which the generating point moves. A **directed line** is one for which it is agreed that the lengths of all segments on it that are directed in one way are to be considered positive and those directed the opposite way are negative. The positive direction on a line is sometimes indicated by an arrow, as in Fig. 11.

A thermometer scale offers a familiar example of directed segments on a directed line. If the top of the mercury column rises 10° from A to B, we say that the temperature change is $+ 10°$ but, if it falls 10°, from B to A, the change is $- 10°$.

In Fig. 11, let us denote by $\overline{AB}$ and $\overline{BA}$ the lengths of the directed segments from A to B and from B to A, respectively, each with its proper sign.* The length of the undirected seg-

---

* We shall also refer to the directed segments themselves by the symbols $\overline{AB}$ and $\overline{BA}$. The undirected segment will similarly be referred to as the segment AB.

14

ment, we shall denote by AB. It follows from the definition that, in the given figure

$$\overline{AB} = AB, \qquad \overline{BA} = -AB.$$

Hence $\qquad \overline{BA} = -\overline{AB}$ or $\overline{AB} + \overline{BA} = 0.$

Let A, B, and C be any three points on a directed line (Figs. 12a, b, c). Then, for all relative positions of these three

FIG. 12a 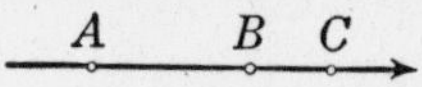   FIG. 12b 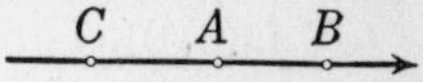   FIG. 12c

points, the following relation holds between the directed segments

$$\overline{AC} + \overline{CB} = \overline{AB}. \tag{1}$$

For, if C lies between A and B (Fig. 12a), the three lengths have the same sign and $\overline{AB}$ equals the sum of the other two. If C lies outside of the segment AB (Figs. 12b and 12c), then $\overline{AC}$ and $\overline{CB}$ have opposite signs but their algebraic sum remains equal to $\overline{AB}$.

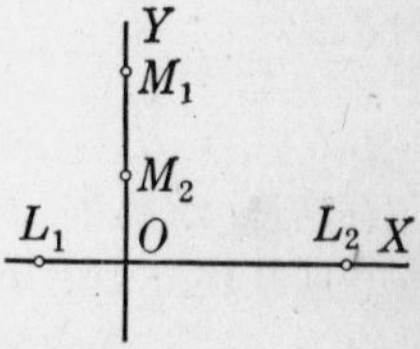

Let $L_1(x_1, 0)$ and $L_2(x_2, 0)$ be any two points on the x-axis. From the definition of the coördinates of a point (Art. 2), we have

$$\overline{OL_1} = x_1 \text{ and } \overline{OL_2} = x_2.$$

FIG. 13

Hence, from (1),

$$\overline{L_1L_2} = \overline{L_1O} + \overline{OL_2} = -\overline{OL_1} + \overline{OL_2} = -x_1 + x_2,$$

or $$\overline{L_1L_2} = x_2 - x_1, \tag{2}$$

that is, *the length of the directed segment L_1L_2, on the x-axis, equals the abscissa of L_2 minus the abscissa of L_1.*

Similarly, if $M_1(0, y_1)$ and $M_2(0, y_2)$ are any two points on the y-axis, we find in exactly the same way that

$$\overline{M_1M_2} = y_2 - y_1, \tag{3}$$

that is, *the length of the directed segment M_1M_2, on the y-axis, equals the ordinate of M_2 minus the ordinate of M_1.*

Formulas (2) and (3) should be carefully memorized, as we shall have frequent occasion to use them in this and subsequent chapters.

EXERCISES

with all ans.

1. Determine the length of the directed segment $\overline{L_1L_2}$ directly from a figure, then check your result by computation from equation (2).

(a) $L_1(3, 0)$, $L_2(6, 0)$ (b) $L_1(-2, 0)$, $L_2(4, 0)$

(c) $L_1(-10, 0)$, $L_2(-4, 0)$ (d) $L_1(12, 0)$, $L_2(5, 0)$

(e) $L_1(1, 0)$, $L_2(-9, 0)$ (f) $L_1(-1, 0)$, $L_2(-4, 0)$.

2. Find the length of the directed segment $\overline{M_1M_2}$ directly from a figure, then check your result by means of equation (3).

(a) $M_1(0, 4)$, $M_2(0, -1)$ (b) $M_1(0, 5)$, $M_2(0, 12)$

(c) $M_1(0, -5)$, $M_2(0, -2)$ (d) $M_1(0, 9)$, $M_2(0, 4)$

(e) $M_1(0, -8)$, $M_2(0, 3)$ (f) $M_1(0, -4)$, $M_2(0, -5)$.

3. Let the feet of the perpendiculars from P_1 and P_2 on the x-axis be L_1 and L_2 and on the y-axis be M_1 and M_2. Find $\overline{L_1L_2}$ and $\overline{M_1M_2}$, given:

(a) $P_1(1, 6)$, $P_2(4, 2)$ (b) $P_1(-3, -2)$, $P_2(2, 10)$

(c) $P_1(4, -2)$, $P_2(-2, 3)$ (d) $P_1(-5, 2)$, $P_2(-1, -4)$

(e) $P_1(3, -4)$, $P_2(-4, -1)$ (f) $P_1(-2, -1)$, $P_2(1, 5)$.

4. In Ex. 3a and 3b, compute the length of P_1P_2 by using the results of these exercises. Check your answer by direct measurement.

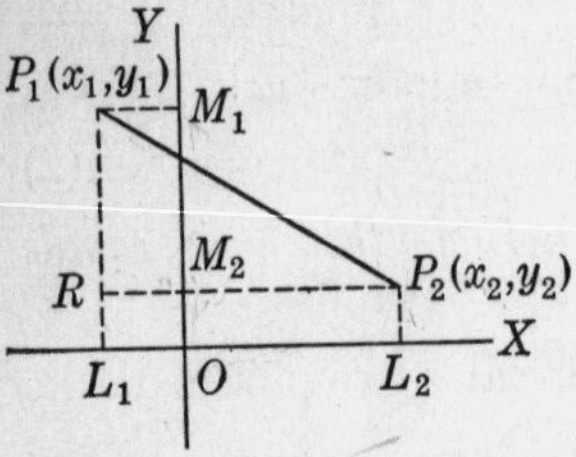

8. Distance between Two Points. Let $P_1(x_1, y_1)$ and $P_2(x_2, y_2)$ be two given points (Fig. 14). Draw the undirected segment P_1P_2. It is required to find the length of this segment in terms of the coördinates of P_1 and P_2.

Fig. 14

Let the feet of the perpendiculars from P_1 on the x- and y-axes be L_1 and M_1, respectively, and from P_2 be L_2 and M_2, respectively. Let P_1L_1 and P_2M_2 (produced if necessary) intersect at R.

Since the angle at R is a right angle, we have, by the Pythagorean theorem,

$$(P_1P_2)^2 = (RP_2)^2 + (RP_1)^2$$
$$= (L_1L_2)^2 + (M_1M_2)^2. \qquad \text{(Why?)}$$

But

$$(L_1L_2)^2 = (\overline{L_1L_2})^2 = (x_2 - x_1)^2$$

and

$$(M_1M_2)^2 = (\overline{M_1M_2})^2 = (y_2 - y_1)^2.$$

Hence

$$(P_1P_2)^2 = (x_2 - x_1)^2 + (y_2 - y_1)^2$$

or

$$\boldsymbol{P_1P_2} = \sqrt{(x_2 - x_1)^2 + (y_2 - y_1)^2}. \qquad (4)$$

This formula gives the length of the undirected segment P_1P_2. If the line through P_1 and P_2 is directed (that is, if a positive direction has been chosen on it) and if the directed length $\overline{P_1P_2}$ is desired, the proper sign must be determined by noticing whether the direction from P_1 to P_2 is positive or negative.

EXERCISES *

1. Derive the distance formula, taking the figure so that
    (a) P_1 is in the third quadrant and P_2 in the first
    (b) P_1 is in the fourth quadrant and P_2 in the second.

Find the distances between the following pairs of points:

2. (a) $(2, 6)$, $(6, 3)$ (b) $(-5, -2)$, $(7, 3)$
3. (a) $(-4, -1)$, $(2, -9)$ (b) $(3, 4)$, $(-2, 1)$
4. (a) $(-2, 3)$, $(6, -3)$ (b) $(2, 1)$, $(-13, 9)$
5. (a) $(8, 1)$, $(1, -2)$ (b) $(-6, -3)$, $(-2, 6)$.

---

* In these, and in all subsequent exercises, the construction of the figure is an essential part of the problem. No exercise in analytic geometry should be considered completely solved until the figure has been drawn. Customarily, the first step in solving an exercise should be to construct a figure since this will usually suggest a method for completing the exercise.

Find the lengths of the sides of a triangle, given that the vertices are:

6. $(3, 4), (2, 2), (5, -3)$ **7.** $(-1, 1), (2, 3), (-3, -1)$
8. $(1, -2), (5, 6), (-2, 3)$ **9.** $(3, 0), (2, 5), (0, -4)$.

Show that the following triangles are isosceles:

10. $(4, 2), (8, 4), (3, 9)$ **11.** $(9, 5), (5, -1), (-1, 3)$
12. $(4, 5), (2, -1), (-3, 4)$ **13.** $(3, 6), (-6, 4), (1, -2)$.

Show that the following triangles are right triangles:

14. $(1, 3), (5, 6), (4, -1)$ **15.** $(7, 4), (4, 5), (1, -4)$
16. $(3, 6), (6, 8), (-1, 12)$ **17.** $(2, 1), (1, 3), (-1, 2)$.

18. Find x, given that $(x, 1)$ is equidistant from $(1, 6)$ and $(9, 4)$.

19. Find y, given that $(6, y)$ lies at a distance 5 from $(3, 2)$. How many solutions?

Express by an equation the fact that a point $P(x, y)$ satisfies the geometric condition indicated by each of exercises 20 to 23. Simplify the resulting equation and draw its graph.

20. The distance of the point $P(x, y)$ from the origin equals 3.
21. The distance of $P(x, y)$ from $(-4, 3)$ equals 5.
22. The distance of $P(x, y)$ from $(2, 1)$ equals its distance from $(1, 0)$.
23. The distance of $P(x, y)$ from $(4, 1)$ equals its distance from $(-1, 2)$.

9. Point Dividing a Segment in a Given Ratio. Let $P_1(x_1, y_1)$

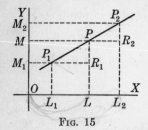

FIG. 15

and $P_2(x_2, y_2)$ be the end points of the given segment and let $P(x, y)$ be the point of the segment such that

$$\frac{\overline{P_1 P}}{\overline{P P_2}} = \frac{n_1}{n_2}$$

where $\dfrac{n_1}{n_2}$ is the given ratio. It is required to determine the coördinates of P in terms of $n_1, n_2,$ and the coördinates of P_1 and P_2.

Let L_1, M_1; L, M; and L_2, M_2 be the feet of the perpendiculars on the x- and y-axes from P_1, P, and P_2, respectively. Let R_1 be the intersection of the lines P_1M_1 and PL and R_2 of PM and P_2L_2. Then

$$\overline{P_1R_1} = \overline{L_1L} = x - x_1 \text{ and } \overline{PR_2} = \overline{LL_2} = x_2 - x.$$

The triangles P_1R_1P and PR_2P_2 are similar. (Why?) Hence we have, both in magnitude and sign,*

$$\frac{n_1}{n_2} = \frac{\overline{P_1P}}{\overline{PP_2}} = \frac{\overline{P_1R_1}}{\overline{PR_2}} = \frac{\overline{L_1L}}{\overline{LL_2}} = \frac{x - x_1}{x_2 - x}. \tag{5}$$

From the same similar triangles, we find also that

$$\frac{n_1}{n_2} = \frac{\overline{P_1P}}{\overline{PP_2}} = \frac{\overline{R_1P}}{\overline{R_2P_2}} = \frac{\overline{M_1M}}{\overline{MM_2}} = \frac{y - y_1}{y_2 - y}. \tag{6}$$

If we equate the first and last members of (5) and solve for x, and the first and last members of (6) and solve for y, we obtain

$$x = \frac{n_2x_1 + n_1x_2}{n_1 + n_2}, \quad y = \frac{n_2y_1 + n_1y_2}{n_1 + n_2}, \tag{7}$$

as the coördinates of the point $P(x, y)$ that divides the segment from $P_1(x_1, y_1)$ to $P_2(x_2, y_2)$ in the ratio $\dfrac{n_1}{n_2}$.

In particular, if P is the midpoint of the segment P_1P_2, then $n_1 = n_2$. (Why?) By substituting $n_1 = n_2$ in (7), and simplifying, we find that *the coördinates of the midpoint of the segment P_1P_2 are*

$$x = \frac{x_1 + x_2}{2}, \quad y = \frac{y_1 + y_2}{2}, \tag{8}$$

that is, *the coördinates of the midpoint of a segment are the half-sums of the coördinates of the end points.*

---

* The elementary geometry theorem concerning the proportionality of the corresponding sides of two similar triangles shows only that the ratios of the lengths of these segments are numerically equal. That the signs of these ratios are also equal must be determined independently, in this problem, by considering the directions of the segments in the figure. This difficulty will arise in all cases in which theorems of elementary geometry are applied to directed segments.

EXERCISES

1. Show that, for one of the points of trisection of the segment from $(-5, 7)$ to $(4, -5)$, $\dfrac{n_1}{n_2} = \dfrac{1}{2}$ and, for the other, $\dfrac{n_1}{n_2} = 2$. Find the coördinates of these two points and check your results by finding the lengths of the three segments.

2. Find the coördinates of the three points of quadrisection of the segment from $(-7, -5)$ to $(9, 3)$.

3. Determine the point which divides in the ratio $2 : 5$ the segment

    (a) from $(-6, 4)$ to $(8, 11)$ (b) from $(8, -3)$ to $(1, 4)$.

4. Determine the point two thirds of the distance from the first of the following pairs of points to the second:

    (a) $(2, 4)$, $(8, 10)$ (b) $(1, -4)$, $(-5, 8)$
    (c) $(2, 10)$, $(14, 1)$ (d) $(6, 5)$, $(1, 9)$.

5. Find the coördinates of the midpoints of the sides and the lengths of the medians of the triangle:

    (a) $(-2, 3)$, $(-6, -5)$, $(8, 1)$ (b) $(-1, 2)$, $(5, -2)$, $(3, 4)$.

6. Determine on each median of the following triangles the point twice as far from the vertex as from the midpoint of the opposite side. State the geometric theorem which shows that these three points coincide.

    (a) $(1, 3)$, $(6, -2)$, $(11, 5)$ (b) $(2, 3)$, $(6, 5)$, $(4, 10)$.

7. Solve Ex. 6 for the triangle whose vertices are (x_1, y_1), (x_2, y_2), and (x_3, y_3).

8. The midpoint of a segment is $(4, 3)$ and one end point is $(10, 12)$. Find the other end point.

9. In what ratio does the point $(5, 8)$ divide the segment from $(-4, 17)$ to $(11, 2)$?

10. Three consecutive vertices of a parallelogram are $(4, 5)$, $(-1, -2)$, and $(-2, 3)$. Find the fourth vertex.

10. Inclination and Slope of a Line.

The **inclination** of a line l (not parallel to the x-axis) is defined as the smallest positive angle for which the initial side (Introd., Art. 6) extends in

the positive direction along the x-axis and the terminal side
extends along l. If l is parallel to the x-axis, its inclination is
defined to be zero.

The tangent of the angle of inclination is called the **slope**
of the line. In analytic geometry, we deal with the slope more
frequently than with the inclination.

We shall denote the inclination of a
line by α and its slope by m, so that

$$m = \tan \alpha. \qquad (9)$$

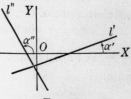

Fig. 16

If the inclination, α, is an acute
angle, then $\tan \alpha$, or m, is *positive* and
the line extends *upward to the right;* but if α is obtuse, m is
negative and the line extends *upward to the left.* Finally, if
$\alpha = 90°$, so that l is perpendicular to the x-axis, $\tan \alpha$ ceases
to exist; that is, *lines perpendicular to the x-axis have no slope.*
When we speak of the slope of a line we shall suppose, accordingly, that the line is not perpendicular to the x-axis.

11. Slope of the Line Through Two Given Points. Let
$P_1(x_1, y_1)$ and $P_2(x_2, y_2)$ $(x_1 \neq x_2 *)$ be the two given points and
let l be the line that passes through them.

Through P_1 draw a line parallel to the x-axis and choose some
point K on this line to the right of P_1. Denote by ϕ the smallest

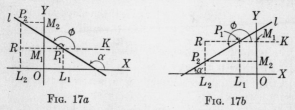

Fig. 17a   Fig. 17b

positive (or zero) angle having the half-line (Introd., Art. 6)
from P_1 through K as initial side and the half-line from P_1
through P_2 as terminal side.

---

* The symbol $\neq$ is read "is not equal to."

If α is the inclination of l, we now have, if $\phi < 180°$ (Fig. 17a)

$$\phi = \alpha \qquad \text{(Why?)}$$

but, if $\phi \geqq 180°$ * (Fig. 17b)

$$\phi = \alpha + 180° \qquad \text{(Why?)}$$

In either case,

$$\tan \phi = \tan \alpha = m. \tag{10}$$

From Figs. 17a and 17b and the definition of the tangent of an angle

$$\tan \phi = \frac{\overline{RP_2}}{\overline{P_1R}} = \frac{\overline{M_1M_2}}{\overline{L_1L_2}} = \frac{y_2 - y_1}{x_2 - x_1};$$

or, since $\tan \phi = m$, by (10), the slope of the line through $P_1(x_1, y_1)$ and $P_2(x_2, y_2)$ is

$$m = \frac{y_2 - y_1}{x_2 - x_1}; \tag{11}$$

that is, *the slope of the line through two given points equals the ordinate of the second minus the ordinate of the first divided by the abscissa of the second minus the abscissa of the first.*

We have supposed throughout this article that $x_1 \neq x_2$. If $x_1 = x_2$, the line is parallel to the y-axis and has no slope (Art. 10).

Example. Find the slope and the inclination of the line through $(2, 1)$ and $(-2, 6)$.

From (11), we find, as the required slope,

$$m = \frac{6 - 1}{-2 - 2} = -\frac{5}{4} = -1.25.$$

To determine the inclination α, we substitute this value of m in (9). We obtain

$$\tan \alpha = -1.25.$$

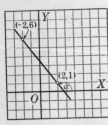

Fig. 18

* The symbol $\geqq$ is read "is greater than or equal to." Similarly, the symbol $\leqq$ is read "is less than or equal to."

By trigonometry, we have

$$\tan (180° - \alpha) = - \tan \alpha = 1.25.$$

From the table of tangents on page 292 we find, to the nearest degree,

$$180° - \alpha = 51° \quad \text{or} \quad \alpha = 129°.$$

EXERCISES

A table of trigonometric functions of angles from 0° to 90° will be found on page 292. If an angle is to be determined, find it to the nearest degree.

Find the slope of a line whose inclination is:

1. (a) 45°   (b) 120°   (c) 71°   (d) 143°.

2. (a) $\dfrac{\pi}{3}$ (b) $\dfrac{5\pi}{6}$ (c) $\dfrac{\pi}{4}$ (d) $\dfrac{2\pi}{3}$.

Find the inclination of a line whose slope is:

3. (a) − 1   (b) $\sqrt{3}$ (c) $-\dfrac{\sqrt{3}}{3}$ (d) 0.

4. (a) 0.3640   (b) 2.1634   (c) − 0.7325   (d) − 4.9352.

Find the slope and the inclination of the line through the points:

5. (a) (3, 1) and (5, 3)   (b) (− 2, 4) and (5, 1).

6. (a) (− 1.736, 2.713) and (1.414, 4.538)
   (b) (4.171, 0.362) and (1.319, 2.536).

7. Draw through the given point the line having the slope indicated.

   (a) (2, 3) $m = 1$ (b) (4, 2) $m = -1$
   (c) (1, − 3) $m = 2$ (d) (1, 4) $m = -9$
   (e) (3, 1) $m = \frac{3}{4}$ (f) (2, 5) $m = -\frac{2}{3}$.

8. An equilateral triangle has two vertices on the y-axis and its third vertex in the first quadrant. Find the slope of two of its sides and show that the third side has no slope.

9. Find the slopes of the bisectors of the angles of the triangle in Ex. 8.

10. Three vertices of a square are (0, a), (0, 0), and (a, 0). Find the slopes of the diagonals of the square.

11. Find from a figure, without using formula (11), the slope of the line through

    (*a*) $(-4, -6)$ and $(1, 5)$ (*b*) $(-1, 4)$ and $(3, -2)$.

12. Express by an equation the condition that the slope of the

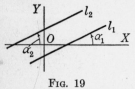

line that passes through the points $(3, 5)$ and (x, y) is equal to 2. What is the graph of this equation?

FIG. 19

12. Parallel and Perpendicular Lines.

Let l_1 and l_2 be two given lines neither of which is parallel to the y-axis.

If the lines l_1 and l_2 are parallel to each other, their inclinations, and hence their slopes, are equal. (Why?) Conversely, if

$$m_1 = m_2, \quad \text{then} \quad \alpha_1 = \alpha_2, \qquad \text{(Why?)}$$

and the lines are parallel.

Hence, *the condition that l_1 and l_2 are parallel is that*

$$m_1 = m_2. \tag{12}$$

If the lines l_1 and l_2 are perpendicular, we have either

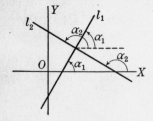

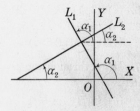

FIG. 20*a*   FIG. 20*b*

$$\alpha_2 = \alpha_1 + 90°, \qquad \text{(Fig. 20}a\text{)}$$

or$$\qquad \alpha_1 = \alpha_2 + 90°. \qquad \text{(Fig. 20}b\text{)}$$

In either case

$$\tan \alpha_1 = -\cot \alpha_2 = -\frac{1}{\tan \alpha_2};$$

or, since$$\qquad \tan \alpha_1 = m_1 \quad \text{and} \quad \tan \alpha_2 = m_2,$$

$$m_1 = -\frac{1}{m_2}, \quad \text{or} \quad m_1 m_2 = -1. \tag{13}$$

Conversely, if

$$m_1 = -\frac{1}{m_2}, \text{ then } \tan \alpha_1 = -\frac{1}{\tan \alpha_2} = -\cot \alpha_2,$$

from which it follows that $\alpha_1 = \alpha_2 \pm 90°$ so that the given lines are perpendicular. Hence, *the condition that l_1 and l_2 are perpendicular is that the product of their slopes equals minus one.*

13. Angle from One Line to Another. In order to choose a definite one among all the angles formed by two given intersecting lines l_1 and l_2, we make the following definition: *the*

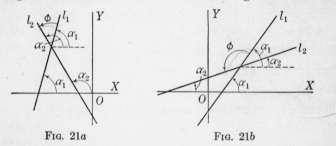

Fig. 21a   Fig. 21b

angle from the line l_1 to the line l_2 is the smallest positive angle through which l_1 must be rotated in order to coincide with l_2. If ϕ is this angle, and if m_1 and m_2 are the slopes of l_1 and l_2, respectively, we shall show that

$$\tan \phi = \frac{m_2 - m_1}{1 + m_1 m_2}. \tag{14}$$

We have, in fact,

Case I. If $\alpha_2 > \alpha_1$ (Fig. 21a)
$$\alpha_2 = \alpha_1 + \phi. \quad \text{(Why?)}$$
So that
$$\phi = \alpha_2 - \alpha_1.$$
Hence,
$$\tan \phi = \tan (\alpha_2 - \alpha_1)$$
$$= \frac{\tan \alpha_2 - \tan \alpha_1}{1 + \tan \alpha_1 \tan \alpha_2}.$$

Case II. If $\alpha_1 > \alpha_2$ (Fig. 21b)
$$\alpha_1 = \alpha_2 + (180° - \phi). \quad \text{(Why?)}$$
So that
$$\phi = 180° + \alpha_2 - \alpha_1.$$
Hence,
$$\tan \phi = \tan (180° + \alpha_2 - \alpha_1)$$
$$= \tan (\alpha_2 - \alpha_1)$$
$$= \frac{\tan \alpha_2 - \tan \alpha_1}{1 + \tan \alpha_1 \tan \alpha_2}.$$

Since $\tan \alpha_1 = m_1$ and $\tan \alpha_2 = m_2$, we have, accordingly, in either case,

$$\tan \phi = \frac{m_2 - m_1}{1 + m_1 m_2},$$

which is the required formula (14).

Example. Find, to the nearest degree, the angles of the triangle

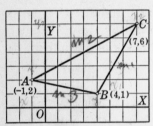

Fig. 22

whose vertices are $A(-1, 2)$, $B(4, 1)$, and $C(7, 6)$.

The slopes m_1, m_2, and m_3, of BC, CA, and AB, respectively, are found by (11) to be

$$m_1 = \tfrac{5}{3}, \quad m_2 = \tfrac{1}{2}, \quad m_3 = -\tfrac{1}{5}.$$

To determine the interior angle of the triangle at A, for example, we notice that, if the line AB is turned about the vertex A through the required angle, it will coincide with AC. Hence

$$\tan A = \frac{\tfrac{1}{2} + \tfrac{1}{5}}{1 - \tfrac{1}{10}} = \tfrac{7}{9} = 0.7778. \qquad A = 38°$$

$$\tan B = \frac{-\tfrac{1}{5} - \tfrac{5}{3}}{1 - \tfrac{1}{3}} = \frac{-14}{5} = -2.8000. \qquad B = 110°$$

$$\tan C = \frac{\tfrac{5}{3} - \tfrac{1}{2}}{1 + \tfrac{5}{6}} = \tfrac{7}{11} = 0.6364. \qquad C = \frac{32°}{180°}$$

EXERCISES

1. Show that $(-5, -1)$, $(1, 1)$, $(7, 7)$, and $(1, 5)$ are the vertices of a parallelogram, and find its acute angle.

2. Show that $(-1, 2)$, $(1, 3)$, $(-5, 10)$, and $(-3, 11)$ are vertices of a rectangle, and find its area.

3. Show that $(5, 4)$, $(1, 6)$, $(2, 3)$, and $(4, 7)$ are the vertices of a square.

4. Show by means of slopes that the following points lie on a line

 (a) $(7, 1)$, $(1, -2)$, $(9, 2)$ (b) $(1, 2)$, $(-3, 4)$, $(7, -1)$.

5. Do the points $(3, 2)$, $(4, -2)$, and $(2, 5)$ lie on a line?

6. Express by an equation the condition that the point (x, y) lies on the line through $(2, 3)$ and $(5, 1)$.

7. Is the line through $(2, 5)$ and $(-6, -11)$ parallel to the line through $(-4, -6)$ and $(3, 8)$?

8. Find to the nearest degree the angle from l_1 to l_2, given:

(a) $m_1 = \frac{5}{3}, m_2 = 2$ (b) $m_1 = -\frac{1}{2}, m_2 = 5$

(c) $m_1 = 7, m_2 = -7$ (d) $m_1 = \frac{1}{9}, m_2 = 9$.

9. Find the slope of l_2, given:

(a) $m_1 = \frac{4}{3}, \phi = 45°$ (b) $m_1 = \frac{7}{6}, \phi = \tan^{-1}(\frac{1}{2})$.

Find the angles of the triangle whose vertices are:

10. $(-1, 1), (4, 5), (3, 2)$.

11. $(6, 7), (9, -7), (-7, -4)$.

12. $(2, 3), (-6, 6), (6, -1)$.

13. The angle from the line through $A(1, 4)$ and $B(x, 8)$ to the line through A and $C(3, 10)$ is $45.°$ Find x.

14. Solve Ex. 3 without using slopes.

15. Solve Ex. 4 without using slopes.

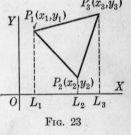

FIG. 23

★ **14. Area of a Triangle.*** Let $P_1(x_1, y_1)$, $P_2(x_2, y_2)$, and $P_3(x_3, y_3)$ be the vertices of a triangle and let L_1, L_2, and L_3 be the feet of the perpendiculars from these three points to the x-axis.

From Fig. 23, we have

Area $\triangle P_1 P_2 P_3$ = area trapezoid $P_1 L_1 L_3 P_3$ − area trapezoid $P_1 L_1 L_2 P_2$ − area trapezoid $P_2 L_2 L_3 P_3$,

or, since the area of a trapezoid equals half the sum of the parallel sides multiplied by the perpendicular distance between them,

$$\text{Area } \triangle P_1 P_2 P_3 = \frac{y_1 + y_3}{2}(x_3 - x_1) - \frac{y_1 + y_2}{2}(x_2 - x_1) - \frac{y_2 + y_3}{2}(x_3 - x_2).$$

By simplifying the right-hand member, we obtain

$$\text{Area } \triangle P_1 P_2 P_3 = \tfrac{1}{2}(x_1 y_2 + x_2 y_3 + x_3 y_1 - x_1 y_3 - x_2 y_1 - x_3 y_2). \quad (15)$$

---

* Articles marked with a ★ may be omitted.

From the definition of a determinant (Introd., Art. 2) it will be seen that this equation may be put in the easily remembered form

$$\text{Area } \triangle P_1 P_2 P_3 = \tfrac{1}{2} \begin{vmatrix} x_1 & y_1 & 1 \\ x_2 & y_2 & 1 \\ x_3 & y_3 & 1 \end{vmatrix} \tag{16}$$

Note. In order that the area of the triangle, as found from equations (15) or (16), may be positive, the vertices must be numbered in the order in which they would be encountered by a person starting from one of them and passing around the perimeter in such a way that the interior of the triangle is always on his left. Otherwise, the value obtained from the formula will be negative. We shall suppose throughout that the vertices have been chosen in such a way that the area, as found from the formula, is positive (or zero).

EXERCISES

Find the area of the triangle whose vertices are

1. (a) $(1, 6)$, $(3, 1)$, $(7, 4)$ (b) $(2, 1)$, $(5, 8)$, $(-1, 4)$.

2. (a) $(9, -4)$, $(-4, 6)$, $(12, 8)$ (b) $(1, 6)$, $(6, 2)$, $(7, 5)$.

3. (a) $(5, 1)$, $(7, 4)$, $(-7, -1)$ (b) $(4, 1)$, $(0, 2)$, $(-7, 4)$.

4. (a) $(-1, -2)$, $(2, 3)$, $(5, -4)$ (b) $(1, 1)$, $(6, 8)$, $(-2, 7)$.

5. Find y, given that the area of the triangle whose vertices are $(2, 1)$, $(4, y)$, and $(5, 3)$ is numerically equal to 10.

6. Show by areas that the following points lie on a line. Check your results by finding the slopes

(a) $(1, 5)$, $(7, 1)$, $(4, 3)$ (b) $(-1, -2)$, $(3, 1)$, $(7, 4)$.

7. Express by an equation that the area of the triangle with vertices $(1, 3)$, $(2, -5)$, and (x, y) is zero. What is the locus of a point (x, y) that satisfies this condition?

8. The vertex of a triangle is $(3, 9)$ and the end points of the base are $(2, 1)$ and $(14, 6)$. Find the altitude.

9. Find the areas of the following quadrilaterals by dividing each of them into two triangles. Check your results by dividing them into triangles in a different way.

(a) $(1, 5)$, $(3, 1)$, $(6, 3)$, $(7, 7)$ (b) $(-2, -5)$, $(3, -3)$, $(5, 6)$, $(0, 3)$.

★ **15. Applications to Elementary Geometry.** Many of the theorems of elementary geometry can be proved more easily by the methods of analytic geometry than by those with which the student is already familiar. In this article, we shall show how the formulas derived in this chapter may be used to demonstrate some of these theorems.

In demonstrating geometric theorems analytically, one can often simplify the computations considerably by a suitable placing of the coördinate axes with reference to the figure. If, for example, it is known that the figure is a rectangle, we may take the coördinate axes along two adjacent sides or, if it is a triangle, we may take the x-axis through two vertices and the y-axis through the third. In doing problems of the type discussed in this article, one should first draw the figure and then make a careful choice of the position of the axes with respect to the figure.

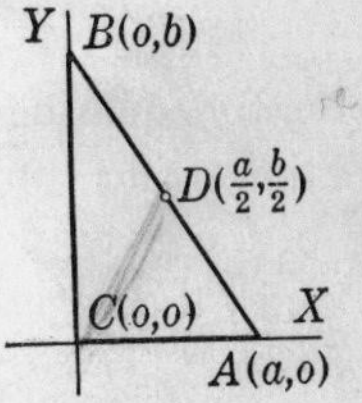

FIG. 24

Example 1. Prove analytically that the midpoint of the hypotenuse of a right triangle is equidistant from the vertices.

Let ABC be the given triangle with a right angle at C and let the lengths of the legs be $CA = a$ and $CB = b$.

If we choose the line CA as x-axis and CB as y-axis (Fig. 24), we find, as the coördinates of the vertices, $C(0, 0)$, $A(a, 0)$, and $B(0, b)$. Let D be the midpoint of AB. By (8), the coördinates of D are $\left(\dfrac{a}{2}, \dfrac{b}{2}\right)$.

By the distance formula, we now have

$$DC = \sqrt{\left(\frac{a}{2} - 0\right)^2 + \left(\frac{b}{2} - 0\right)^2} = \frac{1}{2}\sqrt{a^2 + b^2}$$

$$DA = \sqrt{\left(\frac{a}{2} - a\right)^2 + \left(\frac{b}{2} - 0\right)^2} = \frac{1}{2}\sqrt{a^2 + b^2}$$

$$DB = \sqrt{\left(\frac{a}{2} - 0\right)^2 + \left(\frac{b}{2} - b\right)^2} = \frac{1}{2}\sqrt{a^2 + b^2}$$

Hence, $DC = DA = DB$, which proves the theorem.

Example 2. Prove that, if the diagonals of a parallelogram are equal, the figure is a rectangle.

Let $ABCD$ be the given parallelogram. We choose the line AB as x-axis and the line perpendicular to it at A as y-axis. Since we do not know that the angle at A is a right angle, we should

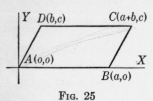

FIG. 25

not take D as a point on the y-axis. The coördinates of A are $(0, 0)$; of B are $(a, 0)$, where a is the length of the side AB of the parallelogram. Denote the coördinates of D by (b, c); then those of C are $(a + b, c)$. (Why?)

If we equate the expressions for the lengths of the diagonals AC and DB, as found from the distance formula, we obtain

$$\sqrt{(a + b - 0)^2 + (c - 0)^2} = \sqrt{(a - b)^2 + (0 - c)^2}$$

By squaring both sides and simplifying, we find that this equation reduces to $4ab = 0$. But $a \neq 0$, since it is the length of a side of the given parallelogram. Hence $b = 0$, so that D lies on the y-axis, the angle at A is a right angle, and the figure is a rectangle.

EXERCISES

Show that, by a suitable choice of coördinate axes:

1. The vertices of any triangle may be taken as:

   (a) $(a, 0)$, $(b, 0)$, $(0, c)$ (b) $(0, 0)$, $(a, 0)$, (b, c).

2. The vertices of any rectangle may be taken as:

   (a) $(0, 0)$, $(a, 0)$, (a, b), $(0, b)$

   (b) (a, b), $(-a, b)$, $(-a, -b)$, $(a, -b)$.

3. The vertices of any trapezoid may be taken as $(0, 0)$, $(a, 0)$, (b, c), (d, c).

Prove the following theorems analytically.

4. The segment joining the midpoints of two sides of a triangle is parallel to the third side and equal in length to half the third side.

5. The diagonals of a rectangle are equal.

6. Two medians of an isosceles triangle are equal.

7. If two medians of a triangle are equal, the triangle is isosceles.

8. The diagonals of a square are perpendicular to each other.

9. The diagonals of a parallelogram bisect each other.

10. If the diagonals of a trapezoid bisect each other, the figure is a parallelogram.

11. The distance between the midpoints of the non-parallel sides of a trapezoid equals half the sum of the parallel sides.

12. The lines joining the midpoints of successive sides of a rectangle form a rhombus.

13. The lines joining the midpoints of successive sides of any quadrilateral form a parallelogram.

14. The lines joining the midpoints of opposite sides of any quadrilateral bisect each other.

15. The sum of the squares of the four sides of a parallelogram equals the sum of the squares of the diagonals.

Solve the following exercises, taking the coördinate axes without any particular reference to the given figure.

16. Prove the theorem of Ex. 4.

17. Prove the theorem of Ex. 9.

18. Prove the theorem of Ex. 12.

19. Prove the theorem of Ex. 14.

POLAR COÖRDINATES

Instead of fixing the position of a point by its directed distances from two fixed lines, as in rectangular coördinates, it is sometimes preferable to locate it by its distance and direction from a given point. When its position is fixed in this way, the point is said to be located by means of *polar coördinates*.

In principle, the method of fixing the position of a point by its polar coördinates is not unfamiliar. We are accustomed, for example, to such statements as that Minneapolis is about 350 miles northwest of Chicago, or that Albany is about 135 miles north of New York.

16. Polar Coördinates. Let O be a fixed point, the **origin,** or **pole,** and let OI be a fixed line through O, the **initial line,** or **polar axis.** The line through the pole perpendicular to the polar axis is the **90° axis.**

Let P be any point in the plane (other than O) * and draw the line through O and P. The position of P is fixed if we know the length r of the segment OP and the angle θ that has

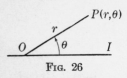

FIG. 26

the half-line (Introd., Art. 6) OI for its initial side and the half-line OP for its terminal side. The quantities (r, θ) are called the **polar coördinates** of P; r is the **radius vector** and θ is the **vectorial angle.**

If the polar coördinates (r, θ) are given, the point P is definitely fixed; but, for a given point P, we can find as many pairs of polar coördinates as we please. For, if we add to θ, or subtract from it, any number of complete revolutions, we do not change the terminal side nor the position of P. Thus, (r, θ), $(r, \theta + 2\pi)$, $(r, \theta - 2\pi)$, etc. are all polar coördinates of the same point P.

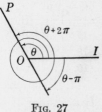

FIG. 27

Moreover, we can also fix the position of P by choosing, for the terminal side of the vectorial angle, the half-line extending from O in the opposite direction from P and considering the length of the radius vector as negative. Thus, $(-r, \theta - \pi)$, $(-r, \theta + \pi)$, $(-r, \theta + 3\pi)$, etc. are also polar coördinates of the point (r, θ).

In most of the applications of polar coördinates, negative values of r are excluded. We shall adhere to this convention except when, in plotting the graphs of certain equations, the values of r, as found from the equation, are negative.

---

* The polar coördinates of the origin O are defined by taking the radius vector, r, equal to zero and the vectorial angle, θ, to be of any magnitude we please.

For plotting points, or drawing graphs, in polar coördinates, it will be found that both speed and accuracy are improved by the use of **polar coördinate paper,** as in Fig. 28.

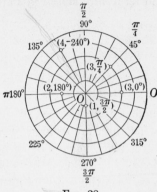

FIG. 28

Example. Plot the points having the polar coördinates $(3, 0°)$, $(4, -240°)$, $(2, 180°)$, $\left(3, \dfrac{\pi}{4}\right)$, $\left(1, \dfrac{3\pi}{2}\right)$.

From OI, as initial side, we measure off the given angle θ and, on its terminal side, lay off the given length of the radius vector. The resulting points are shown in Fig. 28.

17. Relations between Polar and Rectangular Coördinates. If a system of polar coördinates is so related to a system of rectangular coordinates that they have the same origin and the directions OI on the initial line and OX on the x-axis coincide, as in Fig. 29, then the relations between the polar coördinates (r, θ)

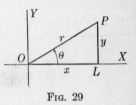

FIG. 29

and the rectangular coördinates (x, y) of a given point P may be found in the following way.

From the definitions of $\sin \theta$ and $\cos \theta$, we have

$$\cos \theta = \frac{x}{r} \text{ and } \sin \theta = \frac{y}{r},$$

so that the values of x and y in terms of r and θ are

$$x = r \cos \theta, \quad y = r \sin \theta. \tag{17}$$

To find r and θ in terms of x and y, we notice (Fig. 29) that $\tan \theta = \frac{y}{x}$ and that r is the hypotenuse of a right triangle whose legs are x and y. Hence

$$r = \sqrt{x^2 + y^2}; \quad \tan \theta = \frac{y}{x} \quad \text{or} \quad \theta = \tan^{-1} \frac{y}{x}. \tag{18}$$

When we determine θ from the last of equations (18), we must bear in mind that there are two angles, differing by 180°, for which $\tan \theta$ has the given value. Before we can determine θ from this equation we must accordingly first find out, by plotting the point on the figure, in what quadrant the given point lies.

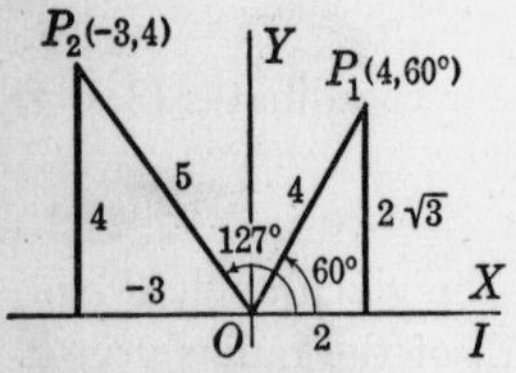

Fig. 30

Example 1. Find the rectangular coördinates of a point given that its polar coördinates are (4, 60°).

Since $\cos 60° = \frac{1}{2}$ and $\sin 60° = \frac{\sqrt{3}}{2}$, we have, from equations (17),

$$x = 4 \cdot \frac{1}{2} = 2, \quad y = 4 \cdot \frac{\sqrt{3}}{2} = 2\sqrt{3}.$$

Hence, the required coördinates are $(2, 2\sqrt{3})$ (Fig. 30).

Example 2. Find the polar coördinates for a point, given that its rectangular coördinates are $(-3, 4)$.

From equations (18), we have

$$r = \sqrt{(-3)^2 + 4^2} = 5, \quad \tan \theta = -\tfrac{4}{3} = -1.3333.$$

Moreover, it is seen from Fig. 30 that P_2 lies in the second quadrant. Hence we may take $\theta = 127°$ and the required coördinates are (5, 127°).

Example 3. Transform the equation $3x - y - 5 = 0$ to polar coördinates.

By substituting for x and y their values in terms of r and θ from (17), we have

$$3r \cos \theta - r \sin \theta - 5 = 0 \quad \text{or} \quad r(3 \cos \theta - \sin \theta) - 5 = 0.$$

Example 4. Transform the polar equation $r = 2 \cos \theta + 3 \sin \theta$ to rectangular coördinates.

In this case, it will be convenient, first, to multiply the given equation by r, giving

$$r^2 = 2r \cos \theta + 3r \sin \theta.$$

From equations (17) and (18) we now obtain

$$x^2 + y^2 = 2x + 3y.$$

EXERCISES

Plot the points having the polar coördinates:

1. $(2, 30°)$, $(5, 45°)$, $(5, -45°)$, $(4, 90°)$, $(3, 225°)$, $(4, 163°)$, $(5, -108°)$.

2. $\left(6, \dfrac{\pi}{3}\right)$, $\left(4, \dfrac{3\pi}{4}\right)$, $\left(5, \dfrac{-\pi}{2}\right)$, $\left(9, \dfrac{3\pi}{2}\right)$, $(7, -\pi)$, $(6, 0.4363)$, $(4, 1.3963)$.

3. Find the rectangular coördinates of the points in Ex. 1.

4. Find polar coördinates for the points whose rectangular coördinates are $(4, 4)$, $(-2, 0)$, $(-2\sqrt{3}, -2)$, $(5, -5)$, $(8, -3)$.

5. Show that the points $(3, 0°)$, $(3, 120°)$, and $(3, 240°)$ are vertices of an equilateral triangle.

6. The center of a square is at the origin and two of its sides are parallel to the polar axis. If the length of the diagonal of the square is 6, find polar coördinates for its vertices.

7. Transform the following equations to polar coördinates and draw the graphs.

(a) $x = 6$ (b) $x + 2y + 9 = 0$ (c) $x^2 + y^2 - 2y = 0$.

8. Transform the following equations to rectangular coördinates and draw the graphs.

(a) $r = 4$ (b) $r \cos (\theta - 45°) = 5\sqrt{2}$ (c) $r = 8 \sec \theta$.

9. What is the locus of a point for which (a) $r = 7$? (b) $\theta = 60°$?

MISCELLANEOUS EXERCISES

1. Find the length of the perimeter of the triangle whose vertices are $(7, 8)$, $(2, -4)$, and $(11, 8)$.

2. The center of a circle is $(5, 9)$ and one end of a diameter is $(8, 2)$. Find the coördinates of the other end.

3. The diagonals of a square lie on the coördinate axes and the length of the side of the square is 8. Find the coördinates of the vertices.

4. Show that the triangle whose vertices are $(2, -1)$, $(6, 1)$, and $(1, 6)$ is isosceles and find its base angles.

5. Show that $(3, 0)$, $(4, 5)$, $(-1, 6)$, and $(-2, 1)$ are the vertices of a square. Find the coördinates of the center and the area.

6. Show (a) by distances and (b) by slopes that $P_1(-1, -2)$, $P_2(4, 8)$ and $P(1, 2)$ lie on a line. In what ratio does the point P divide the segment P_1P_2?

7. Prove in two ways that $(-7, -1)$, $(6, 5)$, and $(1, -5)$ are the vertices of a right triangle and find its acute angles.

8. The center of a regular hexagon is at the origin and one vertex is $(8, 0)$. Find the remaining vertices.

9. A rhombus lies in the first quadrant with one vertex at the origin and another at $(10, 0)$. The angle at the origin is $30°$. Find the remaining vertices.

10. In what ratio is the segment from $(-2, -5)$ to $(6, 7)$ divided by the point in which it intersects the y-axis?

11. Three vertices of a rectangle are $(2, 1)$, $(5, -1)$, and $(9, 5)$. Find the fourth vertex.

12. The angle from a line l_1 through $(-1, 2)$ and $(4, 1)$ to a line l_2 is $45°$. Find the slope of l_2.

13. Find three points each of which, with the points $(2, 4)$, $(4, 5)$, and $(6, 8)$, are the vertices of a parallelogram.

14. The ends of the base of an isosceles triangle are $(-1, 3)$ and $(5, 11)$. The tangents of the base angles are 2. Find the vertex. How many solutions?

15. Express by an equation the condition that the line through (x, y) and $(4, 0)$ is perpendicular to the line through (x, y) and $(-4, 0)$. What is the graph of this equation?

16. Show analytically that, if the diagonals of a parallelogram are perpendicular to each other, the figure is a rhombus.

17. If D is the midpoint of the side AB of the triangle ABC, show that $AC^2 + BC^2 = 2(CD^2 + AD^2)$.

18. Show analytically that the sum of the squares of the three medians of a triangle equals three-fourths of the sum of the squares of the sides.

19. Show that the sum of the squares of the four sides of any quadrilateral equals the sum of the squares of the diagonals plus four times the square of the segment joining the midpoints of the diagonals.

SELECTED EXERCISES

1. Prove the converse of the Pythagorean theorem, that is, if the square of one side of a triangle equals the sum of the squares of the other two sides, the triangle is a right triangle.

2. Let O be the origin and let $P_1(x_1, y_1)$ and $P_2(x_2, y_2)$ be any two given points in the plane. Find the cosine of the angle P_1OP_2 in terms of the coördinates of P_1 and P_2.

3. In a triangle ABC determine a point D such that angle $DAB =$ angle $DBC =$ angle DCA and a point D' such that angle $D'BA =$ angle $D'CB =$ angle $D'AC$. The points D and D' are called the *Brocard points* of the triangle.

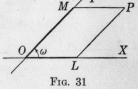

FIG. 31

4. If the angle $\omega = XOY$ between the coördinate axes is not a right angle, and if the line through a given point P parallel to OY intersects OX at L (Fig. 31) and the one through P parallel to OX intersects OY at M, then $\overline{OL} = x$ and $\overline{OM} = y$ are called the **Cartesian** (or **oblique**) **coördinates** of P.

Derive the formula for the distance between two points in terms of their Cartesian coördinates.

5. Find the Cartesian coördinates (Ex. 4) of the point $P(x, y)$ that divides the segment from $P_1(x_1, y_1)$ to $P_2(x_2, y_2)$ in the ratio $n_1 : n_2$.

6. If $ABCD$ is a parallelogram and E and F are the midpoints of BC and CD, respectively, show, by using Cartesian coördinates (Ex. 4), that the points on AE and AF that are twice as far from A as from the latter points are the points of trisection of BD.

7. Derive a formula for the distance between two points in polar coördinates.

8. Derive a formula for the area of a triangle in polar coördinates.

1, 4, 6, 7, 8

19

CHAPTER III

THE LINE

18. Equation of a Line. By the equation of a line, we mean an equation that has the given line for its graph. In order that an equation may be the equation of a given line it is necessary (1) that the coördinates of every point that lies on the line shall satisfy the equation and (2) that every point whose coördinates satisfy the equation shall lie on the line.

In the applications of analytic geometry, it is necessary that we be able to write the equation of a line whenever enough geometric conditions have been given us to fix its position. This information may be stated to us in any one of a number of ways; for example, we may be given its direction and the position of one point on it, or the position of two of its points, and so forth. We shall begin this chapter, accordingly, by showing how the equation of a line may be found when its position has been fixed in various ways.

19. Lines Parallel to the Axes. If the line is parallel to the y-axis, it meets the x-axis in some point $(a, 0)$. It follows from the definition of the coördinates of a point (Art. 2), that the abscissa of any point on the line is $x = a$ and, conversely, that any point that has its abscissa equal to a lies on the given line. (Why?) Hence the equation of any line parallel to the y-axis is

$$x = a. \tag{19}$$

By similar reasoning, we find that the equation of the line parallel to the x-axis that intersects the y-axis at $(0, b)$ is

$$y = b. \tag{20}$$

20. The Point-Slope Form. If the line l whose equation is required passes through a given point $P_1(x_1, y_1)$ and has for its slope a given number m, we shall show that its equation is

$$y - y_1 = m(x - x_1). \qquad (21)$$

This equation is called the *point-slope equation* of the line.

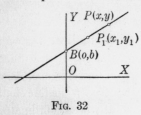

FIG. 32

To show that (21) is the equation of l, we must show that (21) is satisfied by the coördinates of every point that lies on l and that every point whose coördinates satisfy (21) lies on l.

The point P_1 itself lies on l and its coördinates clearly satisfy (21) since, if we assign to x and y the values x_1 and y_1, respectively, both members of the equation are zero.

Next, let $P(x, y)$ be any point on l other than P_1. Then the slope of the line through P_1 and P is m, that is (Art. 11)

$$m = \frac{y - y_1}{x - x_1}, \qquad (22)$$

or $\qquad y - y_1 = m(x - x_1).$

Hence, the coördinates of P satisfy (21).

Conversely, if the coördinates of any point P, other than P_1, satisfy (21), then they also satisfy (22). Hence the slope of the line P_1P is m and P lies on l.

21. The Slope-Intercept Form. If the given line intersects the y-axis at $B(0, b)$, the number b is called its **y-intercept.**

Since $B(0, b)$ is a fixed point on l, we may take its coördinates as (x_1, y_1) in (21). This gives

$$y - b = m(x - 0),$$

or $\qquad y = mx + b. \qquad (23)$

This is the *slope-intercept form* of the equation of the line.

Example. Find the equation of the line through (2, 1) perpendicular to the line through $(-3, -1)$ and $(-1, 2)$.

The slope of the line through $(-3, -1)$ and $(-1, 2)$ is $\frac{3}{2}$. Hence (Art. 12) the slope of the required line is $-\frac{2}{3}$ and, since it passes through (2, 1), its equation is

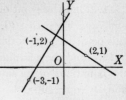

Fig. 33

$$y - 1 = -\tfrac{2}{3}(x - 2) \text{ or } 2x + 3y - 7 = 0.$$

EXERCISES

1. Find the equations of the lines through the following points having the given slopes.

(a) (2, 3) $m = \frac{5}{2}$ (b) (3, -4) $m = -2$
(c) (3, 0) $m = 2$ (d) $(-5, 2)$ $m = -\frac{1}{2}$
(e) (2, 9) $m = 0$ (f) (0, 5) $m = -\frac{8}{9}$.

2. Find the equations of the lines through $(-2, 5)$ whose inclinations are:

(a) $\alpha = 0$ (b) $\alpha = \dfrac{\pi}{3}$ (c) $\alpha = \dfrac{2\pi}{3}$ (d) $\alpha = \dfrac{3\pi}{4}$.

3. Find the equations of the lines for which:

(a) $m = 2, b = 3$ (b) $m = \frac{1}{3}, b = \frac{11}{6}$ (c) $m = -\frac{1}{6}, b = \frac{5}{2}$.

4. Find the equations of the lines through (1, 3) parallel to the lines in Ex. 3.

5. Find the equations of the lines through $(-2, 5)$ perpendicular to the lines in Ex. 3.

6. Find the equation of a line (a) parallel to the y-axis and 4 units to the right of it, (b) parallel to the x-axis and 5 units below it.

7. Find the equations of two lines parallel to the y-axis and at a distance from it numerically equal to 2.

8. Find the equations of the lines through (4, 7) parallel to the x-axis and to the y-axis, respectively.

9. The equation of a line is $2y = 3x + 4$. Find (a) the ordinates of the points on the line for which $x = 2$ and $x = 6$, (b) the slope of the line, and (c) its y-intercept.

10. Find the equation of a line through $(4, -1)$, given that the angle from the line through $(2, -3)$ and $(6, 5)$ to it is $135°$.

11. Find the point of intersection of the lines $4x + 2y + 7 = 0$ and $7x + 3y + 13 = 0$ and write the equation of the line through this point having its slope equal to 3.

12. Find the coördinates of the vertices of a triangle, given that the equations of its sides are $x - 5y + 8 = 0$, $3x + 4y + 5 = 0$, and $4x - y - 6 = 0$.

13. Show that the lines $x + 2y + 6 = 0$, $3x + 4y + 2 = 0$, and $2x + 5y + 20 = 0$ meet in a point.

22. The Two-Point Form. If $P_1(x_1, y_1)$ and $P_2(x_2, y_2)$ are two given points on a line, and if $x_1 \neq x_2$, then the slope of the line through these two points is (Art. 11)

$$m = \frac{y_2 - y_1}{x_2 - x_1}.$$

If we substitute this value of the slope in equation (21), we have

$$y - y_1 = \frac{y_2 - y_1}{x_2 - x_1} (x - x_1). \tag{24}$$

This is the *two-point form* of the equation of a line.

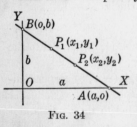

FIG. 34

If $x_1 = x_2$, the line through P_1 and P_2 is parallel to the x-axis and its equation is, by Art. 19,

$$x = x_1. \tag{25}$$

If we multiply equation (24) through by $x_2 - x_1$, transpose all the terms to the right-hand member, and simplify, we find that the resulting equation is equivalent to the following

$$\begin{vmatrix} x & y & 1 \\ x_1 & y_1 & 1 \\ x_2 & y_2 & 1 \end{vmatrix} = 0, \tag{26}$$

as may be seen by expanding this determinant by the rule for evaluating a determinant of the third order (Introd., Art. 2).

The student should verify that this determinant form for the equation of a line through two given points holds also when $x_1 = x_2$, that is, when the line is parallel to the y-axis.

Exercise. Derive the equation of a line in the form of equation (26) by considering the area of the triangle whose vertices are (x, y), (x_1, y_1), and (x_2, y_2) when these three points lie on a line.

23. The Intercept Form. The directed distances $\overline{OA}$ and $\overline{OB}$ (Fig. 34) from the origin to the intersections of a line with the axes are called the x- and y-intercepts, respectively, of the line. We shall denote them by a and b.

Let a and b both be different from zero. Then $A(a, 0)$ and $B(0, b)$ are two fixed points on the line and we find, by taking the coördinates of these points as (x_1, y_1) and (x_2, y_2) in (24), that the equation of this line is

$$y - 0 = \frac{b - 0}{0 - a}(x - a),$$

or $$-ay = bx - ab.$$

If we rearrange this equation, and divide by ab which, by hypothesis, is different from zero, we obtain

$$\frac{x}{a} + \frac{y}{b} = 1, \tag{27}$$

which is the *intercept form* of the equation of the line.

Example 1. Find the equation of the line through the intersection of $x + 2y - 4 = 0$, $x - 3y + 1 = 0$ and also through the midpoint of the segment joining $(2, 5)$ and $(4, 3)$.

The point of intersection of the given lines is found, by solving their equations as simultaneous, to be $(2, 1)$ and the midpoint of the given segment, by Art. 9, is $(3, 4)$. The equation of the line through these two points is

$$y - 1 = \frac{4 - 1}{3 - 2}(x - 2),$$

or $$y = 3x - 5.$$

Example 2. Find the intercepts of the line $3x - 2y - 12 = 0$ and write its equation in the intercept form.

The x-intercept is found, by putting $y = 0$ and solving for x, to be $a = 4$. Similarly, by putting $x = 0$, we find for the y-intercept $b = -6$. Hence the intercept form of the equation is

$$\frac{x}{4} + \frac{y}{-6} = 1.$$

EXERCISES

1. Find the equation of the line through the points:

    (a) $(4, 3), (2, 7)$ (b) $(2, -1), (6, 5)$

    (c) $(7, 9), (-5, 1)$ (d) $(-3, 1), (7, 2)$

    (e) $(2, -5), (-3, 8)$ (f) $(-5, -1), (2, 9)$.

2. Write the equations of the following lines in the intercept form:

    (a) $3x + 5y = 15$ (b) $2x + 3y + 6 = 0$ (c) $3x - 4y + 7 = 0$.

3. Find the slopes of the lines in Ex. 2 and write their equations in the slope-intercept form.

4. Find the ordinate of a point if its abscissa is 5 and it lies on the line through $(-1, 3)$ and $(3, 9)$.

5. Find the equation of a line through $(5, 2)$ for which the x- and y-intercepts are equal.

6. The vertices of a parallelogram are $(-1, -2), (-2, 1),$ $(4, 1),$ and $(3, 4)$. Find (a) the equations of the sides and (b) the equations of the diagonals.

7. Three vertices of a rectangle are $(-3, 5), (3, 2),$ and $(5, 6)$. Write the equations of its sides and find the coördinates of the fourth vertex.

8. Show that the points $(1, 2), (3, -1),$ and $(-3, 8)$ lie on a line and find its equation.

9. The vertices of a triangle are $(1, -4), (3, 2),$ and $(-5, 6)$. Find the equations of its sides.

10. Find the equations of the medians of the triangle in Ex. 9 and show that they meet in a point.

11. Find the equations of the altitudes of the triangle in Ex. 9 and show that they meet in a point.

12. The ends of a diagonal of a square are $(0, 0)$ and $(8, 0)$.

Find the equations of the sides and the coördinates of the other two vertices.

13. Find the equation of a line, given that its x-intercept is a and its slope is m.

24. The General Form. Linear Equations. Any equation of the form

$$Ax + By + C = 0, \qquad (28)$$

wherein A, B, and C are constants and A and B are not both zero, is an *equation of first degree in x and y.*

We have seen in Art. 21 that, if a line is not parallel to the y-axis, it has an equation $y = mx + b$ and, if it is parallel to the y-axis, it has an equation $x = a$ (Art. 19). Both of these equations are of the first degree in x and y. Hence, we have

Theorem I: *Every line has an equation of first degree in x and y.*

We shall now prove

Theorem II: *Every equation of the first degree in x and y, with real coefficients, is the equation of a line.*

There are two cases, according as $B \neq 0$ or $B = 0$.
If $B \neq 0$, we can solve (28) for y, giving

$$y = -\frac{A}{B}x - \frac{C}{B}. \qquad (29)$$

By Art. 21, this is the equation of a line in the slope-intercept form

$$y = mx + b$$

for which the slope and y-intercept have the values

$$m = -\frac{A}{B} \text{ and } b = -\frac{C}{B}. \qquad (30)$$

If $B = 0$, then, since A and B are not both zero, we can solve (28) for x, giving

$$x = -\frac{C}{A}.$$

This is the equation of a line parallel to the y-axis (Art. 19) having its x-intercept equal to $-\dfrac{C}{A}$.

Hence, in both cases, (28) is the equation of a line. It is called the **general form** of the equation of a line.

Because of Theorems I and II, equation (28) is also called a *linear equation* in x and y.*

From equations (29) and (30), we obtain the following useful result: *If the equation of a line is solved for y, the coefficient of x is the slope and the constant term is the y-intercept.*

Example. Given the line $3x + 4y - 24 = 0$. Find its slope and its intercepts and reduce its equation to the slope intercept and to the intercept form.

We first solve the equation for y, giving

$$y = -\tfrac{3}{4}x + 6.$$

This is the slope-intercept form. From it we obtain at once $m = -\tfrac{3}{4}$ and $b = 6$. To find a, we put $y = 0$ and solve for x. We obtain $x = 8$. Hence

$$\frac{x}{8} + \frac{y}{6} = 1$$

is the intercept form of the equation of the given line.

25. The Linear Function. An expression of the form

$$mx + b, \qquad m \neq 0 \tag{31}$$

is called a *linear function* of x.

To find the graph of a linear function, we equate it to y and plot the graph of the resulting equation. We thus find that *the graph of a linear equation is a line.*

---

* The name *linear equation* is also extended to equations of the first degree in any number of variables. Thus, the equation

$$Ax + By + Cz + Dw + Et + F = 0$$

wherein the coefficients of the variables are not all zero, is a linear equation in x, y, z, w, t, although it cannot be represented graphically by a line.

In the applications of mathematics, two variable quantities
are often related in such a way that a change of a given amount
in one produces a proportional change in the other. Under such
circumstances, the second is a linear function of the first.

Example. An automobile, traveling at a constant rate of 40
miles per hour, has gone 100 miles by noon. Express the distance
traveled as a function of the time after noon
and draw the graph.

We have

$$d = 100 + 40t$$

where d is the distance traveled in miles and
t is the time in hours.

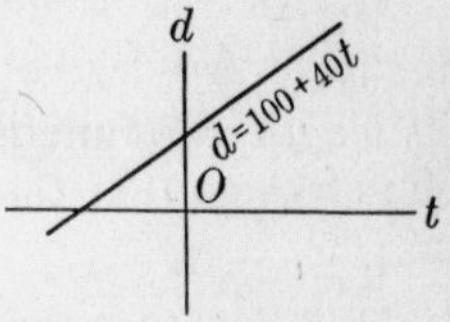

Fig. 35

The graph of d, as a function of t, is given
in Fig. 35. In drawing this graph, we have used a unit on the t-axis
60 times as large as on the d-axis. In the applications, such differ-
ences in units are often necessary to produce satisfactory graphs.

EXERCISES

1. Find the slopes and the intercepts of the following lines.

(a) $5x - 4y + 20 = 0$ (b) $3x + 2y + 18 = 0$
(c) $6x - 9y - 11 = 0$ (d) $5x + 11y + 17 = 0$.

2. Find the angle from the line $2x - y + 3 = 0$ to the line
$5x + 3y - 5 = 0$.

3. Find the equation of a line having an inclination of 30° and
an x-intercept equal to 5.

4. Show that the lines $3x + 6y - 11 = 0$, $6x - 9y + 5 = 0$,
$3y - 2x + 4 = 0$, and $2x + 4y + 5 = 0$ determine a parallelogram.

5. Find the equations of the sides of a rectangle, given that two
sides are parallel to $x + 2y = 11$ and pass through $(- 4, - 2)$ and
$(4, 1)$, respectively, and that the other two sides pass through $(3, 4)$
and $(- 1, 2)$, respectively.

6. Find the coördinates of two points on the line $3x + 2y = 8$.
Check your result by finding the equation of the line through the
two points and reducing it to the given form.

7. The slope of a line is m and its y-intercept is b. Find its x-intercept.

8. Find the slope of a line in terms of its intercepts a and b.

9. Draw the graph of the linear function $-2x + 4$. For what values of x is this function positive? For what values is it negative?

10. Express the amount due in n years on \$100 at 6%, simple interest. Draw the graph of this function.

11. An iron bar one meter long at 0° C. expands 0.012 millimeter for every degree Centigrade of rise in temperature. Express its length as a function of the temperature and draw the graph.

12. Show that the condition that the lines $Ax + By + C = 0$ and $A'x + B'y + C' = 0$ are parallel is $AB' - BA' = 0$.

13. Show that the condition that the lines in Ex. 12 are perpendicular is $AA' + BB' = 0$.

14. Show that, if $C' \neq C$, the lines $Ax + By + C = 0$ and $Ax + By + C' = 0$ are parallel.

15. Show that the lines $Ax + By + C = 0$ and $Bx - Ay + C' = 0$ are perpendicular.

16. Show that the equations $Ax + By + C = 0$ and $A'x + B'y + C' = 0$ determine the same line if, and only if, $A : B : C = A' : B' : C'$.

17. Find the equations of the lines through the given point that are parallel and perpendicular, respectively, to the given line:

(a) $(1, 3)$, $4x + 7y - 9 = 0$;   (b) $(6, 8)$, $2x + y - 1 = 0$;
(c) $(-1, -2)$, $3x - 5y + 4 = 0$;   (d) $(2, -7)$, $8x + y - 1 = 0$;
(e) $(8, 3)$, $2x - 9y + 1 = 0$;   (f) $(2, 5)$, $x + 4 = 0$.

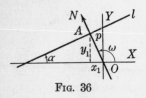

FIG. 36

26. The Normal Form. Let l (Fig. 36) be the given line. Draw through O a line ON perpendicular to l and let ω be the *inclination of this perpendicular*. From Art. 10, we have, $0° \leqq \omega < 180°$. We shall consider ON as a directed line, its positive direction being that of the terminal half-line of ω.

Let $A(x_1, y_1)$ be the intersection of ON with l and denote the length of the directed segment $\overline{OA}$ by p. Then p is positive if A lies above O and negative if it lies below.

From the definitions of sin ω and cos ω (Introd., Art. 8), we find that

$$x_1 = p \cos \omega, \qquad\qquad y_1 = p \sin \omega.$$

Let m be the slope of l. Since ON is perpendicular to l, we have
$$m = - \text{ctn } \omega. \qquad\qquad \text{(Why?)}$$

If we substitute these values of x_1, y_1, and m in the point slope equation (21) of a line, we have

$$y - p \sin \omega = - \text{ctn } \omega(x - p \cos \omega).$$

In this equation, we replace ctn ω by its value $\dfrac{\cos \omega}{\sin \omega}$ and multiply through by sin ω. We thus obtain

$$y \sin \omega - p \sin^2 \omega = - x \cos \omega + p \cos^2 \omega,$$

or $$x \cos \omega + y \sin \omega - p(\sin^2 \omega + \cos^2 \omega) = 0,$$

that is $$x \cos \omega + y \sin \omega - p = 0. \qquad (32)$$

This is the *normal form* of the equation of a line. Its importance arises chiefly from the fact (which we shall prove in Art. 28) that, whenever we are required to determine the distance from a line to a point, we shall need the equation of the line in the normal form.

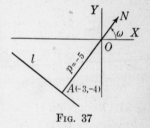

Fig. 37

Example 1. Find the normal form of the equation of the line through $A(-3, -4)$ perpendicular to the line through A and the origin.

Draw the line ON through O and A. From the figure, ω is an acute angle and $\overline{OA}$, or p, is negative. Hence we have

$$p = - \sqrt{(-3)^2 + (-4)^2} = -5, \qquad \sin \omega = \frac{-4}{-5} = \frac{4}{5},$$

$$\cos \omega = \frac{-3}{-5} = \frac{3}{5}.$$

and the required equation is

$$\frac{3x}{5} + \frac{4y}{5} + 5 = 0.$$

Example 2. Two lines of inclination 60° lie at a distance from the origin numerically equal to 10. Find their equations in the normal form.

From the figure, we find $\omega = 60° + 90° = 150°$, so that $\sin \omega = \sin 150° = \frac{1}{2}$ and $\cos \omega = \cos 150° = -\frac{\sqrt{3}}{2}$. For one of the

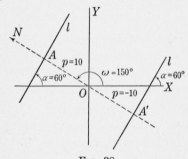

Fig. 38

required lines, $p = 10$ and, for the other $p = -10$. Hence the required equations are

$$-\frac{\sqrt{3}}{2} x + \frac{1}{2} y - 10 = 0 \quad \text{and} \quad -\frac{\sqrt{3}}{2} x + \frac{1}{2} y + 10 = 0.$$

Exercise. Show that the derivation of equation (32) given in the text fails if l is parallel to the y-axis but that equation (32) still holds for these lines also.

27. Reduction of the Equation of a Line to the Normal Form.
Let
$$Ax + By + C = 0 \tag{33}$$
be the equation of a line and let
$$x \cos \omega + y \sin \omega - p = 0 \tag{34}$$
be the normal form of the equation of the same line. To reduce the first equation to the second, we multiply it by a constant k
$$kAx + kBy + kC = 0, \tag{35}$$

and determine k so that the coefficients in this equation and in (34) are equal, that is,

$$kA = \cos \omega, \qquad kB = \sin \omega, \qquad kC = -p. \quad (36)$$

If we square the members of the first two of equations (36) and add, we obtain

$$k^2A^2 + k^2B^2 = \cos^2 \omega + \sin^2 \omega = 1.$$

If we solve this equation for k, we find that

$$k = \frac{1}{\pm \sqrt{A^2 + B^2}}. \quad (37)$$

To determine the sign of the radical, we note that, since $0° \leqq \omega < 180°$, $\sin \omega$ is always positive or zero. Hence, by the second equation of (36), if $B \neq 0$, k and B have the same signs. If, however, $B = 0$, then $\sin \omega = 0$, so that $\omega = 0$, $\cos \omega = 1$ and k agrees in sign with A.

If we substitute the value of k from (37) in (35), we obtain, as the normal form of the equation of the line defined by (33),

$$\frac{A}{\pm \sqrt{A^2 + B^2}}x + \frac{B}{\pm \sqrt{A^2 + B^2}}y + \frac{C}{\pm \sqrt{A^2 + B^2}} = 0, \quad (38)$$

where the signs before the radicals agree with that of B if $B \neq 0$, and with that of A if $B = 0$.

Hence, *to reduce the equation of a line to the normal form, divide each term by* $\pm \sqrt{A^2 + B^2}$, *choosing the sign before the radical so as to make the coefficient of y positive if $B \neq 0$, and the coefficient of x positive if $B = 0$.*

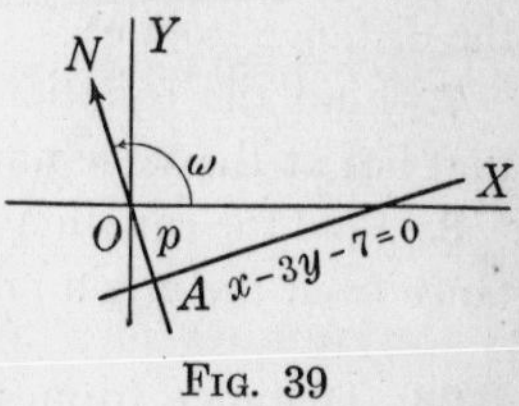

Example. Reduce the equation $x - 3y - 7 = 0$ to the normal form and find the values of ω and p.

Fig. 39

Since $B = -3 < 0$, divide each term by $-\sqrt{1^2 + (-3)^2} = -\sqrt{10}$. The required equation is thus found to be

$$\frac{-x}{\sqrt{10}} + \frac{3y}{\sqrt{10}} + \frac{7}{\sqrt{10}} = 0.$$

By comparing this equation with the normal form (32), we find

$$\cos \omega = -\frac{1}{\sqrt{10}}, \qquad \sin \omega = \frac{3}{\sqrt{10}}, \qquad p = -\frac{7}{\sqrt{10}}.$$

Since ω lies in the second quadrant, we find by the aid of the tables, $\omega = 108°$.

EXERCISES

1. Write the equations of the following lines in the normal form:

(a) $\omega = 30°$, $p = 4$;   (b) $\omega = 0°$, $p = -6$;

(c) $\omega = \dfrac{2\pi}{3}$, $p = 4$;   (d) $\omega = \dfrac{\pi}{2}$, $p = -5$.

2. Write the equations of the following lines in the normal form and find the values of ω and p

(a) $4x - 3y - 15 = 0$;   (b) $12x + 5y + 39 = 0$;   (c) $2x + 3y = 0$;
(d) $x + y - 2 = 0$;   (e) $x - 3 = 0$;   (f) $2y + 5 = 0$.

3. Find the equation of a line through $(-2, 5)$ for which

(a) $\omega = 45°$, (b) $\omega = \dfrac{5\pi}{6}$.

4. Find the equation of the line through $(-7, 24)$, perpendicular to the line joining this point to the origin.

5. Find the equations of two lines of inclination $135°$ that lie at a distance from the origin numerically equal to 6.

6. Find the equations of two lines parallel to $8x - 15y - 68 = 0$ that lie at a distance from the origin numerically equal to 2. Find the distance from each of these lines to the given line.

7. Find the equation of the line parallel to $2x - 3y - 6 = 0$ that lies at the same numerical distance from the origin.

8. Find the equations of two lines through $(1, 7)$ that lie at a distance from the origin numerically equal to 5.

28. Distance from a Line to a Point. Let $P_1(x_1, y_1)$ be the given point and let the normal form of the equation of the given line be

$$x \cos \omega + y \sin \omega - p = 0$$

wherein $p = \overline{OA}$ (Fig. 40).

If l' is the line through P_1 parallel to l, we may write its equation in the normal form

$$x \cos \omega + y \sin \omega - p' = 0 \qquad \text{(Why?)}$$

wherein $p' = \overline{OA'}$.

Since P_1 lies on l', its coördinates satisfy this equation, that is,

$$x_1 \cos \omega + y_1 \sin \omega - p' = 0. \tag{39}$$

Let Q_1 be the foot of the perpendicular from P_1 on l and let us choose the positive direction on the line through Q_1 and P_1 to agree with that on ON. Then we have, for the required distance d,

$$d = \overline{Q_1 P_1} = \overline{AA'} = \overline{OA'} - \overline{OA} = p' - p.$$

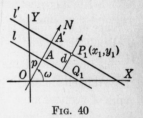

If we substitute for p' in this equation its value from (39), we have

$$d = x_1 \cos \omega + y_1 \sin \omega - p \tag{40}$$

that is, *to find the distance from a line to a point, substitute the coördinates of the point in the left-hand member of the normal form of the equation of the line. The resulting number is the required distance.*

Fig. 40

The distance d, or $\overline{Q_1 P_1}$, determined by (40), is a directed distance. It is positive if $\overline{Q_1 P_1}$ agrees in direction with the positive direction on ON and it is negative in the contrary case.

If the equation of the line is given in the general form

$$Ax + By + C = 0$$

and we wish to find the distance of the point $P_1(x_1, y_1)$ from it, we first reduce the equation of the line to the normal form, as in equation (38), and then substitute the coördinates of P_1 in it. The result is

$$d = \frac{Ax_1 + By_1 + C}{\pm \sqrt{A^2 + B^2}} \tag{41}$$

wherein the sign before the radical agrees with that of B if $B \neq 0$, and agrees with that of A if $B = 0$.

Example. Find the distance from the line $2x - y - 4 = 0$ to each of the points $P_1(-1, -2)$, $P_2(5, 0)$, and $P_3(3, 5)$.

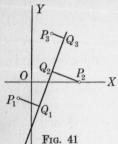

We first reduce the given equation to the normal form by dividing through by $-\sqrt{2^2 + (-1)^2} = -5$. The result is

$$\frac{2x - y - 4}{-\sqrt{5}} = 0.$$

By substituting the coördinates of the given points in the left-hand member of this equation, we find as the required distances

Fig. 41

$$d_1 = \frac{4}{\sqrt{5}}, \qquad d_2 = -\frac{6}{\sqrt{5}}, \qquad d_3 = \frac{3}{\sqrt{5}}.$$

Since d_1 and d_3 are positive and d_2 is negative, the points P_1 and P_3 lie above the line and P_2 lies below it (Fig. 41).

29. Bisectors of the Angles Formed by Two Lines. It is proved in elementary geometry that the two lines that bisect the pairs of vertical angles formed by two given lines constitute the locus of a point equidistant from the two given lines. We shall use this theorem to find the equations of these bisectors, as is shown in the following example.

Example. Find the bisectors of the pairs of vertical angles formed by the lines $x + 7y - 5 = 0$ and $x - y + 3 = 0$.

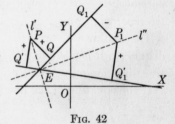

Fig. 42

Let E (Fig. 42) be the intersection of the given lines and let $P(x, y)$ be any point on the bisector l'. If P lies above E, it also lies above both given lines and its distances from both of them, as found from (41), are positive.

Similarly, if P lies on l' but below E, its distances from both given lines are negative. Hence, in both cases, its distances from the given lines as found from formula (41) are equal, both in magnitude and sign, so that

$$\overline{QP} = \overline{Q'P}.$$

If P_1 is any point, other than E, on the bisector l'', it is similarly seen that it lies above one of the given lines and below the other, so that
$$\overline{Q_1 P_1} = -\overline{Q_1' P_1}.$$

Finally, the point E itself lies on both bisectors and its directed distances from the two given lines, being zero, satisfy both of the above equations.

The equation of l' is accordingly found, by equating the distances of $P'(x, y)$ from the given lines, to be
$$\frac{x - y + 3}{-\sqrt{2}} = \frac{x + 7y - 5}{\sqrt{50}}$$
or
$$3x + y + 5 = 0.$$

The equation of l'' is similarly found, by equating the negative of one distance to the other, to be
$$\frac{x - y + 3}{-\sqrt{2}} = -\frac{x + 7y - 5}{\sqrt{50}}$$
or
$$x - 3y + 5 = 0.$$

EXERCISES

1. Find the distance from the given line to the point indicated and state, in each case, whether the given point lies above the given line or below it.

(a) $4x + 3y - 15 = 0$ $(6, 4)$ (b) $12x - 5y + 65 = 0$ $(-4, 2)$
(c) $7x + 24y = 0$ $(-6, 4)$ (d) $3x + 7y + 4 = 0$ $(8, -5)$.

2. Show that $(-1, 5)$ and $(3, -2)$ lie on opposite sides of the line $3x + 2y - 6 = 0$.

3. Show that $(1, 3)$ lies between the parallel lines $x - 2y + 4 = 0$ and $2x - 4y + 13 = 0$.

4. Find the equation of the locus of a point whose distances from the two lines in Ex. 3 are numerically equal but opposite in sign. What is this locus?

5. Find the distance between the parallel lines

(a) $4x - 3y - 5 = 0$
$8x - 6y + 1 = 0$

(b) $2x - 5y + 3 = 0$
$6x - 15y + 28 = 0$.

6. Find the equations of the lines perpendicular to $12x + 5y - 15 = 0$ that lie at a distance from $(4, 2)$ numerically equal to 2.

7. Find the equation of the locus of a point that lies at a distance from $7x + 24y - 20 = 0$ equal (a) to -3, (b) to 1. What loci are defined by these equations?

8. Determine two points that are equidistant from $(5, 6)$ and $(1, -2)$ and lie at a distance from $3x - 4y + 9 = 0$ numerically equal to 2.

9. Find the altitudes of the triangle whose vertices are $(3, -1)$, $(4, 7)$, and $(9, -3)$.

10. Find the equations of the bisectors of the pairs of vertical angles formed by the lines $7x + 6y - 9 = 0$ and $2x - 9y + 6 = 0$.

11. Find the equation of the bisector of that pair of vertical angles formed by the lines $5x - 12y + 9 = 0$ and $4x - 3y - 8 = 0$ in which the point $(-1, 2)$ lies.

12. Find the equations of the bisectors of the interior angles of the triangle whose sides are $9x + 2y - 7 = 0$, $6x + 7y + 10 = 0$, and $2x - 9y + 14 = 0$. Show that these three bisectors meet in a point and find its coördinates. What is this point called?

13. Find the equations of the bisectors of the interior angles, and the coördinates of the center and the radius of the inscribed circle, of the triangle whose sides are $3x + 4y - 3 = 0$, $4x - 3y + 4 = 0$, and $7x - 24y + 1 = 0$.

30. Families of Lines. Parameters. If, in the equation

$$3x + 5y + k = 0 \qquad (42)$$

we substitute for k any number we please, we determine a line. For example, if we put $k = 10$, we obtain

$$3x - 5y + 10 = 0$$

which is the equation of a line; and similarly for any other value we may assign to k (Fig. 43).

All the lines that can be determined by substituting values for k in (42) are parallel since their slopes all equal $-\frac{3}{5}$. Moreover, by substituting a suitable value for k in (42), we can obtain the equation of any given line of slope $-\frac{3}{5}$. Equation

(42) is, consequently, called the equation of the *family* of lines of slope $-\frac{3}{5}$ and k is the *parameter* of the family.

More generally, if the coefficients in the equation of a line contain a quantity k such that, by letting k run through all possible values, we obtain a whole system of lines satisfying some geometric condition, then we say that the given equation defines a **family** of lines and that k is the **parameter** of the family.

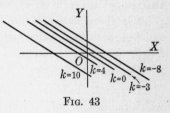

Fig. 43

For our purposes, the importance of the consideration of families of lines lies in the fact that, if the required line is known to belong to a given family, we may first write the equation of this family and then find from the conditions of the problem the value of k that fixes the required line. The following examples will indicate the procedure.

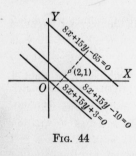

Fig. 44

Example 1. Find the equations of the lines parallel to $8x + 15y - 10 = 0$ that lie at a distance from $(2, 1)$ numerically equal to 2.

The equation of the family of lines parallel to the given line is
$$8x + 15y + k = 0.$$

Since we have to do with the distance from this line to a point, we first reduce its equation to the normal form
$$\frac{8}{17} x + \frac{15}{17} y + \frac{k}{17} = 0.$$

The condition that the distance from this line to $(2, 1)$ is equal to ± 2 is now found, by substituting the coördinates of $(2, 1)$ in the left-hand member of the above equation and equating the result to ± 2, to be $\dfrac{31 + k}{17} = \pm 2$. Hence $k = 3$ or $k = -65$ and the required lines are
$$8x + 15y + 3 = 0 \quad \text{and} \quad 8x + 15y - 65 = 0.$$

Example 2. Find the line perpendicular to $x + 2y - 4 = 0$ that passes through (4, 1).

The equation of the family of lines perpendicular to $x + 2y - 4 = 0$ is $y = 2x + k$. (Why?) To determine the line of this family that passes through (4, 1), we substitute the coördinates of this point in the equation of the family and find the value of k that satisfies the resulting equation. We have $1 = 2 \cdot 4 + k$ or $k = -7$. The equation of the required line is, accordingly, $y = 2x - 7$.

Example 3. Find the equations of the lines through (6, − 1) for which the product of the intercepts equals 3.

Let a and b be the intercepts. From the statement of the problem, $ab = 3$, or $b = \dfrac{3}{a}$. If we substitute this value of b in the intercept form $\dfrac{x}{a} + \dfrac{y}{b} = 1$ of the equation of a line, we obtain

$$\frac{x}{a} + \frac{ay}{3} = 1 \quad \text{or} \quad a^2 y + 3x - 3a = 0.$$

This is the equation of the family of lines for which the product of the intercepts is equal to 3.

The condition that a line of this family passes through (6, − 1) is that the coördinates of this point satisfy the equation of the family, that is, that $-a^2 - 3a + 18 = 0$. Hence $a = 3$ or $a = -6$ and, by substituting these values of a in the equation of the family, we obtain, as the equations of the required lines

$$x + 3y - 3 = 0 \quad \text{and} \quad x + 12y + 6 = 0.$$

31. Family of Lines Through the Intersection of Two Given Lines. If

$$A_1 x + B_1 y + C_1 = 0 \quad \text{and} \quad A_2 x + B_2 y + C_2 = 0$$

are the equations of two intersecting lines, then we shall show that the coördinates of their point of intersection satisfy the equation

$$A_1 x + B_1 y + C_1 + k(A_2 x + B_2 y + C_2) = 0 \qquad (43)$$

for *all* values of k. For, the coördinates of the point of intersection satisfy both of the given equations (Why?) and hence, when substituted in (43), reduce this equation to $0 + k \cdot 0 = 0$ which is true for all values of k.

Moreover, (43) is of first degree in x and y and thus, by Art. 24, defines a line for all real values of k. It is the equation of the *family of lines through the intersection of the given lines*. Its importance lies in the fact that it enables us to find the equation of a line through the point of intersection of two given lines without ever actually determining the coördinates of this point.

Example. Find the equation of the line through the intersection of $8x - 2y + 3 = 0$ and $5x + 10y + 17 = 0$ that makes an angle of $135°$ with the x-axis.

It is unnecessary actually to find this point of intersection. Instead, we proceed as follows: The required line belongs to the family

$$8x - 2y + 3 + k(5x + 10y + 17) = 0,$$

or $$(8 + 5k)x + (-2 + 10k)y + 3 + 17k = 0.$$

The slope of the required line is $\tan 135°$ or -1, so that

$$-\frac{8 + 5k}{-2 + 10k} = -1$$

or $$8 + 5k = 10k - 2.$$

On solving, we find that $k = 2$, so that the required equation is

$$8x - 2y + 3 + 2(5x + 10y + 17) = 0 \quad \text{or} \quad 18x + 18y + 37 = 0.$$

EXERCISES

1. Write the equations of the following families of lines. Assume, in each case, five values for the parameter and draw the corresponding lines.

(*a*) Parallel to $3x - 2y - 1 = 0$

(*b*) Perpendicular to $5x - 3y + 7 = 0$

(*c*) Of slope 2

(*d*) Passing through $(4, 7)$

(*e*) Having $\omega = \dfrac{\pi}{4}$

(*f*) Having equal intercepts

(*g*) At a distance from the origin numerically equal to 3.

(*h*) Passing through the intersection of $2x + y - 9 = 0$ and $2x - 3y + 3 = 0$.

2. Draw four lines of each of the following families and state a geometrical property common to all the lines of each family.

(*a*) $y = 4x + b$ (*b*) $\dfrac{x}{2} + \dfrac{y}{b} = 1$

(*c*) $y = b$ (*d*) $x \cos 30° + y \sin 30° - p = 0$

(*e*) $y - 1 = m(x + 3)$ (*f*) $x \cos \omega + y \sin \omega \pm 7 = 0$.

3. Find the line of the family $y = 5x + b$ that passes through (*a*) $(-1, 3)$, (*b*) $(4, -2)$.

4. Find the line of the family $y - 6 = m(x + 2)$ that is (*a*) parallel, and (*b*) perpendicular, to the lines of the family $y = 3x + b$.

5. Determine a line through $(2, 5)$ for which the *y*-intercept is three times the *x*-intercept.

6. Find two lines through $(2, -3)$ for which the sum of the intercepts is 4.

7. Determine two lines of slope -2 each of which forms, with the coördinate axes, a triangle of area 9.

8. Find the equation of the line through the intersection of $4x - 3y - 9 = 0$ and $2x + y + 5 = 0$ that is perpendicular to $3x - y + 2 = 0$.

9. Find the lines through the intersection of $x + 3y - 8 = 0$ and $2x - 5y + 11 = 0$ and the points of trisection of the segment from $(-5, -1)$ to $(7, 5)$.

10. Find the equations of the altitudes of the triangle defined by $x + y - 3 = 0$, $4x + y - 2 = 0$, and $x - 3y - 5 = 0$.

11. The angle from the line $x - 2y - 1 = 0$ to a certain line through the intersection of $x + 5y + 7 = 0$ and $x - 3y - 6 = 0$ is 45°. Find the equation of this line.

32. Factorable Equations. The equation $x^2 - 4y^2 = 0$ may be written in the equivalent form

$$(x - 2y) \cdot (x + 2y) = 0.$$

The coördinates of a point will satisfy this equation if, and only if, they make one of the factors of the left-hand member equal to zero.* It follows that the graph of this equation consists of the two lines

$$x - 2y = 0 \quad \text{and} \quad x + 2y = 0.$$

Similarly, we may write the equation $x^2y + xy^2 + 3xy = 0$ in the equivalent form

$$x \cdot y \cdot (x + y + 3) = 0$$

from which it follows that the given equation is satisfied by the coördinates of those points, and no others, that lie on the lines

$$x = 0, \quad y = 0, \quad \text{and} \quad x + y + 3 = 0.$$

The graph of the given equation thus consists of these three lines.

EXERCISES

Draw the graphs of the following equations:

1. $x(y - 2) = 0$ **2.** $4x^2 - 9y^2 = 0$
3. $x^2 - 3xy + 2y^2 = 0$ **4.** $(x - y)^2 - 9 = 0$
5. $x^2 + 2xy + y^2 - 4 = 0$ **6.** $x^3 - 3x^2 - 10x = 0$

7. Write a single equation whose graph consists of the two lines
    (a) $x + 3y = 0, 3x + y = 0$ (b) $x - y + 1 = 0, x - y - 1 = 0$.

8. Explain the fallacy of the following statement: The graph of the equation $x \cdot y = 1$ consists of the two lines $x = 1$ and $y = 1$.

POLAR COÖRDINATES

33. Polar Equations of a Line. By substituting the values (Art. 17)

$$x = r \cos \theta \qquad\qquad y = r \sin \theta$$

of x and y in terms of r and θ in the general form $Ax + By + C = 0$ of the equation of a line, we obtain, as the **general polar form** of the equation of a line

$$r(A \cos \theta + B \sin \theta) + C = 0. \tag{44}$$

---

* It is an axiom of algebra that the product of two numbers is zero if, and only if, one of the numbers is equal to zero.

If we make the same substitution in the normal form $x \cos \theta + y \sin \theta - p = 0$ of the equation of a line, we obtain

$$r(\cos \theta \cos \omega + \sin \theta \sin \omega) - p = 0$$

which simplifies (Introd., Art. 11) to the **polar normal form**

$$r \cos (\theta - \omega) - p = 0. \tag{45}$$

The following special cases of the polar normal equation of a line are encountered frequently.

If the given line is perpendicular to the polar axis, $\omega = 0$ and (45) reduces to

$$r \cos \theta - p = 0 \quad \text{or} \quad r = p \sec \theta. \tag{46}$$

Similarly, if the line is parallel to the polar axis, $\omega = \dfrac{\pi}{2}$ and the normal equation becomes

$$r \sin \theta - p = 0 \quad \text{or} \quad r = p \csc \theta. \tag{47}$$

EXERCISES

Draw the lines:

1. $r(3 \cos \theta + 4 \sin \theta) - 8 = 0$

2. $r(2 \cos \theta - 5 \sin \theta) + 10 = 0$

3. $r \cos \theta + 4 = 0$ **4.** $r \cos \left(\theta - \dfrac{\pi}{4}\right) - 6 = 0$

5. $r = 3 \sec \left(\theta - \dfrac{2\pi}{3}\right)$ **6.** $\tan \theta = \dfrac{2}{5}$

Transform the following equations to polar coördinates:

7. $x + y - 6 = 0$ **8.** $3x - y - 10 = 0$

9. $2x - 5y - 11 = 0$ **10.** $6x + 11y + 3 = 0$

11. $y - x = 0$ **12.** $y - 5 = 0$

Transform the following equations to rectangular coördinates:

13. $r = 4 \sec \theta$ **14.** $r \cos \left(\theta - \dfrac{3\pi}{4}\right) = 5$ **15.** $\tan \theta = 2$

Write the equation of a line:

16. Perpendicular to the polar axis and passing through
(a) $(3, 0)$, (b) $(4, \pi)$, (c) $\left(6, \dfrac{\pi}{4}\right)$.

17. Parallel to the polar axis and passing through (a) $\left(5, \dfrac{\pi}{2}\right)$, (b) $\left(2, -\dfrac{\pi}{2}\right)$, (c) $\left(4, \dfrac{3\pi}{4}\right)$.

18. Through $\left(4, \dfrac{\pi}{6}\right)$, perpendicular to the line through the origin and the given point.

19. Through $(6, 0°)$, making an angle of $150°$ with the initial line.

20. Through $(2, \pi)$, making an angle $\dfrac{\pi}{4}$ with the initial line.

21. Through $\left(3, \dfrac{\pi}{4}\right)$, perpendicular to the line in Ex. 20.

22. Find the length of the segment of the line $r \cos\left(\theta - \dfrac{\pi}{3}\right) = 3$ included between the polar axis and the $90°$ axis.

23. A regular hexagon has its center at the origin and one vertex at $(a, 0)$. Find the equations of its sides.

24. Derive directly from a figure the polar normal form of the equation of a line and deduce from it the rectangular normal form.

MISCELLANEOUS EXERCISES

1. Find the equation of a line inclined to the x-axis at an angle of $135°$ and having its x-intercept equal to -6.

2. Find the equations of the lines through the origin and the points of trisection of the segment from $(2, -5)$ to $(8, -2)$.

3. Find a point on the y-axis equidistant from $(-2, 4)$ and $(6, 2)$. Find also the angle at the vertex of the isosceles triangle formed by these three points.

4. Find the intercepts of the line through $(3, -2)$ and $(-2, 8)$.

5. Find the equation of a line if the foot of the perpendicular to it from $(2, 1)$ is $(7, 3)$.

6. Find two points on the x-axis at a distance from the line $12x - 5y - 18 = 0$ numerically equal to 6.

7. Find a line through the origin that divides into two triangles of equal area the triangle formed by the coördinate axes and the line $5x + 2y = 20$.

8. A triangle has a right angle at $(3, 4)$. The hypotenuse lies on

$3x + 2y - 1 = 0$ with one end point at $(-1, 2)$. Find the other end point.

9. Two adjacent sides of a parallelogram are on $x + 3y - 5 = 0$ and $2x - 3y + 12 = 0$. If $(-3, 7)$ is a vertex, find the equations of the other two sides.

10. The equations of two sides and a diagonal of a rectangle are $8x + 3y + 1 = 0$, $8x + 3y - 13 = 0$, and $2x - y - 5 = 0$, respectively. Find the equations of the other two sides and the area of the rectangle.

11. Find the coördinates of the foot of the perpendicular from $(7, -4)$ to $3x - 5y - 7 = 0$.

12. Find four points that are equidistant from $3x - 4y + 4 = 0$, $7x - 24y + 2 = 0$ and also equidistant from $x + 5y - 6 = 0$, $5x - y + 2 = 0$.

13. Find the equation of the locus of a point whose distance from $x - 7y + 5 = 0$ is numerically equal to $\frac{3}{5}$ of its distance from $x + y - 3 = 0$.

14. Find the equation that must be satisfied by the coefficients in the equation $Ax + By + C = 0$ if the line

    (*a*) Passes through the origin

    (*b*) Passes through $(4, -3)$

    (*c*) Is parallel to $3x - 7y - 8 = 0$

    (*d*) Is perpendicular to $4x + 9y = 0$

    (*e*) Lies at a distance 4 from $(0, 0)$

    (*f*) Lies at a distance 2 from $(3, 1)$

    (*g*) Has its *y*-intercept equal to 5

    (*h*) Has equal intercepts.

15. Write the equation of each of the families of lines in Ex. 14.

16. Find two lines through the intersection of $3x + y - 2 = 0$ and $4x + 3y - 4 = 0$ for which the product of the intercepts equals 2.

17. Two vertices of an equilateral triangle are $(a, 0)$ and $(0, a)$ and the third vertex lies in the first quadrant. Find the equations of its sides.

18. The equations of two sides and a diagonal of a parallelogram are $3x - 5y - 7 = 0$, $3x - 5y + 21 = 0$, and $x + 3y - 7 = 0$, respectively. The other diagonal passes through the origin. Find the equations of the other two sides.

19. The equal sides of an isosceles triangle lie on $2x + 9y - 6 = 0$ and $7x - 6y + 10 = 0$. The base lies on a line through $(5, 2)$. Find the equation of this line. How many solutions?

20. Find the area of the triangle whose vertices are $(-1, -2)$, $(4, 2)$, and $(-2, 4)$ by finding the length of one side and the length of the perpendicular from the third vertex to that side. Check your result by the formula of Art. 14.

21. Derive the formula for the area of the triangle whose vertices are (x_1, y_1), (x_2, y_2), and (x_3, y_3) by the method of Ex. 20.

22. Find the equation of the locus of a point which forms, with $(-2, 1)$ and $(2, 4)$, the vertices of a triangle of area numerically equal to 10.

23. Show that the feet of the perpendiculars from $(1, -3)$ on the sides of the triangle $x = 0$, $y = 0$, $x - 2y - 4 = 0$ lie on a line.

24. Show that the equation of any line not parallel to the x-axis can be written in the form $x = y \operatorname{ctn} \alpha + a$, where α is the inclination and a is the x-intercept of the line.

25. Let l_1, l_2, l_3, and l_4 be four given lines such that l_3 is perpendicular to l_1 and l_4 to l_2. Show analytically that the angle from l_1 to l_2 is equal to the angle from l_3 to l_4.

26. Find the polar coördinates of the point of intersection of the lines $r = 3\sqrt{3} \sec \theta$, $r = 3 \csc \theta$.

27. Find the polar coördinates of the point of intersection of the lines $r \cos (\theta - 120°) = 2$ and $r \cos (\theta - 60°) = 2$.

SELECTED EXERCISES

1. Find the coördinates of the foot of the perpendicular from (x_1, y_1) on the line $Ax + By + C = 0$. Derive the formula for the distance from the given line to the given point as the distance between these two points.

2. Show that, if $B^2 - 4AC > 0$, the equation $Ax^2 + Bxy + Cy^2 = 0$ defines two lines through the origin. Find the condition that these two lines are perpendicular.

3. Find the equation of a family of lines such that the directed

distances of any line of the family from two given points are
(a) equal, (b) equal but opposite in sign.

 4. Show analytically that, in any triangle, the following sets of
three lines meet in a point (a) the altitudes, (b) the medians,
(c) the perpendicular bisectors of the sides.

 5. Show that the three points defined in Ex. 4 lie on a line and
find the ratio in which the intersection of the medians divides the
segment joining the other two points.

6. Let $A_1x + B_1y + C_1 = 0$, $A_2x + B_2y + C_2 = 0$, and $A_3x + B_3y + C_3 = 0$ be the equations of three lines. Show that these
lines meet in a point or are parallel if, and only if, $\begin{vmatrix} A_1 & B_1 & C_1 \\ A_2 & B_2 & C_2 \\ A_3 & B_3 & C_3 \end{vmatrix} = 0.$

7. Let A', B', and C' be points on the sides BC, CA, and AB,
respectively, of a triangle ABC. Show that A', B', and C' lie on a
line if, and only if,

$$\frac{\overline{BA'}}{\overline{A'C}} \cdot \frac{\overline{CB'}}{\overline{B'A}} \cdot \frac{\overline{AC'}}{\overline{C'B}} = -1. \qquad \text{Theorem of Menelaus}$$

8. With the configuration of Ex. 7, show that the lines AA',
BB', and CC' meet in a point or are parallel if, and only if

$$\frac{\overline{BA'}}{\overline{A'C}} \cdot \frac{\overline{CB'}}{\overline{B'A}} \cdot \frac{\overline{AC'}}{\overline{C'B}} = 1. \qquad \text{Theorem of Ceva}$$

 9. Write the equation, in polar coördinates, of the line through
(r_1, θ_1) and (r_2, θ_2).

CHAPTER IV

THE CIRCLE

34. Equation of a Circle in Terms of Its Center and Radius.
A circle is defined as the locus of a point that moves so that its distance from a fixed point, the center, is equal to a constant, the radius.

To find the equation of a circle from its definition, we let $C(h, k)$ be its center and let a be the radius. If $P(x, y)$ is any point on the circle, the expression for its distance from $C(h, k)$ is

FIG. 45

$$\sqrt{(x - h)^2 + (y - k)^2}$$

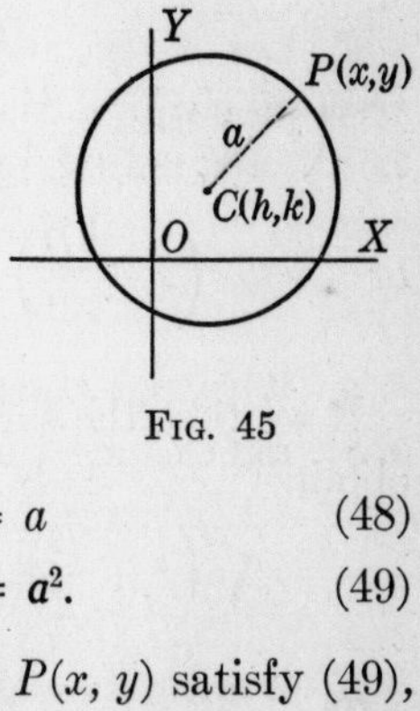

and, since this distance is equal to a, we have, as the equation of the circle,

$$\sqrt{(x - h)^2 + (y - k)^2} = a \tag{48}$$

or
$$(x - h)^2 + (y - k)^2 = a^2. \tag{49}$$

Conversely, if the coördinates of a point $P(x, y)$ satisfy (49), they also satisfy (48) so that the distance from P to C is equal to a and P lies on the circle. Equation (49) is thus the *equation of the circle with center $C(h, k)$ and radius a.*

In particular, if h and k are both equal to zero, equation (49) reduces to
$$x^2 + y^2 = a^2 \tag{50}$$

which is the equation of the circle in the important special case when the center of the circle lies at the origin.

35. General Form of the Equation of a Circle. If we expand equation (49), we obtain

$$x^2 + y^2 - 2hx - 2ky + h^2 + k^2 - a^2 = 0. \tag{51}$$

67

This equation is of the form

$$x^2 + y^2 + Dx + Ey + F = 0 \qquad (52)$$

so that every circle has an equation of the form (52).

We now wish to find out whether, conversely, every equation of the form (52) is the equation of a circle. For this purpose, we rewrite (52) in the equivalent form

$$(x^2 + Dx \qquad) + (y^2 + Ey \qquad) = \qquad -F$$

and complete the squares in the two parentheses by adding $\dfrac{D^2}{4}$ and $\dfrac{E^2}{4}$ to both sides of the equation. We now have

$$\left(x^2 + Dx + \frac{D^2}{4}\right) + \left(y^2 + Ey + \frac{E^2}{4}\right) = \frac{D^2}{4} + \frac{E^2}{4} - F$$

or $$\left(x + \frac{D}{2}\right)^2 + \left(y + \frac{E}{2}\right)^2 = \frac{D^2 + E^2 - 4F}{4}.$$

If we take the square root of both sides of this equation, we obtain

$$\sqrt{\left(x + \frac{D}{2}\right)^2 + \left(y + \frac{E}{2}\right)^2} = \frac{1}{2}\sqrt{D^2 + E^2 - 4F}. \qquad (53)$$

The left-hand member of (53) is the formula for the distance of the point (x, y) from the point $\left(-\dfrac{D}{2}, -\dfrac{E}{2}\right)$ and the right-hand member is a constant. The appearance of the graph of the equation is accordingly found to depend on the value of the quantity $D^2 + E^2 - 4F$, as follows:

(a) If $D^2 + E^2 - 4F > 0$, the right-hand member of (53) is real and greater than zero, so that the locus of (53), and hence of (52), is a circle of

Center $\left(-\dfrac{D}{2}, -\dfrac{E}{2}\right)$ and radius $\frac{1}{2}\sqrt{D^2 + E^2 - 4F}$ (54)

(b) If $D^2 + E^2 - 4F = 0$, the graph of the given equation reduces to a single point, the center $\left(-\dfrac{D}{2}, -\dfrac{E}{2}\right)$. In this case, (52) is said to define a **point circle,** or **circle of zero radius.**

(c) If $D^2 + E^2 - 4F < 0$, there can be no points on the graph since neither $\left(x + \dfrac{D}{2}\right)^2$ nor $\left(y + \dfrac{E}{2}\right)^2$ can be negative. In this case, (52) is said to define an **imaginary circle,** with the center and radius defined by (54).

If the definition of a circle is extended as in (b) and (c), equation (52) defines a circle for all real values of D, E, and F. It is called the **general form** of the equation of a circle. It is often a more convenient form to work with than equation (49) is, because the coefficients enter in it to the first power only.

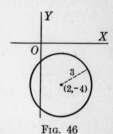

FIG. 46

Example 1. Find the center, the radius, and the coördinates of the intersections with the axes, of the circle $x^2 + y^2 - 4x + 8y + 11 = 0$.

To complete the squares in the left-hand member, we first write the equation in the form

$$(x^2 - 4x \qquad) + (y^2 + 8y \qquad) = \qquad - 11.$$

Inside the parentheses, the coefficients of x^2 and y^2 are unity. Hence these expressions become perfect squares by adding the square of half the coefficient of x and of y, respectively. On making these additions, we obtain

$$(x^2 - 4x + 4) + (y^2 + 8y + 16) = 4 + 16 - 11$$

or
$$(x - 2)^2 + (y + 4)^2 = 9.$$

The given equation thus defines a circle with center $(2, -4)$ and radius 3.

To find the intersections with the x-axis, put $y = 0$ and solve for x.

We have $\qquad\qquad x^2 - 4x + 11 = 0.$

Hence $\qquad\qquad\qquad x = 2 \pm \sqrt{-7}.$

Since these values of x are imaginary, the curve does not intersect the x-axis (Fig. 46).

Similarly, on putting $x = 0$, we obtain

$$y^2 + 8y + 11 = 0$$

so that

$$y = -4 \pm \sqrt{5}.$$

Hence the intersections with the y-axis are $(0, -4 + \sqrt{5})$ and $(0, -4 - \sqrt{5})$.

Example 2. Find the equation of the circle of radius 5 that lies in the first quadrant and is tangent to both axes.

Since the distance from the center of a circle to a tangent is numerically equal to the radius, the coördinates of the center of the

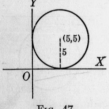

FIG. 47

required circle are $(5, 5)$ (Fig. 47), and its equation is, from (49),

$$(x - 5)^2 + (y - 5)^2 = 5^2$$

or

$$x^2 + y^2 - 10x - 10y + 25 = 0.$$

To verify that the circle defined by this equation is tangent to the x-axis, we put $y = 0$ in the final equation, giving

$$x^2 - 10x + 25 = 0.$$

Since the roots of this equation are equal, the circle is tangent to the x-axis. The point of tangency is found, by solving the above equation, to be $(5, 0)$.

The corresponding discussion for the y-axis is left as an exercise for the student.

EXERCISES

1. Write the equations of the following circles:

(a) Center $(-1, 3)$, radius 2   (b) Center $(2, 5)$, radius 6
(c) Center $(-3, -4)$, radius 5   (d) Center $(1, -4)$, radius 0
(e) Center $(-1, 7)$, radius 7   (f) Center $(-3, -3)$, radius 3.

2. Write the equation of a circle with:

(a) Center $(-4, 2)$ and passing through the origin
(b) Center $(2, -3)$ and passing through $(3, -5)$
(c) Center $(6, -5)$ and tangent to the x-axis

(d) Center $(-4, 3)$ and tangent to the y-axis

(e) Radius a, lying in the second quadrant, and tangent to both axes

(f) Center on the y-axis, radius a, and passing through the origin.

3. Find the center and radius of the following circles and draw the graph when it exists:

(a) $x^2 + y^2 - 6x + 10y - 2 = 0$

(b) $x^2 + y^2 + 10x + 8y + 25 = 0$

(c) $x^2 + y^2 + 4x - 12y = 0$

(d) $x^2 + y^2 + 4x - 6y - 7 = 0$

(e) $x^2 + y^2 + 5x + y + 8 = 0$

(f) $x^2 + y^2 + 4x - 10y + 29 = 0$

(g) $3x^2 + 3y^2 + 24x + 10y = 0$

(h) $4x^2 + 4y^2 - 3x + 5y - 6 = 0$.

4. Find the equation of a circle for which $(5, 2)$ and $(-1, 8)$ are ends of a diameter.

5. Find the equation of the circle that passes through $(5, 8)$ and is concentric with the circle $x^2 + y^2 - 3x - 7y + 2 = 0$. Find also the intersections of both circles with the coördinate axes.

6. Find the coördinates of six points on the circle $x^2 + y^2 - 2x - 4y - 20 = 0$.

7. Find the points of intersection of the circles $x^2 + y^2 - 4x + 2y - 8 = 0$ and $x^2 + y^2 - 2x - 8y + 4 = 0$.

8. Write the equation of the family of circles:

(a) With center at the origin

(b) With center at $(5, 2)$

(c) With center on the x-axis and passing through the origin

(d) With center on the line $y = x$ and passing through the origin.

9. Show analytically that the line through the center of a circle and the midpoint of a chord is perpendicular to the chord.

36. Circle Determined by Three Conditions.   Each of the standard forms of the equation of a circle

$$(x - h)^2 + (y - k)^2 = a^2 \quad \text{and} \quad x^2 + y^2 + Dx + Ey + F = 0$$

contains three constants. In order to find the equation of a required circle, we must, accordingly, be given enough information about the circle so that we can set up three equations from which to determine these constants. We can, for example, determine the constants if we know that the circle passes through three given points, or that it passes through two known points and that its center lies on a given line, and so on.

In any given problem, we must first decide which of the above two standard forms of the equation of the circle to use. If the coördinates of the center and the radius can be determined conveniently from the statement of the problem, it is usually best to find these numbers and substitute them in the first standard form. In most other cases, it is easier to use the general form of the equation of the circle, since the constants D, E, and F enter

Fig. 48

in this equation to the first power only.

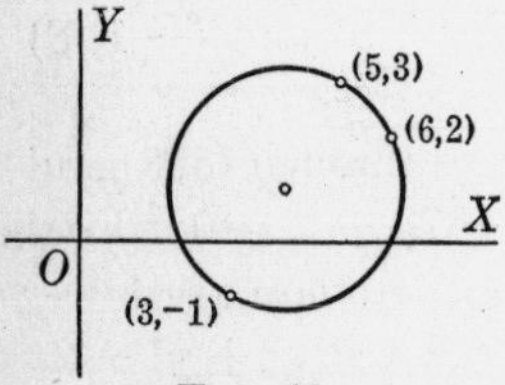

Example 1. Find the equation of the circle through the points $(5, 3)$, $(6, 2)$, and $(3, -1)$.

In problems of this type, we shall use the general form (52).

To find D, E, and F, we impose the condition that the coördinates of each of the given points satisfy the equation of the circle, that is,

$$25 + 9 + 5D + 3E + F = 0$$
$$36 + 4 + 6D + 2E + F = 0$$
$$9 + 1 + 3D - E + F = 0.$$

On solving these equations for D, E, and F, we find that

$$D = -8, \quad E = -2, \quad F = 12.$$

When these values of D, E, and F are substituted in equation (52), we have, as the required equation of the circle through the given points, $$x^2 + y^2 - 8x - 2y + 12 = 0.$$

Example 2. Find the equations of the circles that pass through $(-1, 1)$ and $(1, 3)$ and are tangent to the line $x + 3y = 0$.

In this case, we shall use equation (49).

Since the coördinates of each of the given points satisfy the equation of the circle, we have

$$(-1 - h)^2 + (1 - k)^2 = a^2$$

and $(1 + h)^2 + (3 - k)^2 = a^2.$

Since the distance from the center to the given tangent line is numerically equal to the radius, we have also

$$\frac{h + 3k}{\sqrt{10}} = \pm a.$$

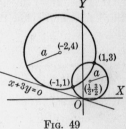

Fig. 49

By subtracting the second equation from the first, and simplifying, we obtain

$$h + k - 2 = 0. \tag{55}$$

If we substitute the value of a from the third equation in the first, and simplify, we have

$$9h^2 - 6hk + k^2 + 20h - 20k + 20 = 0. \tag{56}$$

On solving (55) and (56) as simultaneous and substituting the resulting solutions in the first of the above equations to find a, we obtain

$$h = -2, k = 4, a = \sqrt{10} \quad \text{and} \quad h = \frac{1}{2}, k = \frac{3}{2}, a = \frac{\sqrt{10}}{2}.$$

By substituting these sets of values of h, k, and a in (49), we obtain, as the equations of the required circles,

$$(x + 2)^2 + (y - 4)^2 = 10 \quad \text{and} \quad (x - \tfrac{1}{2})^2 + (y - \tfrac{3}{2})^2 = \tfrac{5}{2}$$

or $x^2 + y^2 + 4x - 8y + 10 = 0$ and $x^2 + y^2 - x - 3y = 0.$

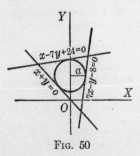

Fig. 50

Example 3. Find the equation of the circle inscribed in the triangle formed by the lines $x + y = 0$, $x - 7y + 24 = 0$, and $7x - y - 8 = 0$.

The distance from each of the sides of the triangle to the center is numerically equal to the radius a. To find this distance, we first write the equation of each side in the normal form

$$\frac{x+y}{\sqrt{2}} = 0, \quad \frac{x-7y+24}{-5\sqrt{2}} = 0, \quad \frac{7x-y-8}{-5\sqrt{2}} = 0.$$

It is seen from the figure that the center lies above the first and third sides and below the second, hence

$$a = \frac{h+k}{\sqrt{2}} = -\frac{h-7k+24}{-5\sqrt{2}} = \frac{7h-k-8}{-5\sqrt{2}}. \qquad (57)$$

On solving these equations, we find $h = 0$, $k = 2$, $a = \sqrt{2}$. Hence the equation of the required circle is

$$x^2 + (y-2)^2 = 2 \quad \text{or} \quad x^2 + y^2 - 4y + 2 = 0.$$

If we change the sign of any one of the directed distances in (57), the resulting equations determine the center and radius of an *escribed circle;* that is, a circle that is exterior to the triangle but is tangent to the three lines that define its sides.

EXERCISES

1. Find the equation of the circle that passes through the following points:

(a) $(0, 0)$, $(4, 0)$, $(3, 1)$ (b) $(0, 0)$, $(1, 8)$, $(2, 3)$

(c) $(0, 5)$, $(-3, 9)$, $(-1, 7)$ (d) $(4, 1)$, $(-5, 4)$, $(2, 3)$

(e) $(2, 3)$, $(4, -1)$, $(5, 2)$ (f) $(5, 9)$, $(-1, 1)$, $(1, 7)$

(g) $(1, 5)$, $(3, 1)$, $(-2, 2)$ (h) $(3, 2)$, $(2, 4)$, $(7, 1)$.

Find all the circles that satisfy the following conditions:

2. Passing through $(1, 3)$; center at the origin.

3. Passing through the origin; center at $(1, 3)$.

4. Passing through $(-2, 3)$ and $(6, -9)$; center on the line $3x - 2y + 3 = 0$.

5. Passing through $(-2, -3)$; center on the lines $x + y - 3 = 0$ and $2x - y - 12 = 0$.

6. Passing through $(4, 2)$ and $(-3, 1)$; radius 5.

7. Abscissa of center -11, radius 17, passing through $(4, 6)$.

8. Concentric with the circle $x^2 + y^2 - 8x - 4y = 0$; tangent to the line $7x - 24y - 55 = 0$.

9. Tangent to the line $3x - 4y - 7 = 0$ at $(5, 2)$; radius 5.

10. Tangent to the line $x + 3y - 2 = 0$ at $(-1, 1)$; passing through $(-5, -3)$.

11. Tangent to the line $3x + y = 0$; passing through $(2, -2)$ and $(6, 2)$.

12. Passing through $(-1, 2)$; tangent to both axes.

13. Circumscribed about the triangle $x + y + 1 = 0$, $3x + y - 5 = 0$, $2x + y - 4 = 0$.

14. Inscribed in the triangle $x = 0$, $y = 0$, $3x + 4y - 24 = 0$.

15. Inscribed in the triangle $9x + 2y - 18 = 0$, $2x + 9y + 7 = 0$, $7x - 6y + 2 = 0$.

16. Escribed to the triangle in Ex. 14.

★ **37. The Family $S + kS' = 0$.** Let

$$S \equiv x^2 + y^2 + Dx + Ey + F = 0$$

and $$S' \equiv x^2 + y^2 + D'x + E'y + F' = 0 \qquad (58)$$

be the equations of two circles. Consider the family of curves defined by the equation

$$S + kS' \equiv x^2 + y^2 + Dx + Ey + F + k(x^2 + y^2 + D'x + E'y + F') = 0. \quad (59)$$

For all values of k except $k = -1$, the curves of this family are circles, since, if we exclude the value $k = -1$, we may write the equation of the family in the form

$$x^2 + y^2 + \frac{D + kD'}{1 + k}\, x + \frac{E + kE'}{1 + k}\, y + \frac{F + kF'}{1 + k} = 0 \quad (60)$$

which is the equation of a circle.

If the circles $S = 0$ and $S' = 0$ intersect (Fig. 51a), all the circles (60) pass through their points of intersection. For, let $P_1(x_1, y_1)$ be a point the coördinates of which satisfy both equations (58). When we substitute the coördinates of P_1 in (59), the resulting equation reduces to $0 + k \cdot 0 = 0$ (Why?), which is true for all values of k, so that P_1 lies on all of the curves (59).

If $S = 0$ and $S' = 0$ do not intersect (Fig. 51b), the family of circles (60) still exists but no two circles of the family intersect.

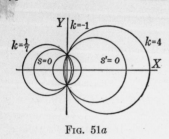

FIG. 51a

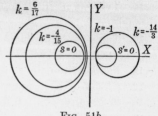

FIG. 51b

If the circles $S = 0$ and $S' = 0$ are not concentric, the curve of the family (59) defined by putting $k = -1$ is the line

$$(D - D')x + (E - E')y + F - F' = 0. \qquad (61)$$

This line is the **radical axis** of the family of circles (60).

If $S = 0$ and $S' = 0$ intersect in two points, the radical axis (61) passes through these two points and is thus the common chord of all the circles of the family (60).

EXERCISES

Draw the curve of the family $S + kS' = 0$ for $k = -5, -1, 0, 1, 8$, given:

1. $S \equiv x^2 + y^2 - 6x - 16 = 0$ $S' \equiv x^2 + y^2 + 6x - 16 = 0$.
2. $S \equiv x^2 + y^2 - 1 = 0$ $S' \equiv x^2 + y^2 - 10x + 21 = 0$.

3. In Ex. 1, find the points of intersection of $S = 0$ and $S' = 0$ and show that every circle through these two points belongs to the given family.

4. Show that there are two point circles in the family of Ex. 2 and find their equations.

5. Find the equation of the circle that passes through $(1, -3)$ and through the intersections of the circles $x^2 + y^2 + 3x - 5y - 2 = 0$ and $x^2 + y^2 - 8x - 4y - 1 = 0$.

6. Find the equation of the circle that passes through the intersections of $x^2 + y^2 - 2x - y - 9 = 0$ and $x^2 + y^2 - x + 3y - 4 = 0$ and has its center on the line $x - 2y - 4 = 0$.

Write the equations of the following families of circles, determine the radical axis, and the points of intersection when they exist.

7. $S \equiv x^2 + y^2 + 6x + 2y + 5 = 0$
$S' \equiv x^2 + y^2 - 6x - 4y - 3 = 0$

8. $S \equiv x^2 + y^2 - 25 = 0$
$S' \equiv x^2 + y^2 + 3x + 4y = 0$

9. $S \equiv x^2 + y^2 - 2x - 6y + 9 = 0$
$S' \equiv x^2 + y^2 + 6x + 2y - 15 = 0.$

10. If $S = 0$ and $S' = 0$ are not concentric, show that the centers of all the circles $S + kS' = 0$ lie on the line through the centers of $S = 0$ and $S' = 0$. This line is called the *line of centers* of the family $S + kS' = 0$.

11. Show that the line of centers (Ex. 10) of $S + kS' = 0$ is perpendicular to its radical axis.

12. Let $P_1(x_1, y_1)$ be a point external to the circle $(x - h)^2 + (y - k)^2 - a^2 = 0$, let T be the point of tangency of a tangent line from P_1 to this circle, and put $P_1 T = t$. Show that $t^2 = (x - h)^2 + (y - k)^2 - a^2$. The number t is called the *length of the tangent from P_1 to the circle.*

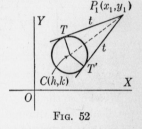

FIG. 52

13. If the lengths of the tangents (Ex. 12) from P to the circles $S = 0$ and $S' = 0$ are equal, show that P lies on the radical axis of $S + kS' = 0$, and conversely.

14. Let $S = 0$, $S' = 0$, and $S'' = 0$ be three circles whose centers do not all lie on a line. Find a point from which the lengths of the tangents to the three circles are all equal. This point is the *radical center* of the three circles.

15. Find the radical center (Ex. 14) of the circles

$$x^2 + y^2 - 6x - 4y - 9 = 0$$
$$x^2 + y^2 + 2x - 8y + 3 = 0$$
$$x^2 + y^2 - 4x + 2y + 1 = 0.$$

38. Loci Problems Leading to Lines and Circles. Analytic geometry is a particularly useful device for solving problems of loci. It is accordingly important to be able to carry through the process of setting up the equation of the locus defined by a given geometric condition. This process usually involves the following sequence of acts:

(1) *Choose a pair of axes located as conveniently as possible with respect to the data.*

(2) *Assume a point anywhere on the locus and call its coördinates* (x, y).

(3) *State, by means of an equation, the condition imposed on this point in order that it may lie on the locus.*

The graph of this equation is the required locus.

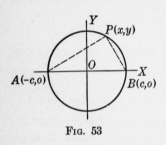

Fig. 53

The following examples will illustrate how the above principles are actually applied.

Example 1. Given two points A and B such that the length of the segment $AB = 2c$. Find the locus of a point such that the sum of the squares of its distances from A and B is equal to $4c^2$.

We choose the line through A and B as x-axis and the line perpendicular to it through the midpoint of the segment AB as y-axis. Then the coördinates of A are $(-c, 0)$ and of B $(c, 0)$.

Let $P(x, y)$ be a point anywhere on the locus.

From the statement of the problem, we have

$$AP^2 + BP^2 = 4c^2$$

and, on replacing AP^2 and BP^2 by their values from the distance formula, we obtain, as the equation of the required locus,

$$(x + c)^2 + (y - 0)^2 + (x - c)^2 + (y - 0)^2 = 4c^2.$$

This equation may be simplified to

$$x^2 + y^2 = c^2.$$

The required locus is thus a circle on AB as a diameter.

Example 2. Given two vertices A and B of a triangle. Find the locus of the third vertex C if $CB = 2CA$.

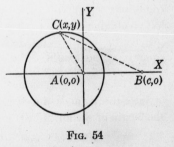

Fig. 54

We choose the line through A and B as x-axis, the line perpendicular to it through A as y-axis, and denote the coördinates of B by $(c, 0)$.

Let $C(x, y)$ be any point on the locus.

From the statement of the problem:

$$\sqrt{(x - c)^2 + y^2} = 2\sqrt{x^2 + y^2}.$$

Hence, $\qquad x^2 - 2cx + c^2 + y^2 = 4x^2 + 4y^2$

or $\qquad\qquad x^2 + y^2 + \dfrac{2}{3}cx - \dfrac{c^2}{3} = 0.$

This locus is a circle which has, as a diameter, the segment joining the two points $\left(\dfrac{c}{3}, 0\right)$ and $(-c, 0)$ on the line through A and B whose undirected distances from B are twice as great as from A.

Example 3. Given the base of a triangle and the lengths of the altitude and the median from the vertex to the base. Find the vertex of the triangle.

Take the midpoint of the base as origin and the line that contains the base as x-axis. Denote the length of the base, the altitude, and the median by $2c$, h, and m, respectively. Then the coordinates of the ends of the base are $A(-c, 0)$ and $B(c, 0)$.

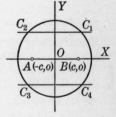

Let $C(x, y)$ be the required vertex.

The statement of the problem imposes two conditions on C. We shall determine the locus of a point that satisfies each of these conditions separately. Then any point of intersection of the two loci so obtained may be taken as the required vertex.

Fig. 55

Since the distance of C from the midpoint $(0, 0)$ of the base is equal to m, the length of the median, C lies on the circle

$$x^2 + y^2 = m^2. \tag{62}$$

Since the distance of C from the x-axis is *numerically* equal to h, the length of the altitude, C lies on one of the lines

$$y = h \text{ or } y = -h.$$

The intersections of these lines with the circle (62), that is, the points

$$(\sqrt{m^2-h^2},\, h),\ (-\sqrt{m^2-h^2},\, h),\ (\sqrt{m^2-h^2},\, -h),\ (-\sqrt{m^2-h^2},\, -h)$$

are the required positions of the vertex C.

The four triangles having the segment AB as base, and any one of the above four points as vertex, are congruent.

If $m^2 - h^2 < 0$, the triangle cannot be constructed.

EXERCISES

1. Solve Ex. 1 in the text when the coördinate axes are taken without special reference to the points A and B.

2. Solve Ex. 2 in the text when the coördinate axes are taken without special reference to the points A and B.

3. Solve Ex. 1 in the text, given that the sum of the squares of the distances of P from A and B is equal to k, where k is a given constant, and find the smallest value of k for which you can draw the graph.

Find the equation of the locus of a point, given that:

4. The distances from it to the points $(3, 5)$ and $(4, 2)$ are equal.

5. The square of its distance from $(6, 3)$ exceeds by 40 the square of its distance from $(-1, 2)$.

6. The sum of the squares of its distances from the lines $x + 3y - 2 = 0$ and $3x - y + 4 = 0$ is equal to 4.

7. The square of its distance from $(6, 2)$ equals 10 times its directed distance from $3x + 4y + 5 = 0$.

8. A segment of length 12 has one end on the y-axis and the other on the x-axis. Find the locus of the midpoint of the segment.

9. Find the locus of a point such that the midpoint of the segment joining it to $(0, b)$ lies on the circle $x^2 + y^2 = a^2$.

Choose a suitable pair of axes and determine the locus of a point that moves so that:

10. Its distances from two given points are equal.

11. Its distance from a fixed point A equals k times its distance from a fixed point B.

12. The algebraic sum of its directed distances from three given lines is equal to a given constant.

13. The sum of the squares of its distances from two adjacent sides of a square equals the sum of the squares of its distances from the other two sides.

14. The angle from the line through it and a fixed point A to the line through it and a fixed point B is a constant.

15. The feet of the perpendiculars from it to the sides of a given triangle lie on a line.

In the following exercises, choose the coördinate axes with reference to the figure so that the coördinates of two vertices are known. Determine the third vertex as a point of intersection of two loci, given:

16. The base, the length of one side, and the altitude.

17. One of the equal sides of an isosceles triangle and the angle that the median to it makes with that side.

18. One of the equal sides of an isosceles triangle and the length of the median to that side.

19. The base, the angle at the vertex, and the altitude.

20. The base and the lengths of the medians from the ends of the base.

POLAR COÖRDINATES

39. Polar Equation of a Circle. Let $C(c, \gamma)$ be the center and a the radius of the given circle and let $P(r, \theta)$ be any point on the circle. If we apply the law of cosines (Introd., Art. 13) to the triangle COP, we obtain

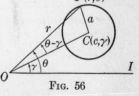

$$r^2 - 2cr \cos (\theta - \gamma) + c^2 = a^2 \quad (63)$$

which is the polar equation of a circle with center (c, γ) and radius a.

Fig. 56

The following special cases are of importance:

(*a*) If the center lies on the polar axis and the circle passes through the origin, the coördinates of the center are $(a, 0)$ or (a, π) (Why?) and equation (63) reduces to

$$r = 2a \cos \theta \quad \text{or} \quad r = -2a \cos \theta, \tag{64}$$

the first equation holding if the center is to the right of the origin and the second if it is to the left.

(b) If the center lies on the 90° axis, and the circle passes through the origin, the coördinates of the center are $\left(a, \pm \dfrac{\pi}{2}\right)$ and equation (63) reduces to

$$r = 2a \sin \theta \quad \text{or} \quad r = -2a \sin \theta, \tag{65}$$

according as the center lies above or below the origin.

(c) If the center lies at the origin, $c = 0$ and the equation may be simplified to

$$r = a. \tag{66}$$

EXERCISES

1. Find the polar equations of the following circles:

(a) Center at the origin, radius 5   (b) Center $(3, 0)$, radius 3

(c) Center $\left(8, \dfrac{\pi}{4}\right)$, radius 4   (d) Center $\left(4, \dfrac{\pi}{2}\right)$, radius 4

(e) Center $\left(4, \dfrac{5\pi}{4}\right)$, radius 2   (f) Center $\left(6, \dfrac{\pi}{6}\right)$, radius 6

(g) Center $\left(a, \dfrac{3\pi}{2}\right)$, radius a (h) Center $(a, 3\pi)$, radius a.

2. Find the center and the radius of the following circles:

(a) $r = -20 \sin \theta$ (b) $r = 7 \cos \theta$

(c) $r = 6 \cos \left(\theta - \dfrac{\pi}{4}\right)$ (d) $r = -4 \cos \left(\theta - \dfrac{\pi}{3}\right)$

(e) $r^2 - 8r \cos \theta + 5 = 0$ (f) $r^2 - 4r \sin \theta = 5$

(g) $r^2 - 6r \cos \left(\theta - \dfrac{\pi}{6}\right) + 5 = 0$

(h) $r^2 - 10r \cos \left(\theta - \dfrac{5\pi}{4}\right) = 11$.

3. Write the equations of the circles in Ex. 2 in rectangular coördinates.

4. Show by changing to rectangular coördinates that the equation $r = a \cos \theta + b \sin \theta$ defines a circle and state the geometrical meaning of a and b.

5. Write the equations of the following circles in polar coördinates:

(a) $x^2 + y^2 = 16$

(b) $x^2 + y^2 + 2y = 0$

(c) $x^2 + y^2 - 2x = 0$

(d) $x^2 + y^2 - 4x - 4y - 28 = 0$

(e) $x^2 + y^2 - 7\sqrt{3}x - 7y + 24 = 0$

(f) $x^2 + y^2 - 5x + 5\sqrt{3}y - 39 = 0$.

6. Write the equations of the following circles in the form of equation (63) and state the coördinates of their centers and their radii:

(a) $r = 6 \cos \theta + 8 \sin \theta$.   (b) $r^2 + 10r \cos \theta + 24r \sin \theta - 120 = 0$.

MISCELLANEOUS EXERCISES

1. Find the equation of the circle:

(a) That has its center on the lines $4x - 3y + 2 = 0$ and $2x + y + 2 = 0$ and passes through $(3, 1)$.

(b) That has as a diameter the segment of $2x - 3y + 11 = 0$ from $(- 1, 3)$ to its intersection with $2x - 5y + 25 = 0$.

(c) That passes through $(2, 3)$ and $(6, 1)$ and has its center on $2x - 3y + 2 = 0$.

(d) That has as a diameter the segment from $(1, 3)$ to the foot of the perpendicular from that point to the line $2x + 3y - 37 = 0$.

(e) That passes through $(- 6, - 4)$ and the points of trisection of the segment from $(4, - 2)$ to $(1, 1)$.

(f) That touches the x-axis at $(6, 0)$ and passes through $(3, 1)$.

(g) Circumscribed about the triangle $x + y - 8 = 0$, $5x + 3y - 28 = 0$, $2x + y - 11 = 0$.

2. Do the following points lie on a circle?

(a) $(5, 10)$, $(7, - 4)$, $(1, - 2)$, $(- 1, 2)$

(b) $(3, 3)$, $(5, - 1)$, $(2, 4)$, $(4, 2)$.

3. Show that the circle $x^2 + y^2 - 6x + 10y + 9 = 0$ touches the x-axis and intersects the y-axis in two distinct points.

4. Find the length of the chord that is cut from the line $y = 4x - 22$ by the circle $x^2 + y^2 - 4x - 6y - 21 = 0$.

5. The midpoint of a chord of the circle $x^2 + y^2 - 2x + 4y - 47 = 0$ is $(6, -1)$. Find the length of the chord.

6. Find the equation of the circle circumscribing the equilateral triangle whose vertices are $(-a, 0)$, $(a, 0)$, and $(0, a\sqrt{3})$.

7. Find two circles of radius 25 that touch the line $24x - 7y - 13 = 0$ at $(2, 5)$.

8. Show that the perpendicular from any point on a circle to a diameter is a mean proportional between the segments into which it divides the diameter.

9. Find the equation of the locus of a point the sum of the squares of whose distances from the three vertices of a triangle is constant.

10. Show that the locus of a point for which the sum of the squares of the distances from n given points is constant is a circle.

11. If $P_1(x_1, y_1)$ is a point on the circle $x^2 + y^2 = a^2$, show that the line $x_1x + y_1y = a^2$ is tangent to the circle at P_1.

12. Show that all the lines of the family $y = mx \pm a\sqrt{m^2 + 1}$, m being the parameter, are tangent to the circle $x^2 + y^2 = a^2$. What is the geometric meaning of the parameter?

13. Find the equations of the two lines tangent to $x^2 + y^2 = 25$ and:

(a) Parallel to $2x - y + 6 = 0$ (b) Passing through $(1, 7)$.

14. Find the points of intersection of the curves:

(a) $r = 12 \cos \theta$ (b) $r = 4 \sin \theta$
    $r \cos \theta = 3$ $r \cos \theta = \sqrt{3}$.

SELECTED EXERCISES

1. Show that, in any triangle, the circle through the midpoints of the sides passes also through the feet of the altitudes and through the points midway between the vertices and the point of intersection of the altitudes. This circle is called the *nine point circle* of the given triangle.

2. A navigator, about to enter a harbor, is uncertain as to his position P. He selects three objects A, B, and C on the shore whose positions are given on the chart and measures the directed angles APB and BPC. Show that his position P is fixed by these angles except when P lies on the circle through A, B, and C.

Note. This problem is of importance in practical navigation.

3. The angle between two intersecting circles is defined as equal to the angle between their tangents at a point of intersection. If ϕ is the angle between the intersecting circles $x^2 + y^2 + Dx + Ey + F = 0$ and $x^2 + y^2 + D'x + E'y + F' = 0$, show that

$$\cos \phi = \pm \frac{DD' + EE' - 2F - 2F'}{\sqrt{D^2 + E^2 - 4F} \sqrt{D'^2 + E'^2 - 4F'}}.$$

4. Using the results of Ex. 3, find the condition that the given circles are (a) tangent, (b) orthogonal, that is, that they intersect at right angles.

5. Let P be any point, other than the origin, and let P' be the point collinear with P and the origin and situated so that, using directed segments,

$$\overline{OP} \cdot \overline{OP'} = k^2$$

where k is a constant. The transformation of the points of the plane obtained by replacing each point P by its corresponding point P' is called an *inversion*. Show that the coördinates of $P'(x', y')$ are determined in terms of those of $P(x, y)$ by the equations

$$x' = \frac{k^2 x}{x^2 + y^2}; \quad y' = \frac{k^2 y}{x^2 + y^2}.$$

6. Show that the locus of a point that is transformed into itself by an inversion is a circle. This circle is called the *circle of inversion*.

7. If P is exterior to the circle of inversion (Ex. 6), show that P' is the intersection with OP of the line joining the points of tangency of the tangents from P to the circle of inversion.

8. Show that, by an inversion:

(a) A line that passes through O is transformed into itself.

(b) A line not passing through O is transformed into a circle through O, and conversely.

(c) A circle not passing through O is transformed into a circle.

CHAPTER V

THE CONIC SECTIONS

40. Plane Sections of a Right Circular Cone. The curve of section of a right circular cone by any plane is called a **conic section** or, simply, a **conic.** If the cutting plane does not pass through the vertex of the cone, the conic belongs to one of the following three types:

(*a*) If the cutting plane cuts entirely across one nappe of the cone (Fig. 57*a*), the conic is called an **ellipse.**

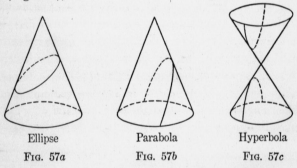

| Ellipse | Parabola | Hyperbola |
| Fig. 57*a* | Fig. 57*b* | Fig. 57*c* |

(*b*) If the cutting plane is parallel to a rectilinear element of the cone (Fig. 57*b*), it cuts the cone in a **parabola.**

(*c*) If the plane cuts both nappes of the cone (Fig. 57*c*), the conic is a **hyperbola.**

These three types of curves were named, and discussed very thoroughly, by the ancient Greek mathematicians, who studied them by the aid of methods very similar to those we now use in elementary geometry. By means of these very inefficient methods, they succeeded in proving essentially all of the properties of these curves that will be considered in this course. In particular, they found properties that will serve to define the conics as loci in their planes and which we shall use, in place of the definitions given on page 86, to derive the equations of these curves.

41. General Equation of the Second Degree. Standard Forms. It is an important and very useful fact of analytic geometry that the equation of a conic in rectangular coördinates is always of second degree, that is, it is of the form

$$Ax^2 + Bxy + Cy^2 + Dx + Ey + F = 0, \qquad (67)$$

wherein A, B, C, D, E, and F are constants, of which the first three are not all zero. Equation (67) is called the **general form** of the equation of a conic.

The general form (67) of the equation of a conic is comparatively long but, for any *given* conic, it is always possible to choose the position of the coördinate axes so that several of the coefficients in its equation are zero. When the axes are so chosen that the equation of a given conic is in the simplest possible form, this simplest form is called the **standard form** of the equation of the given conic. In this chapter, we shall derive the equations of the conics, and determine some of their properties, when the axes are chosen so that the equation of the conic is in its standard form.

THE PARABOLA

42. Definitions. *A parabola is the locus of a point that moves in such a way that its undirected distances from a fixed point and from a fixed line are equal.*

Thus, in Fig. 58, let F be the fixed point and $D'D$, the fixed line. The locus of the points P such that

$$FP = RP,$$

where R is the foot of the perpendicular from P to $D'D$, is a parabola. If we plot a number of these points and draw a smooth curve through them, we obtain a figure to represent this curve.

The fixed point F (Fig. 58) is called the **focus,** and the fixed line $D'D$ the **directrix,** of the parabola.   The line $A'A$, through the focus perpendicular to the directrix, is called the **axis** of the

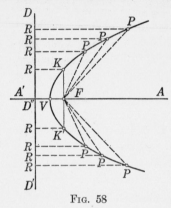

FIG. 58

parabola.   The point V that lies on the axis midway between the focus and the directrix is the **vertex.**   The chord $K'K$ of the parabola through the focus, parallel to the directrix, and terminated by the curve, is called the **latus rectum.**

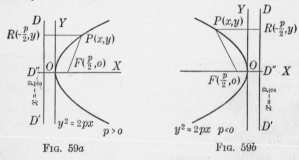

FIG. 59a   FIG. 59b

43. Standard Form of the Equation of the Parabola.   To obtain the standard form of the equation of the parabola, we take the axis of the curve as the x-axis and the vertex as the origin. Let F be the focus and let $D'D$ (Figs. 59a and 59b) be the directrix.   Let D'' be the intersection of the directrix with the axis and let the length of the directed segment $\overline{D''F} = p$.

Then the coördinates of F are $\left(\dfrac{p}{2}, 0\right)$, of D'' are $\left(-\dfrac{p}{2}, 0\right)$, and the equation of the directrix is $x = -\dfrac{p}{2}$.

Let $P(x, y)$ be any point on the parabola. Draw FP and RP, where R is the foot of the perpendicular from P to the directrix. From the definition of a parabola,

$$FP = RP, \text{ or } FP^2 = RP^2. \tag{68}$$

From the distance formula, we have

$$FP^2 = \left(x - \frac{p}{2}\right)^2 + (y - 0)^2.$$

Also, $$RP^2 = \left(x + \frac{p}{2}\right)^2. \tag{Why?}$$

By substituting these values of FP^2 and RP^2 in (68), we obtain

$$\left(x - \frac{p}{2}\right)^2 + y^2 = \left(x + \frac{p}{2}\right)^2.$$

On simplifying this equation, we have

$$y^2 = 2px. \tag{69}$$

Conversely, if the coördinates of P satisfy (69), we find, by adding $\left(x - \dfrac{p}{2}\right)^2$ to both sides of the equation, that they satisfy

$$\left(x - \frac{p}{2}\right)^2 + y^2 = \left(x + \frac{p}{2}\right)^2.$$

Hence, $$FP^2 = RP^2$$

or, since FP and RP, being undirected, are both positive,

$$FP = RP$$

so that P lies on the parabola.

Equation (69) is the equation of the parabola when the axis of the parabola is the x-axis and the vertex is the origin. If p is positive, the focus is to the right of the origin (Fig. 59a) and, if p is negative, the focus is to the left (Fig. 59b).

If the axis of the parabola is taken as the y-axis, and the vertex as the origin, we find in a similar way that the equation of the parabola is

$$x^2 = 2py \tag{70}$$

where the focus lies above the x-axis if p is positive, and below it if p is negative.

Equations (69) and (70) are the standard forms (Art. 41) of the equation of a parabola.

44. Discussion of the Equation. If we solve equation (69) for y, we find

$$y = \pm \sqrt{2px}.$$

If p is positive (as in Fig. 59a), there are no points on the curve for which x is negative since, for such values of x, y is imaginary. Similarly, if p is negative, there are no points on the curve for which x is positive (Fig. 59b).

If $x = 0$, then $y = 0$, so that the vertex, which we have taken as origin, lies on the curve. The parabola does not intersect either axis in any other point since, if we put $x = 0$, the only value of y that satisfies the resulting equation is $y = 0$, and if we put $y = 0$, the only solution is $x = 0$.

To each value of x agreeing in sign with p, there correspond two values of y which are numerically equal but opposite in sign. This fact is expressed by saying that the curve is *symmetric* (Art. 5) to the x-axis.

As x increases numerically, the corresponding two values of y also increase numerically. It follows that the curve extends indefinitely far away from both axes.

Since the latus rectum (Art. 42) is parallel to the y-axis, its length is the sum of the numerical values of the ordinates of its end points. To find these ordinates, put $x = \dfrac{p}{2}$ (Why?) in the equation of the curve. We then have

$$y^2 = p^2 \text{ or } y = \pm p.$$

Hence, *the length of the latus rectum is the numerical value of $2p$.*

Example 1. Locate the vertex, focus, axis, and directrix and find the length of the latus rectum of the parabola $y^2 = -6x$.

Since the equation is in the standard form (69), with $p = -3$, the coördinates of the vertex are $(0, 0)$ and of the focus are $(-\frac{3}{2}, 0)$. The equation of the axis of the parabola is $y = 0$ and of its directrix is $x - \frac{3}{2} = 0$. The length of the latus rectum is 6 (Fig. 60).

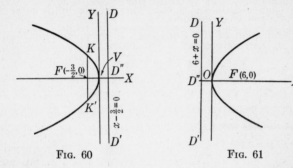

FIG. 60   FIG. 61

Example 2. Find the equation of a parabola, the coördinates of its focus, and the equation of its directrix, if the vertex is at the origin, the focus is on the x-axis to the right of the vertex, and the length of the latus rectum is 24.

Since the focus is to the right of the vertex, p is positive and equal to one-half of the length of the latus rectum, or 12. Since the coördinate axes are placed so that the equation of the parabola is in the standard form (69), the required equation of the curve is $y^2 = 24x$, the coördinates of the focus are $(6, 0)$, and the equation of the directrix is $x + 6 = 0$ (Fig. 61).

45. Applications. The parabola is frequently encountered in the applications of analytic geometry. Only a few of the best known of these applications can be mentioned here.

The path of a projectile near the surface of the earth (air resistance being neglected) is a parabola.

A cable of a suspension bridge, if the load is uniformly distributed along the bridge, assumes a parabolic form.

A parabolic mirror is one whose reflecting surface may be

generated by revolving a parabola about its axis. The construction of locomotive headlights is based on the principle that, if a source of light is placed at the focus of such a mirror, the rays striking the mirror will be reflected parallel to the axis of the mirror. In the construction of reflecting telescopes, also, use is made of the fact that, if the axis of a parabolic mirror is pointed toward a star, the rays from the star that strike the mirror will all be reflected to the focus.

★ **46. Constructions for a Parabola.** (1) *Continuous Construction.* An arc of a parabola can

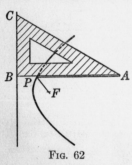

Fig. 62

readily be drawn in the following way: At the vertex A of a draftsman's triangle (Fig. 62) fasten one end of a string of length AB. Fasten the other end at the focus F of the required parabola and place the other leg BC of the triangle along the directrix. Hold the string taut by pressing it against the side of the triangle with the point of a pencil at P. If the side BC of the triangle is now made to slide along the directrix, the point P will describe an arc of the parabola.

(2) *Point by Point Construction.* As many points on the parabola as may be desired can be found by means of the following construction with ruler and compasses: Through the focus F draw the axis of the parabola perpendicular to the directrix and meeting it at D''. Through any point L on the axis that lies nearer to F than to D'', draw a line $A'A$ parallel to the directrix and,

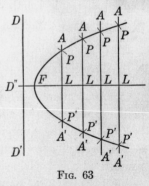

Fig. 63

with F as center and radius $D''L$, draw a circle intersecting $A'A$ at P and P'. Then P and P' lie on the parabola.

EXERCISES

1. Draw the following parabolas, find the length of the latus rectum, locate the vertex, focus, axis, and directrix, and plot them on the figure.

(a) $y^2 = 6x$ (b) $x^2 = 4y$ (c) $x^2 + 10y = 0$

(d) $y^2 = -8x$ (e) $y^2 + 5x = 0$ (f) $3y^2 + 8x = 0$

(g) $2x^2 - 9y = 0$ (h) $7y^2 = 4x$.

2. Find the equation of the parabola having its vertex at the origin and the x-axis as its axis, given that:

(a) Its focus is $(3, 0)$.

(b) Its directrix is $x + 5 = 0$.

(c) It passes through $(2, 5)$.

(d) Its directrix passes through $(4, 11)$.

(e) Its directrix is $x + a = 0$.

(f) Its focus lies on $2x + 3y - 6 = 0$.

(g) The length of its latus rectum is 20. (Two solutions)

3. Determine the points of intersection of the parabolas:

(a) $y^2 = 5x$, $x^2 = 5y$ (b) $y^2 = 24x$, $x^2 = 3y$

(c) $2y^2 = 9x$, $3x^2 = 4y$ (d) $y^2 = 2x$, $x^2 = y$.

4. Find the equation of the circle that has the latus rectum of $y^2 = 2px$ as a diameter.

5. Find the equation of the line through the points of the parabola $x^2 = 12y$ for which the abscissas are 3 and 4.

6. Find the length of the chord of the parabola $y^2 = 18x$ that lies on the line $y = x + 4$.

7. The *focal radius* of a point on a parabola is its distance from the focus. Show that the focal radius of a point $P_1(x_1, y_1)$ that lies on the parabola $y^2 = 2px$ is numerically equal to $x_1 + \dfrac{p}{2}$.

8. Find the focal radii (Ex. 7) of the points on the parabola $y^2 = 12x$ for which: (a) $x = 3$, (b) $y = 18$, (c) $y = x$, (d) $x^2 + y^2 = 22x$.

9. Determine the points on the parabola $y^2 = 24x$ for which the focal radii are equal in length to the latus rectum.

10. Show that the lines drawn from the point of intersection of the directrix and the axis of a parabola to the ends of the latus rectum are perpendicular to each other.

11. A circle passes through $(a, 0)$ and touches the line $x + a = 0$. Find the locus of its center.

12. Find the locus of a point whose undirected distance from $(3, 0)$ exceeds by 3 its directed distance from the y-axis.

13. Find the loci of the ends of the latera recta * of the family of parabolas $y^2 = 2px$, p being the parameter of the family.

14. The distance between the towers of Brooklyn Bridge is about 1600 feet and the lowest point of the cables is about 140 feet below these points of support. Assuming that the form of the cables is parabolic, take the lowest point of one of them as origin, the y-axis vertical, and find the equation of the parabola.

The equations of the following parabolas are not in the standard form. Find the required equations by determining the focus and directrix and using the definition of a parabola (Art. 42).

15. (a) Focus $(3, 1)$, directrix $y = 0$
  (b) Vertex $(2, -1)$, directrix $y + 3 = 0$
  (c) Vertex $(2, 1)$, focus $(5, 1)$
  (d) Vertex $(2, 9)$, focus $(2, 5)$.

16. (a) Focus $(0, 0)$, directrix $x + 2y - 5 = 0$
  (b) Focus $(3, -2)$, directrix $x + y + 1 = 0$
  (c) Focus $\left(\dfrac{a}{2}, \dfrac{a}{2}\right)$, directrix $x + y = 0$.

17. Prove that the constructions in Art. 46 lead to parabolas.

THE ELLIPSE

47. Standard Form of the Equation of the Ellipse. *An ellipse is the locus of a point that moves so that the sum of its undirected distances from two fixed points is equal to a constant.* The two fixed points are called the **foci** and the point midway between them is the **center** of the ellipse.

---

* The plural of latus rectum is latera recta.

To derive the standard form of the equation of the ellipse, we take the line through the foci as the x-axis and the center as the origin.   Let F and F' (Fig. 64) be the foci and let $2c$ be the distance between them, so that the coördinates of F are $(c, 0)$ and of F' are $(-c, 0)$.

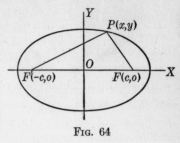

Let $P(x, y)$ be any point on the ellipse and let the sum of its distances from the foci be $2a$, so that

Fig. 64

$$F'P + FP = 2a, \tag{71}$$

or $\qquad \sqrt{(x + c)^2 + y^2} + \sqrt{(x - c)^2 + y^2} = 2a.$

If we transpose the second radical, square, and solve for the radical expression, we find that

$$\sqrt{(x - c)^2 + y^2} = a - \frac{c}{a} x. \tag{72}$$

By squaring again, and simplifying, we obtain

$$\frac{a^2 - c^2}{a^2} x^2 + y^2 = a^2 - c^2 \tag{73}$$

or

$$\frac{x^2}{a^2} + \frac{y^2}{a^2 - c^2} = 1. \tag{74}$$

But $a > c$, since, in the triangle $F'PF$, the sum of the two sides $F'P + FP$, which equals $2a$ by (71), is greater than the third side $F'F$, which is equal to $2c$.   Hence $a^2 - c^2$ is positive. We shall denote this positive number by b^2, that is

$$b^2 = a^2 - c^2. \tag{75}$$

If we substitute this value for $a^2 - c^2$ in (74), we have

$$\frac{x^2}{a^2} + \frac{y^2}{b^2} = 1. \tag{76}$$

$c^2 = a^2 - b^2$

It can be proved conversely (see page 105, Ex. 11) that, if the coördinates of a point $P(x, y)$ satisfy (76), then $F'P + FP = 2a$, so that P lies on the ellipse.

Equation (76) is thus the equation of the ellipse. It is the standard form obtained by taking the line through the foci as the x-axis and the center as the origin.

If we choose the coördinate axes so that the foci are $(0, \pm c)$ on the y-axis, we obtain in a precisely similar way

$$\frac{x^2}{b^2} + \frac{y^2}{a^2} = 1 \tag{77}$$

as the standard form when the line through the foci is the y-axis and the center is the origin.

To distinguish, in numerical problems, between the cases in which the foci are on the x-axis (equation 76) or on the y-axis (equation 77) we notice that, because of (75), the number a, for the ellipse, cannot be less than b. It is equal to b only if $c = 0$, in which case the ellipse becomes a circle.

48. Discussion of the Equation. If we solve equation (76) for y and for x, we obtain

$$y = \pm \frac{b}{a} \sqrt{a^2 - x^2} \quad \text{and} \quad x = \pm \frac{a}{b} \sqrt{b^2 - y^2} \tag{78}$$

respectively.

From the first of these equations, it follows that if $x^2 > a^2$, y is imaginary and, from the second, that if $y^2 > b^2$, then x is imaginary. There are thus no points on the ellipse outside of the rectangle formed by the lines $x = \pm a$ and $y = \pm b$.

To any value of x numerically less than a, there correspond two values of y, numerically equal but opposite in sign. Hence the curve is symmetric (Art. 5) to the x-axis. By similar reasoning, from the second of equations (78), we find that it is also symmetric to the y-axis.

If $x = 0$, $y = \pm b$; and, as x increases numerically, the numerical value of y decreases and becomes zero when $x = \pm a$.

49. Definitions. The ellipse defined by equation (76) intersects the x-axis at the points $V(a, 0)$ and $V'(-a, 0)$ (Fig. 65). These points are called the **vertices** of the ellipse. The chord $V'V$ joining the vertices is the **major axis** of the ellipse. Its length is $2a$ and it is the longest chord that can be drawn in the ellipse. The chord of the ellipse on the y-axis is of length $2b$

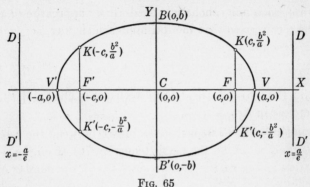

Fig. 65

and is called the **minor axis**. The numbers a and b are thus the lengths of the **semi-major axis** and the **semi-minor axis**, respectively.

Latus Rectum. The chord $K'K$, through either focus perpendicular to the major axis, is called the **latus rectum**. Its length is obviously twice the ordinate of K. To find this ordinate, put $x = \pm c$ in (76) and solve for y. We find, by the aid of (75), that

$$y = \pm \frac{b}{a} \sqrt{a^2 - c^2} = \pm \frac{b^2}{a}.$$

Hence, *the length of the latus rectum is* $\dfrac{2b^2}{a}$.

Eccentricity. The fraction $\dfrac{c}{a}$ is called the **eccentricity** and is denoted by the letter e. We have, by (75),

$$e = \frac{c}{a} = \frac{\sqrt{a^2 - b^2}}{a}. \tag{79}$$

Since, for an ellipse, c is always less than a, it follows that *the eccentricity of an ellipse is always less than unity.*

The shape of the ellipse (but not its size) is determined by its eccentricity. Thus, if $e = 0$, then $c = 0$, $b = a$, and the ellipse is a circle with its foci coincident at the center. As e increases from zero, the ellipse becomes more and more flattened. If we let e approach unity, holding a fixed, then c approaches a and b approaches zero so that the foci approach the vertices and the ellipse becomes very narrow.

Directrices. If $e \neq 0$, the two lines $x = \pm \dfrac{a}{e}$ (the lines $D'D$ in Fig. 65) are called the **directrices.** Their importance will appear in Art. 50.

Example 1. The vertices of an ellipse are $(\pm 4, 0)$ and its eccentricity is $e = \dfrac{\sqrt{3}}{2}$. Find its equation, locate the foci, and find the length of the latus rectum.

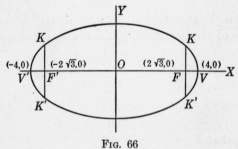

Fig. 66

We have $c = ae = 4 \cdot \dfrac{\sqrt{3}}{2} = 2\sqrt{3}$. The coördinates of the foci are thus $(\pm 2\sqrt{3}, 0)$. Moreover, $b^2 = a^2 - c^2 = 16 - 12 = 4$. Hence $b = 2$. The length of the latus rectum, as found from the formula $\dfrac{2b^2}{a}$, is equal to 2.

The equation of the ellipse, as found by substituting the values of a and b in equation (76), is $\dfrac{x^2}{16} + \dfrac{y^2}{4} = 1$.

Example 2. The equation of an ellipse is $25x^2 + 9y^2 = 225$. Find the coördinates of the vertices and of the foci and the equations of the directrices.

If we write the given equation in the form

$$\frac{x^2}{9} + \frac{y^2}{25} = 1,$$

we find, by the last paragraph of Art. 47, that the foci are on the y-axis. We have

$$a = 5, \quad b = 3, \quad c = \sqrt{a^2 - b^2} = 4,$$

and $e = \dfrac{c}{a} = \dfrac{4}{5}$.

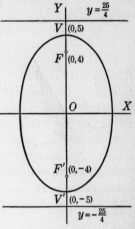

Fig. 67

The coördinates of the vertices are $(0, \pm 5)$ and of the foci are $(0, \pm 4)$. The equations of the directrices are $y = \pm \frac{25}{4}$.

EXERCISES

1. Find the vertices, foci, eccentricity, lengths of the semi-axes, and equations of the directrices of the following curves.

(a) $16x^2 + 25y^2 = 400$ (b) $9x^2 + 4y^2 = 36$

(c) $x^2 + 4y^2 = 4$ (d) $25x^2 + 4y^2 = 100$

(e) $2x^2 + 4y^2 = 50$ (f) $x^2 + 4y^2 = 9$

(g) $3x^2 + 2y^2 = 6$ (h) $81x^2 + 100y^2 = 100$.

2. Find the equation of the ellipse having:

(a) Vertices $(\pm 13, 0)$, foci $(\pm 8, 0)$

(b) Vertices $(\pm 5, 0)$, directrices $x = \pm \frac{25}{3}$

(c) Foci $(0, \pm 2)$, $e = \frac{2}{5}$

(d) Foci $(\pm 1, 0)$, directrices $x = \pm 2$

(e) Ends of minor axis $(\pm 3, 0)$, latus rectum 3

(f) Foci $(0, \pm 5)$, ends of minor axis $(\pm 5, 0)$.

3. Find the equation, in one of the standard forms, of an ellipse that passes through the points

(a) $\left(\dfrac{2\sqrt{3}}{3}, 1\right)$ and $\left(1, \dfrac{\sqrt{6}}{2}\right)$ (b) $(2, \sqrt{3})$ and $\left(\dfrac{\sqrt{10}}{3}, 2\right)$.

4. Find the points of intersection of the line $3x - 4y + 30 = 0$ with the ellipse $9x^2 + 4y^2 = 360$.

5. Find the points of intersection of the ellipses $9x^2 + 4y^2 = 72$ and $2x^2 + y^2 = 17$.

6. Show both analytically and graphically that the ellipses $4x^2 + 9y^2 = 36$ and $25x^2 + 16y^2 = 400$ do not intersect.

7. The ends of the base of a triangle are $(\pm 5, 0)$ and the sum of the lengths of the other two sides is 26. Find the equation of the locus of the vertex of the triangle.

8. Find the equation of the circle that passes through the four ends of the two latera recta of the ellipse $x^2 + 9y^2 = 81$.

9. Show that the length of the segment from a focus of an ellipse to an end of the minor axis is equal to the semi-major axis.

10. Find the equation of the locus of the midpoints of the ordinates of the points on the circle $x^2 + y^2 = a^2$.

11. Let $P(x, y)$ be any point on the circle $x^2 + y^2 = a^2$ and let P' be the point whose coördinates are $\left(x, \dfrac{by}{a}\right)$. Find the equation of the locus of P'.

12. Find the equation of the parabola with vertex at the origin that passes through the ends of the latus rectum to the right of the origin of the ellipse $\dfrac{x^2}{a^2} + \dfrac{y^2}{b^2} = 1$.

13. The earth's orbit is an ellipse with the sun at one of the foci. If the semi-major axis of the ellipse is 92.9 million miles and the eccentricity is 0.0168, find, to three significant figures, the greatest and the least distances of the earth from the sun.

50. A Second Definition of the Ellipse. We shall prove the following theorem: *The ellipse* $\dfrac{x^2}{a^2} + \dfrac{y^2}{b^2} = 1$ *is the locus of a point that moves in such a way that the ratio of its undirected distance from the focus* $F(ae, 0)$ *to its undirected distance from the directrix* $x - \dfrac{a}{e} = 0$ *is equal to* e, *the eccentricity.*

Let $P(x, y)$ be any point such that $\dfrac{FP}{RP} = e$, that is, such that

$$FP = eRP \quad \text{or} \quad FP^2 = e^2RP^2.$$

From the distance formula, we have

$$FP^2 = (x - ae)^2 + (y - 0)^2.$$

Moreover, $\qquad RP^2 = \left(\dfrac{a}{e} - x\right)^2.$ \qquad (Why?)

If we substitute these values of FP^2 and RP^2 in the above equation, we have

$$(x - ae)^2 + (y - 0)^2 = e^2\left(\dfrac{a}{e} - x\right)^2.$$

If we simplify this equation and multiply by a^2, we obtain:

$$a^2(1 - e^2)x^2 + a^2y^2 = a^4(1 - e^2). \qquad (80)$$

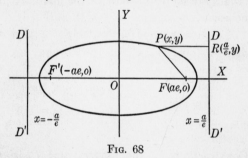

Fig. 68

But, with the aid of equations (79) and (75), we find that

$$a^2(1 - e^2) = a^2 - a^2e^2 = a^2 - c^2 = b^2$$

and, on making these substitutions in (80), we have

$$b^2x^2 + a^2y^2 = a^2b^2. \qquad (81)$$

Hence P lies on the given ellipse.

Conversely, if $P(x, y)$ lies on the ellipse, its coördinates satisfy (81) and, by reversing the steps in the above proof, we find that

$$\frac{FP}{RP} = e$$

that is, P satisfies the conditions of the theorem.

From the symmetry of the figure with respect to the y-axis,

it follows at once that the theorem of this article remains true
if we replace the focus $F(ae, 0)$ by $F'(- ae, 0)$ and the directrix
$x - \dfrac{a}{e} = 0$ by the second directrix $x + \dfrac{a}{e} = 0$.

The focus $(ae, 0)$ and the directrix $x - \dfrac{a}{e} = 0$ are said to be
a *corresponding* focus and directrix. Similarly, $(- ae, 0)$ and
$x + \dfrac{a}{e} = 0$ are a corresponding focus and directrix.

51. Some Applications of the Ellipse. The orthogonal projection of a circle on a plane oblique to the plane of the circle
is an ellipse.

Elliptic gears are used in machines, such as hay presses and
power punches, where a slow, powerful motion is needed in a
part, only, of each revolution.

The arches of stone, and of concrete, bridges are frequently
constructed in the form of semi-ellipses.

The orbits in which the planets, including the earth, revolve
around the sun, are ellipses.

A crescent, such as the crescent moon, is bounded by a semi-
circle and a semi-ellipse.

★ **52. Constructions for the Ellipse.** (1) *Continuous Construction.* Fasten thumb tacks at the two foci F' and F of the

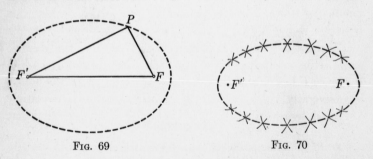

Fig. 69   Fig. 70

ellipse. Form a loop of thread of length $2a + 2c$, pass it around
the thumb tacks, and draw it taut with the point of a pencil.

If the pencil is now made to move around the foci, holding the thread constantly taut, the pencil point will describe an ellipse.

(2) *Point by Point Constructions.*   As many points as may be desired can be found by the following ruler and compass constructions.

(*a*) With centers at the foci F and F', draw circles of radii r and r' such that $r + r' = 2a$. The points of intersection of these circles lie on the ellipse.

(*b*) With center C and radii b and a, draw two circles. Draw through C a fixed line CA and, from C, draw any half-line

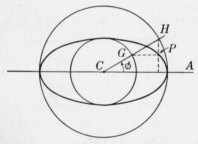

Fig. 71

intersecting the smaller circle at G and the larger at H.   Draw through G a line parallel to CA and through H a line perpendicular to it.   Then the point P of intersection of these two lines lies on the ellipse.

The angle $\phi = ACH$, in construction (*b*), is called the *eccentric angle* of the point P of the ellipse.   The circle of radius a is the *major auxiliary circle* and the one of radius b is the *minor auxiliary circle*.

EXERCISES

1. Find the equation of the ellipse with center at the origin, given:

(*a*) Focus $(3, 0)$, $e = \frac{1}{2}$ (*b*) Directrix $x = 6$, $e = \frac{2}{3}$

(c) Focus $(2, 0)$, directrix $x = 8$

(d) Vertex $(0, -3)$, directrix $y = 4$

(e) End of minor axis $(8, 0)$, $e = \frac{3}{5}$

(f) Vertex $(6, 0)$, $e = \frac{1}{3}$.

2. A square with sides parallel to the coördinate axes is inscribed in the ellipse $\dfrac{x^2}{a^2} + \dfrac{y^2}{b^2} = 1$. Find the coördinates of its vertices and its area.

3. A line segment AB, of length 12, moves so that A is always on the x-axis and B is on the y-axis. Find the equation of the locus of a point $P(x, y)$ of the segment that is twice as far from A as from B.

4. The arch of a bridge is a semi-ellipse with major axis horizontal. The span is 30 feet and the top of the arch is 10 feet above the major axis. The roadway is horizontal and two feet above the top of the arch. Find, at five-foot intervals, the vertical distance from the roadway to the arch.

5. Prove that, if two ellipses have the same eccentricity, their semi-axes are proportional.

6. Prove the theorem of Art. 50, using the focus $F'(-ae, 0)$ and the directrix $x + \dfrac{a}{e} = 0$.

7. The distances of a point P on an ellipse from the foci are called the *focal radii* of P. Show that the focal radii of $P(x, y)$ on the ellipse $b^2x^2 + a^2y^2 = a^2b^2$ are $a - ex$ and $a + ex$.

Hint. Use the theorems of Art. 50.

8. Find the focal radii (Ex. 7) of the point:

(a) $(1, \frac{3}{2})$ on the ellipse $3x^2 + 4y^2 = 12$

(b) $(3, -2)$ on the ellipse $x^2 + 2y^2 = 17$.

9. The equations of the following ellipses are not in the standard form. Find their equations by using the definition in Art. 47.

(a) Foci $(-2, 2)$, $(0, 2)$; $a = 5$

(b) Foci $(0, 0)$, $(-4, -3)$; $a = 3$.

10. For the following ellipses, the given focus and directrix are corresponding focus and directrix. Find the equations of these ellipses, using the theorems of Art. 50, and explain why the resulting equations are not in the standard form.

(a) Focus $(7, 1)$, directrix $x = 5$, $e = \dfrac{\sqrt{3}}{2}$;

(b) Focus $(-1, 2)$, directrix $y = 8$, $e = \frac{1}{3}$;

(c) Focus $(4, -1)$, directrix $x + y + 1 = 0$, $e = \frac{2}{3}$.

11. Carry out the details of the following proof of the converse for the derivation of the equation of an ellipse in Art. 47.

If the coördinates of a point satisfy equation (76), then, by reversing the steps given in Art. 47, we obtain

$$\pm F'P \pm FP = 2a.$$

But we know that (1), by hypothesis, $a > c > 0$, (2) $F'P$ and FP are positive (or zero), and (3) the difference between the lengths of two sides of a triangle cannot be greater than the length of the third side. Hence show that the signs in the left-hand member must both be positive and that P lies on the ellipse.

THE HYPERBOLA

53. Standard Form of the Equation of the Hyperbola. *A hyperbola is the locus of a point that moves so that the difference of its undirected distances from two fixed points is equal to a constant.*

The two fixed points are called the *foci* and the point midway between them is the **center** of the hyperbola. We shall denote the distance between the foci by $2c$ and the difference of the distances of a point on the hyperbola from the foci by $2a$. Then $a < c$, since the difference of two sides of a triangle is less than the third side.

The derivation of the standard form of the equation of the hyperbola parallels that of the ellipse (Art. 47). We take the line through the foci as the x-axis and the center as the origin, so that the coördinates of the foci are $F(c, 0)$ and $F'(-c, 0)$ (Fig. 72).

Let $P(x, y)$ be any point on the curve. From the definition of the hyperbola, we have

$$F'P - FP = \pm 2a,$$

the positive sign holding for the points on the curve that lie

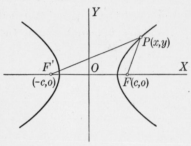

FIG. 72

to the right of the y-axis and the negative sign for the points to the left.

On substituting for $F'P$ and FP their values from the distance formula, we have

$$\sqrt{(x + c)^2 + y^2} - \sqrt{(x - c)^2 + y^2} = \pm 2a.$$

By transposing the second radical, squaring, and simplifying, we find that

$$cx - a^2 = \pm a\sqrt{(x - c)^2 + y^2}.$$

If we square again and collect terms, we obtain

$$(c^2 - a^2)x^2 - a^2y^2 = a^2(c^2 - a^2). \tag{82}$$

We have seen that, for the hyperbola, $a < c$, hence we may put

$$b^2 = c^2 - a^2. \tag{83}$$

If we make this substitution in (82), that equation becomes

$$b^2x^2 - a^2y^2 = a^2b^2.$$

or

$$\frac{x^2}{a^2} - \frac{y^2}{b^2} = 1. \tag{84}$$

The proof that, conversely, if the coördinates of a point $P(x, y)$ satisfy (84) then P lies on the hyperbola is left as an exercise for the student (see p. 116, Ex. 13).

Equation (84) is the standard form of the equation of the hyperbola when the foci are taken at $(\pm c, 0)$ on the x-axis. When the axes are taken so that the foci are at $(0, \pm c)$ on the y-axis, we obtain similarly the equation of the curve in the standard form

$$\frac{y^2}{a^2} - \frac{x^2}{b^2} = 1. \tag{85}$$

In the equation of a hyperbola a may be less than, equal to, or greater than b. To determine, in a numerical problem, whether the foci are on the x-axis or on the y-axis, we first write the equation in the form (84) or (85), then notice whether the coefficient of x^2, or of y^2, is positive.

54. Discussion of the Equation. Asymptotes. If we solve equation (84) for y and for x, we obtain

$$y = \pm \frac{b}{a}\sqrt{x^2 - a^2} \quad \text{and} \quad x = \pm \frac{a}{b}\sqrt{y^2 + b^2} \tag{86}$$

respectively.

From the first of these equations it is seen at once that the curve is symmetric to the x-axis and, from the second, that it is symmetric to the y-axis. (Why?) From the first equation we find that if $x^2 < a^2$, y is imaginary. There are thus no points on the curve between the lines $x = -a$ and $x = a$. For every real value of y, however, there are two real values of x. These values of x are numeri-

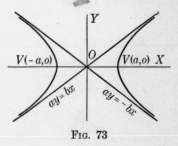

Fig. 73

cally smallest, and equal to $\pm a$, when $y = 0$. They increase indefinitely as y becomes numerically larger, so that the curve extends indefinitely far from both axes in each quadrant.

To determine how the curve approaches infinity, we may write the first of equations (86) in the form

$$y = \pm \frac{b}{a}x\sqrt{1 - \frac{a^2}{x^2}}.$$

If x is numerically very large, the expression $\sqrt{1 - \frac{a^2}{x^2}}$ is very nearly unity and we obtain, as an *approximation* to the form of the curve a long way from the origin, the lines

$$y = \frac{bx}{a} \quad \text{and} \quad y = -\frac{bx}{a}. \tag{87}$$

These lines are called the **asymptotes** to the hyperbola (84).

It can be shown (see page 115, Ex. 11) that, if a point P_1 recedes along the curve indefinitely far from the origin, its distance from one of these asymptotes becomes indefinitely small.

It is sometimes desirable to combine the equations of the two asymptotes into the single equation

$$\frac{x^2}{a^2} - \frac{y^2}{b^2} = 0 \tag{88}$$

which is satisfied by the coördinates of those points (and no others) that lie on the asymptotes.

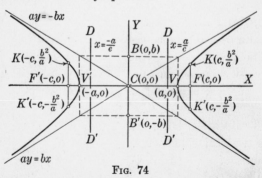

FIG. 74

55. Definitions. The intersections of the hyperbola (84) with the x-axis are found, by putting $y = 0$ in the equation, to be $(\pm a, 0)$. These points, V' and V (Fig. 74), are the **ver-tices**. The segment $V'V$, of length $2a$, that joins the vertices is the **transverse axis** of the hyperbola. Although the hyperbola does not intersect the y-axis (Why?), the segment from $B'(0, -b)$ to $B(0, b)$, of length $2b$, is the **conjugate axis**. The numbers a and b are thus the lengths of the **semi-transverse** and of the **semi-conjugate** axis, respectively.

The chord $K'K$ of the hyperbola through either focus per-pendicular to the transverse axis is the **latus rectum**. Its length is found, as in Art. 49, to be $\dfrac{2b^2}{a}$.

The quotient $\dfrac{c}{a}$ is denoted by e and is called the **eccentricity**. From (83), we have

$$e = \frac{c}{a} = \frac{\sqrt{a^2 + b^2}}{a}. \tag{89}$$

Since, for a hyperbola, a is always less than c, it follows that *the eccentricity of a hyperbola is always greater than unity.*

The lines $x = \dfrac{a}{e}$ and $x = -\dfrac{a}{e}$ are the **directrices**.

Example 1. Determine the ver-tices, foci, eccentricity, and the equations of the asymptotes and directrices of the hyperbola $16x^2 - 9y^2 = 144$.

If we write the given equation in the standard form $\dfrac{x^2}{9} - \dfrac{y^2}{16} = 1$, we find that $a = 3$, $b = 4$, $c = \sqrt{a^2 + b^2} = 5$, and $e = \dfrac{c}{a} = \dfrac{5}{3}$.

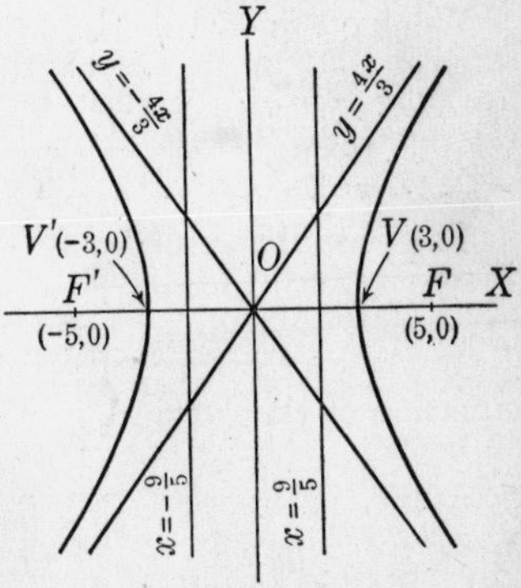

Fig. 75

Since the transverse axis is on the x-axis, the vertices are $(\pm 3, 0)$ and the foci $(\pm 5, 0)$.

The equations of the asymptotes are $y = \frac{4}{3}x$ and $y = -\frac{4}{3}x$. The equations of the directrices are $x = \frac{9}{5}$ and $x = -\frac{9}{5}$.

If one wishes to draw a hyperbola free-hand, it is usually best to draw its asymptotes first, then to plot the vertices and to locate, from the equation, a few points on the curve. The hyperbola can then be drawn to pass through these points and to approach the asymptotes.

Example 2. The vertices of a hyperbola are $(0, \pm 4)$ and the equations of the directrices are $y = \pm \frac{8}{3}$. Find the eccentricity,

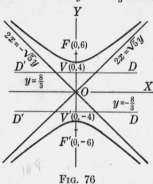

Fig. 76

the coördinates of the foci, the equation of the curve, and of its asymptotes.

We have $a = 4$. Moreover, the equations of the directrices are $y = \dfrac{a}{e} = \dfrac{8}{3}$. Hence $e = \dfrac{3}{2}$, $c = ae = 6$, and $b = \sqrt{c^2 - a^2} = \sqrt{20} = 2\sqrt{5}$.

The coördinates of the foci are, accordingly, $(0, \pm 6)$, the equations of the asymptotes are $x = \pm \dfrac{b}{a}y$, or $2x = \pm \sqrt{5}\,y$, and the equation of the curve is $\dfrac{y^2}{16} - \dfrac{x^2}{20} = 1$.

EXERCISES

1. Find the vertices, foci, eccentricity, the lengths of the latera recta, and the equations of the asymptotes of the following hyperbolas:

(a) $16x^2 - 25y^2 = 400$ (b) $y^2 - 4x^2 = 8$

(c) $100x^2 - 36y^2 = 3600$ (d) $9y^2 - 16x^2 = 144$

(e) $5y^2 - 2x^2 = 40$ (f) $x^2 - y^2 = 16$

(g) $9y^2 - x^2 = 36$ (h) $3x^2 - 2y^2 = 5.$

2. Find the equations of the following hyperbolas:

(a) Vertices $(\pm 6, 0)$, eccentricity $\dfrac{\sqrt{13}}{2}$

(b) Vertices $(0, \pm 4)$, foci $(0, \pm 8)$

(c) Directrices $5y = \pm 2$, eccentricity 2

(d) Directrices $x = \dfrac{\pm 3\sqrt{10}}{\sqrt{5}}$, length of transverse axis $6\sqrt{2}$

(e) Asymptotes $3y = \pm x$, ends of conjugate axis $(0, \pm 2)$

(f) Foci $(\pm 15, 0)$, asymptotes $4y = \pm 3x.$

3. Find the equation, in the standard form (84), of the hyperbola which:

(a) Passes through $(2, 3)$ and has its eccentricity equal to 2

(b) Passes through $(6, 2)$ and has $2x \pm 3y = 0$ as asymptotes

(c) Passes through $(-3, 2)$ and $(3\sqrt{3}, 4)$

(d) Passes through $(-5, 2)$ and $(7, 10).$

4. Find, directly from the definition, the equations of the hyperbolas:

(a) With foci $(\pm 5, 0)$, $a = 3$ (b) With foci $(0, \pm 3)$, $a = 1.$

5. Find the equation of the ellipse of eccentricity $\frac{1}{2}$ that has the same foci as the hyperbola $x^2 - 4y^2 = 4.$

6. The ends of the base of a triangle are $(\pm 6, 0)$ and the difference between the lengths of the other two sides is 8. Find the locus of the vertex.

7. Find the points of intersection of the hyperbola $x^2 - y^2 = 1$ and the ellipse $4x^2 + 9y^2 = 36.$

8. Show that the segment of an asymptote of a hyperbola included between the directrices is equal in length to the transverse axis.

9. Find the length of the perpendicular from a focus of the hyperbola $b^2x^2 - a^2y^2 = a^2b^2$ to an asymptote.

56. A Second Definition of the Hyperbola.

The following property of a hyperbola is sometimes used to define the curve:

The hyperbola $b^2x^2 - a^2y^2 = a^2b^2$ is the locus of a point that moves in such a way that the ratio of its undirected distance from the focus $F(ae, 0)$ to its undirected distance from the directrix

$x - \dfrac{a}{e} = 0$ *is equal to e, its eccentricity.*

The proof of this theorem, which parallels that given in Art. 50 for the ellipse, is left as an exercise for the student. For the hyperbola, we have $e > 1$, and

$$b^2 = c^2 - a^2 = a^2(e^2 - 1)$$

which changes the sign of b^2 from the value given in the derivation of equation (81).

From the symmetry of the figure with respect to the y-axis, it follows at once that the above theorem remains true if we replace the focus $F(ae, 0)$ by $F'(-ae, 0)$ and the directrix

$x - \dfrac{a}{e} = 0$ by $x + \dfrac{a}{e} = 0$.

The focus $(ae, 0)$ and the directrix $x - \dfrac{a}{e} = 0$ are called a *corresponding* focus and directrix, as are also $(-ae, 0)$ and

$x + \dfrac{a}{e} = 0$.

57. Conjugate Hyperbolas. The two hyperbolas

$$\frac{x^2}{a^2} - \frac{y^2}{b^2} = 1 \quad \text{and} \quad \frac{x^2}{a^2} - \frac{y^2}{b^2} = -1$$

are so related that *the transverse axis of each coincides with the conjugate axis of the other.* For, the ends of the transverse axis of the first are $(a, 0)$ and $(-a, 0)$ and the ends of its conjugate axis are $(0, b)$ and $(0, -b)$ (Art. 55). But these are precisely the ends of the conjugate and the transverse axes, respectively, of the second hyperbola.

Two hyperbolas related in this way are said to be a pair of **conjugate hyperbolas** and each of them is called the **conjugate hyperbola** of the other (Fig. 77).

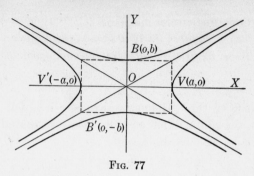

Fig. 77

The student should show that the asymptotes of any given hyperbola coincide with those of its conjugate.

58. Equilateral Hyperbola. If we put $b = a$ in equation (84), that equation becomes

$$x^2 - y^2 = a^2. \tag{90}$$

In this special case, the hyperbola is called an **equilateral (or rectangular) hyperbola.** It bears substantially the same relation to hyperbolas that the circle does to ellipses.

The eccentricity of the equilateral hyperbola is found, by putting $b = a$ in (89), to be $e = \sqrt{2}$. Its asymptotes are the lines $y = x$ and $y = -x$ which are perpendicular to each other.

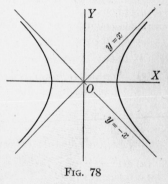

Fig. 78

If the coördinate axes are rotated through $-45°$, so that the asymptotes of the hyperbola become the coördinate axes, we shall show (Art. 65) that the equation of the equilateral hyperbola becomes

$$2xy = a^2. \tag{91}$$

In the applications of analytic geometry, the equation of the equilateral hyperbola is often encountered in this form.

★ **59. Constructions for the Hyperbola.** (1) *Continuous Construction.* At one focus F' of the required hyperbola, fasten one end of a ruler of length l. Attach one end of a string of

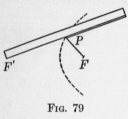

length $l - 2a$ at the free end of the ruler and the other end at the second focus F. Hold the string taut by pressing it with the point of a pencil against the side of the ruler. If the ruler is now rotated about F', the point of the pencil will describe an arc of the hyperbola.

Fig. 79

(2) *Point by Point Construction.* With centers at the foci F' and F, draw circles of radii r' and r such that $r' - r = \pm 2a$. The points of intersection of these circles will lie on the hyperbola.

EXERCISES

1. Using the second definition of the hyperbola (Art. 56), derive the equation of a hyperbola with center at the origin, given:

(a) Focus $(6, 0)$, directrix $2x = 3$

(b) Focus $(0, -9)$, directrix $y + 1 = 0$

(c) Vertex $(0, 6)$, $e = \frac{3}{2}$

(d) Focus $(0, 5)$, end of conjugate axis $(3, 0)$

(e) Directrix $y = 2$, $e = 2$

(f) Vertex $(3, 0)$, asymptote $y = 2x$.

2. Find the equation of the hyperbola conjugate to each of the following hyperbolas. Determine, for the given curve and for its conjugate, the asymptotes, vertices, foci, and directrices.

(a) $9x^2 - 4y^2 = 36$ (b) $6y^2 - 5x^2 = 30$

(c) $x^2 - 4y^2 = 4$ (d) $7y^2 - 2x^2 = 14$

(e) $4x^2 - 9y^2 = 20$ (f) $2x^2 - 3y^2 = 12$.

3. Show that the four foci of two conjugate hyperbolas lie on a circle. Find the center and radius of this circle.

4. If e and e' are the eccentricities of two conjugate hyperbolas, show that $e^2 + e'^2 = e^2 e'^2$.

5. The distances of a point P on a hyperbola from the foci are called the *focal radii* of P. Show that the focal radii of the point $P(x, y)$ on the hyperbola $b^2x^2 - a^2y^2 = a^2b^2$ are numerically equal to $ex + a$ and $ex - a$.

6. Find the focal radii (Ex. 5) of:

(a) the point $(5, 6)$ on $4x^2 - y^2 = 64$

(b) The point $(4, -2)$ on $x^2 - y^2 = 12$.

7. The equations of the following hyperbolas are not in the standard form. Derive their equations by using the definition of Art. 53.

(a) Foci $(1, 3)$ and $(11, 3)$, $a = 3$

(b) Foci $(-1, -10)$ and $(-1, 16)$, $a = 5$

(c) Foci $(1, 2)$ and $(-1, -2)$, $a = 1$

(d) Foci $(-1, 2)$ and $(3, 4)$, $a = 1$.

8. Find the equations of the following hyperbolas, using the definition of Art. 56.

(a) Focus $(2, 3)$, corresponding directrix $y = 5$, $e = \sqrt{3}$

(b) Focus $(5, 2)$, corresponding directrix $x = 0$, $e = 2$

(c) Focus $(2, -3)$, corresponding directrix $3x - y + 7 = 0$, $e = \sqrt{5}$.

9. A focus of a hyperbola is (a, a), the corresponding directrix is $x + y - a = 0$, and its eccentricity is $\sqrt{2}$. Show that the curve is an equilateral hyperbola which has its asymptotes as coördinate axes.

10. A point moves so that the product of its directed distances from the lines $y - mx = 0$ and $y + mx = 0$ is equal to a constant k^2. Show that its locus is a hyperbola that has these lines as asymptotes.

11. If the point $P_1(x_1, y_1)$ lies on the hyperbola (84), so that $b^2x_1^2 - a^2y_1^2 = a^2b^2$, show that the distance d to P_1 from the asymptote $bx - ay = 0$ can be written in the form

$$d = \frac{bx_1 - ay_1}{\sqrt{a^2 + b^2}} = \frac{a^2b^2}{\sqrt{a^2 + b^2}(bx_1 + ay_1)}.$$

Hence, show that, if P_1 recedes along the hyperbola indefinitely far from the origin in the first or third quadrants, its distance from the asymptote $bx - ay = 0$ becomes indefinitely small. State and prove the corresponding theorem for the asymptote, $bx + ay = 0$.

12. Show that the product of the distances of any point on a hyperbola from its asymptotes is a constant.

13. Prove the converse of the theorem of Art. 53 by showing that, if the coördinates of a point satisfy equation (84), we obtain, by reversing the steps of that article,

$$\pm F'P \pm FP = 2a.$$

Hence, show, since $0 < 2a < 2c$, that

$$F'P - FP = \pm 2a$$

so that P lies on the hyperbola. Show further that the sign in the right-hand member of the above equation is positive or negative according as P lies on the right-hand or the left-hand branch of the hyperbola.

POLAR COÖRDINATES

60. Standard Polar Equation of a Conic. By combining the definitions of Arts. 42, 50, and 56, we obtain the following single definition which holds for either the ellipse, parabola, or hyperbola: *A conic is the locus of a point that moves in such a way that the ratio of its undirected distance from a fixed point (a focus) to its undirected distance from a fixed line (the corresponding directrix) is equal to a constant e, the eccentricity.*

The conic is

> *an ellipse if $e < 1$*
> *a parabola if $e = 1$*
> *a hyperbola if $e > 1$.*

We shall derive the standard polar equation of these three conics from the above definition. We take the focus as origin,* the line through the focus perpendicular to the directrix as

---

* Since the focus is not the origin in any one of the standard rectangular equations of a conic, a transformation of the standard polar equation into rectangular coördinates will, in no case, lead to the standard rectangular equation.

polar axis, and we shall suppose that this polar axis is directed away from the directrix (Fig. 80).

Let D'' be the foot of the perpendicular from O to the directrix and denote the length of the segment $D''O$ by p.

Let $P(r, \theta)$ * be any point on the conic and let R and L (Fig. 80) be the feet of the perpendiculars from P to the directrix and to the polar axis, respectively. From the definition of the conic, we have

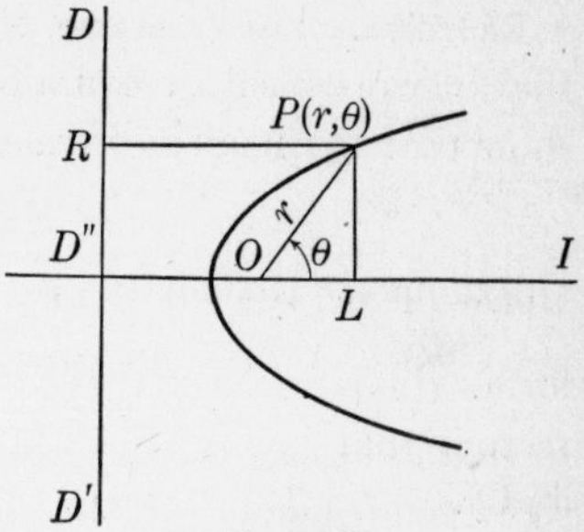

Fig. 80

$$OP = e \cdot RP.$$

But $$OP = r$$

and $$RP = D''L = D''O + \overline{OL} = p + r \cos \theta.$$

Hence $$r = e(p + r \cos \theta) = ep + er \cos \theta.$$

If we solve the last of these equations for r, we obtain

$$r = \frac{ep}{1 - e \cos \theta}. \tag{92}$$

Conversely, if the coördinates of a point P satisfy (92), we find, by reversing the steps in the above proof, that $OP = e \cdot RP$ so that P lies on the given conic.

In deriving (92), we supposed that the polar axis was directed away from the directrix. If it is directed toward the directrix, we find in a similar way that

$$r = \frac{ep}{1 + e \cos \theta}. \tag{93}$$

---

* The following proof supposes (1) that the polar coördinates of P have been chosen so that r is positive and (2) that P and the origin lie on the same side of the directrix. Supposition (1) can always be made but (2) fails for one branch of the hyperbola. In that case, however, we are led to the same final equation if we suppose the coördinates of P chosen so that r is negative.

Equations (92) and (93) are the standard polar equations when the focus is the pole and the axis of the conic is the polar axis.

Exercise. Find the coördinates·of the points of intersection of the conics defined by equations (92) and (93) with the 90° axis and show that the length of the latus rectum is $2ep$.

Example. Reduce the equation $r = \dfrac{6}{2 - \cos \theta}$ to the standard form. Locate the vertices, the center, and the ends of the latus rectum that passes through the origin. Find the values of e, a, and b.

To reduce the equation to the standard form, we must make the first term in the denominator unity by dividing each term in numerator and denominator by 2. We thus obtain

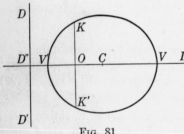

$r = \dfrac{3}{1 - \frac{1}{2} \cos \theta}.$ By comparing this equation with (92), we find that $e = \frac{1}{2}$. The curve is thus an ellipse.

The vertices of the ellipse are found, as the intersections of the polar axis with the

Fig. 81

curve, to be $(6, 0)$ and $(2, \pi)$. Since the center is midway between the vertices, its coördinates are $(2, 0)$. The distance from the center to either vertex is a; hence $a = 4$.

The ends of the latus rectum are the intersections of the 90° axis with the curve. Their coördinates are $\left(3, \dfrac{\pi}{2}\right)$ and $\left(3, -\dfrac{\pi}{2}\right)$. The length of the latus rectum is the distance between these points, which is 6.

By Art. 49, the length of the latus rectum is $\dfrac{2b^2}{a}$. Hence, $\dfrac{2b^2}{a} = \dfrac{2b^2}{4} = 6$, so that $b = \sqrt{12} = 2\sqrt{3}$.

EXERCISES

1. Find the eccentricity, the length of the latus rectum, the coördinates of the vertex or vertices, and draw the curve, given:

(a) $r = \dfrac{21}{3 - \cos \theta}$
(b) $r = \dfrac{6}{1 - 2 \cos \theta}$

(c) $r = \dfrac{4}{1 - \cos \theta}$
(d) $r = \dfrac{12}{3 + 4 \cos \theta}$

(e) $r = \dfrac{15}{3 + 2 \cos \theta}$
(f) $r = \dfrac{10}{3 + 3 \cos \theta}$

(g) $r = \dfrac{8}{1 - 2 \cos \theta}$
(h) $r = \dfrac{10}{1 + 3 \cos \theta}$

2. Find, for each of the curves of Ex. 1, the polar equation of the directrix corresponding to the focus at the origin.

3. Show that if the conic (92) is an ellipse, the length of its major axis is $\dfrac{2ep}{1 - e^2}$ and if it is a hyperbola, the length of its transverse axis is $\dfrac{2ep}{e^2 - 1}$.

4. If the conic defined by (92) is a parabola, find the coördinates of the vertex and the equation of the directrix.

5. Show that, if the conic is a parabola, equations (92) and (93) may be reduced to $r = \dfrac{p}{2} \csc^2 \dfrac{\theta}{2}$ and $r = \dfrac{p}{2} \sec^2 \dfrac{\theta}{2}$, respectively.

6. Draw the parabolas (a) $r = 3 \csc^2 \dfrac{\theta}{2}$;   (b) $r = 5 \sec^2 \dfrac{\theta}{2}$.

7. Show from a figure that, if a focus of the conic is at the origin and the corresponding directrix is parallel to the initial line, the equation of the conic is $r = \dfrac{ep}{1 - e \sin \theta}$ or $r = \dfrac{ep}{1 + e \sin \theta}$ according as the directrix lies below or above the initial line.

8. Draw the curves:

(a) $r = \dfrac{6}{2 - \sin \theta}$
(b) $r = \dfrac{4}{1 - 2 \sin \theta}$

(c) $r = \dfrac{5}{1 + \sin \theta}$
(d) $r = \dfrac{8}{4 + 3 \sin \theta}$.

9. Transform equations (92) and (93) to rectangular coördinates.

10. Transform the standard rectangular equations of the conics to polar coördinates. Explain why the resulting equations differ from the standard polar forms.

MISCELLANEOUS EXERCISES

1. Find the equation of the parabola of the form $y^2 = 2px$ that passes through the point $(-3, 6)$.

2. Find the equation of an ellipse given that its foci are $(0, \pm 2)$ and that its eccentricity is $\frac{1}{2}$.

3. Find the equation of the hyperbola that has the lines $x = \pm 3$ as directrices and $y = \pm 2x$ as asymptotes.

4. Find the points on the parabola $y^2 = 8x$ for which the distance from the focus is equal to three times the length of the latus rectum.

5. Determine graphically the number of real points of intersection of the conics $x^2 + 2y^2 = 6$ and $x^2 - y^2 = 3$. Find the coördinates of these points algebraically.

6. Find the equation of the hyperbola that has the foci of $4x^2 + 9y^2 = 36$ for vertices and the vertices for foci.

7. Find the equation of the chord of the parabola $x^2 = 10y$ that is bisected at the point $(2, 4)$.

8. Show that the lines joining a vertex of a hyperbola to the ends of the conjugate axis are parallel to the asymptotes.

9. Find the eccentricity of an ellipse if the lines joining a focus to the ends of the minor axis are perpendicular.

10. Show that the eccentricity of the hyperbola $b^2x^2 - a^2y^2 = a^2b^2$ is numerically equal to the secant of the angle made by an asymptote with the x-axis.

11. A triangle inscribed in the parabola $y^2 = 2px$ has a right angle at the origin. Show that the position of the point of intersection of the hypotenuse with the x-axis is independent of the slopes of the sides of the triangle.

12. Show that the midpoints of all chords of the parabola $y^2 = 2px$ that are parallel to the line $y = mx$ lie on the line $y = \dfrac{p}{m}$.

SELECTED EXERCISES

1. Show that the lines of the family $y = mx + \dfrac{p}{2m}$, in which m is the parameter, are tangent to the parabola $y^2 = 2px$. What is the geometrical meaning of the parameter?

Hint. Algebraically, the condition that a line is tangent to a conic is that its two intersections with the conic coincide.

2. Show that the lines of the family $y = mx \pm \sqrt{a^2m^2 + b^2}$, in which m is the parameter, are tangent to the ellipse $b^2x^2 + a^2y^2 = a^2b^2$.

3. Find the condition on k that the line $y = mx + k$ is tangent to the hyperbola $b^2x^2 - a^2y^2 = a^2b^2$. Hence find the equation of the family of lines tangent to this hyperbola.

4. Show that, if the point $P_1(x_1, y_1)$ lies on the parabola $y^2 = 2px$, then the line $y_1y = p(x + x_1)$ is tangent to the parabola at P_1.

5. Show that, if the point $P_1(x_1, y_1)$ lies on the ellipse $b^2x^2 + a^2y^2 = a^2b^2$ then the line $b^2x_1x + a^2y_1y = a^2b^2$ is tangent to the ellipse at P_1.

6. Show that, if the point $P_1(x_1, y_1)$ lies on the hyperbola $b^2x^2 - a^2y^2 = a^2b^2$, then the line $b^2x_1x - a^2y_1y = a^2b^2$ is tangent to the hyperbola at P_1.

7. Show that the tangent to a parabola at a point P_1 on it bisects the angle from the line through P_1 parallel to the axis of the parabola to the line through the focus and P_1.

Note. It is on this property that the applications of the parabolic mirror (Art. 45) are based.

8. Show that the tangent line to an ellipse or a hyperbola at a point P_1 on the curve bisects a pair of vertical angles formed by the lines through P_1 and the foci.

9. Given the family of conics $\dfrac{x^2}{a^2 + k} + \dfrac{y^2}{b^2 + k} = 1$, in which k is the parameter. Show (a) that all the conics of this family are confocal (that is, that they have the same foci), (b) that through any point P_1 in the plane (not lying on a coördinate axis) there pass two conics of the family, (c) that the tangent lines at P_1 to the two conics that pass through P_1 are perpendicular.

CHAPTER VI

TRANSFORMATION OF COÖRDINATES

61. Changing the Coördinate Axes. It frequently happens that the solution of a problem in analytic geometry can be simplified by the use of a different pair of coördinate axes from the one employed in the statement of the problem. The process of changing from one pair of coördinate axes to another is called a **transformation of coördinates.**

If the new axes are parallel, respectively, to the old ones, and if they have the same positive directions, the transformation is

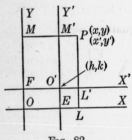

FIG. 82

called a **translation of axes.** If the origin remains unchanged, and the new axes are obtained by revolving the old ones about the origin through a certain angle, then the transformation is a **rotation of axes.**

62. Translation of Axes. Let OX and OY (Fig. 82) be the original axes and let $O'X'$ and $O'Y'$ be the new ones, parallel, respectively, to the old and having the same positive directions. Let the coördinates of O', referred to OX and OY, be (h, k).

Let P be any given point in the plane and let its coördinates, referred to the old axes, be (x, y) and, referred to the new ones, be (x', y'). It is required to find the values of x and y in terms of x' and y'.

Let L and L' be the feet of the perpendiculars from P on OX and $O'X'$, respectively, and M and M' the feet of the perpendiculars on OY and $O'Y'$. We have

122

$$x = \overline{OL} = \overline{OE} + \overline{EL} = \overline{OE} + \overline{O'L'} = h + x'$$
$$y = \overline{OM} = \overline{OF} + \overline{FM} = \overline{OF} + \overline{O'M'} = k + y'.$$

Hence *the formulas for a translation of axes are:*

$$x = x' + h \qquad y = y' + k \tag{94}$$

wherein (h, k) are the old coördinates of the new origin.

Equations (94) are frequently spoken of as defining a *translation of the origin to the point* (h, k).

Example 1. Find the equation of the conic $4x^2 - y^2 + 16x - 2y + 19 = 0$ when the origin is translated to the point $(-2, -1)$.

We have from (94), since $h = -2$ and $k = -1$,

$$x = x' - 2, \qquad y = y' - 1.$$

If we substitute these values of x and y in the given equation, we obtain

$$4(x' - 2)^2 - (y' - 1)^2 + 16(x' - 2) - 2(y' - 1) + 19 = 0.$$

By expanding and simplifying this equation, we find, as the equation of the given conic referred to the new axes,

$$y'^2 - 4x'^2 = 4.$$

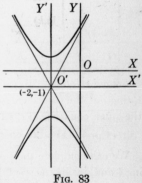

This is the standard equation of a hyperbola with its center at the new origin and its transverse axis on the y'-axis. If we draw, with reference to the new axes, the curve defined by this last equation, the resulting locus will also be the graph of the original equation referred to the old axes (Fig. 83).

Fɪɢ. 83

Example 2. Find a translation of axes that will transform the equation $9x^2 + 4y^2 + 18x - 24y + 9 = 0$ into one in which the coefficients of the first degree terms are zero.

First solution. If we substitute the values of x and y from (94) in the given equation and collect the coefficients of the various powers of x' and y', we have

$$9x'^2 + 4y'^2 + (18h + 18)x' + (8k - 24)y'$$
$$+ 9h^2 + 4k^2 + 18h - 24k + 9 = 0.$$

Equating to zero the coefficients of x' and y' gives

$$18h + 18 = 0 \quad \text{and} \quad 8k - 24 = 0$$

so that $h = -1$ and $k = 3$.

On substituting these values of h and k in the transformed equation, we obtain

$$9x'^2 + 4y'^2 - 36 = 0.$$

The curve is an ellipse which has its center at the new origin, its major axis on the y'-axis, and semi-axes $a = 3$ and $b = 2$.

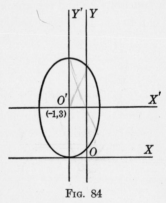

FIG. 84

Second solution. By collecting the terms in x and in y, and factoring out the coefficients of x^2 and y^2, respectively, we may write the given equation in the form

$$9(x^2 + 2x \quad) + 4(y^2 - 6y \quad) = -9.$$

We can complete the square inside the first parenthesis by adding 1 and, inside the second, by adding 9. (Why?) Because of the coefficients outside these parentheses, by inserting these numbers we add 9 and 36, respectively, to the left-hand member. To preserve the equality, we must add the same numbers to the right-hand member. We then have

$$9(x^2 + 2x + 1) + 4(y^2 - 6y + 9) = -9 + 9 + 36$$

or
$$9(x + 1)^2 + 4(y - 3)^2 = 36.$$

If we now translate the origin by putting $x + 1 = x'$, $y - 3 = y'$, that is
$$x = x' - 1, \quad y = y' + 3,$$
we obtain as the required transformed equation
$$9x'^2 + 4y'^2 = 36.$$

This method of solving the given problem is considerably shorter than the first one but it calls for more skill in algebraic manipulation.

63. The Quadratic Function.

The expression
$$ax^2 + bx + c \qquad (a \neq 0)$$
is called a **quadratic function** of x and the graph of the equation obtained by equating it to y is the *graph of the quadratic function.*

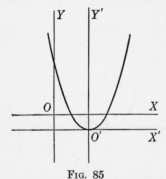

Fig. 85

We shall show that the graph of the quadratic function, that is, of the equation
$$y = ax^2 + bx + c \qquad (95)$$
is a parabola by reducing this equation, by a translation of axes, to one of the standard forms of the equation of the parabola.

We may write the given equation in the form
$$y = a\left(x^2 + \frac{b}{a}x + \frac{b^2}{4a^2}\right) + c - \frac{b^2}{4a}$$
or
$$y + \frac{b^2 - 4ac}{4a} = a\left(x + \frac{b}{2a}\right)^2.$$

If we now translate the coördinate axes by means of the equations

$$x = x' - \frac{b}{2a}, \qquad y = y' - \frac{b^2 - 4ac}{4a}$$

the given equation reduces to

$$y' = ax'^2 \tag{96}$$

which is the equation of a parabola with vertex at the new origin and focus on the y'-axis.

If $a > 0$, the parabola (95) opens upward and the vertex is the lowest point on it.   Similarly, if $a < 0$, the vertex is the highest point on the curve.   Hence we have the following useful property of the quadratic function: *The value of x for which* $ax^2 + bx + c$ *takes its least value if* $a > 0$, *and its greatest value if* $a < 0$, *is* $x = -\dfrac{b}{2a}$. *This extreme value of the function is*

$$\frac{4ac - b^2}{4a}.$$

EXERCISES

1. Find the new coördinates of the following points when the origin is translated to the point $(1, 4)$:

(a) $(7, 6)$ (b) $(8, 1)$ (c) $(1, -2)$
(d) $(-2, 2)$ (e) $(9, 4)$ (f) $(-1, 5)$.

2. Find the coördinates in Ex. 1 when the origin is translated to $(2, -3)$.

Transform the following equations by translating the origin to the point indicated:

3. $x - 3y - 5 = 0$ $(2, -1)$
4. $x^2 + y^2 - 4x - 6y - 3 = 0$ $(2, 3)$
5. $x^2 + 4y^2 + 4x - 8y - 8 = 0$ $(-2, 1)$
6. $25x^2 - 9y^2 - 50x + 36y - 236 = 0$ $(1, 2)$
7. $y = x^2 + 3x - 1$ $(-\frac{3}{2}, -\frac{13}{4})$.   From your graph, estimate to one decimal place the roots of $x^2 + 3x - 1 = 0$.

Remove the first degree terms from each of the following equations by translation of axes:

8. $x^2 + 4y^2 + 6x - 16y - 11 = 0$.

9. $4x^2 + 9y^2 - 24x - 72y + 144 = 0$.

10. $2x^2 - 3y^2 + 8x + 18y - 25 = 0$.

11. $4x^2 - y^2 + 24x + 2y + 36 = 0$.

12. Reduce the equations of the following parabolas to a standard form by translation of axes:

(a) $3y = 2x^2 + 8x + 11$ (b) $5x = y^2 + 6y - 1$.

13. If a projectile is fired from the origin with an initial velocity of 100 feet per second in a direction making an angle of 45° with the x-axis, the equation of its path is $y = x - \dfrac{32.2x^2}{(100)^2}$. Find to the nearest foot the highest point in its path.

14. What is the largest rectangular area that can be enclosed by a fence 400 feet long?

15. Show that $\dfrac{(x - h)^2}{a^2} + \dfrac{(y - k)^2}{b^2} = 1$ is the equation of an ellipse with center at (h, k) and axes parallel to the coördinate axes. Find the coördinates of the foci and vertices and the equations of the directrices.

16. Show that $\dfrac{(x - h)^2}{a^2} - \dfrac{(y - k)^2}{b^2} = 1$ is the equation of a hyperbola with transverse axis parallel to the x-axis. Find the coördinates of the foci and vertices and the equations of the directrices and the asymptotes.

17. Show that $(y - k)^2 = 2p(x - h)$ and $(x - h)^2 = 2p(y - k)$ are the equations of parabolas with vertices at (h, k) and axes parallel to the x-axis and y-axis, respectively.

Derive the equation of each of the following conics from one of the definitions and reduce the resulting equation to a standard form by a translation of axes.

18. Foci $(5, 1)$ and $(5, -7)$, $a = 5$.

19. Foci $(1, 2)$ and $(9, 2)$, $a = 2$.

20. Focus $(-1, -2)$, directrix $y = 3$, $e = 1$.

21. Focus $(2, 1)$, corresponding directrix $x = 6$, $e = \frac{2}{3}$.

22. Focus $(-5, 3)$, corresponding directrix $y + 1 = 0$, $e = 2$.

64. Rotation of Axes. Let OX and OY be the old axes, OX' and OY', the new ones, and denote the angle XOX' by ϕ (Fig. 86).

Let P be any given point in the plane. Denote its coördinates,

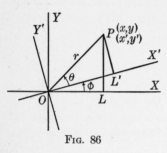

referred to the old axes, by (x, y) and, referred to the new ones, by (x', y'). It is required to find the values of x and y in terms of x' and y'.

FIG. 86

Draw OP and let $OP = r$ and the angle $X'OP = \theta$. From the definition of the sine and cosine of an angle, we have

$$x = \overline{OL} = r \cos (\theta + \phi), \qquad y = \overline{LP} = r \sin (\theta + \phi),$$

and

$$x' = \overline{OL'} = r \cos \theta, \qquad\qquad y' = \overline{L'P} = r \sin \theta.$$

From the formulas for the cosine and the sine of the sum of two angles, we now have

$$x = r \cos (\theta + \phi) = r \cos \theta \cos \phi - r \sin \theta \sin \phi$$
$$= x' \cos \phi - y' \sin \phi$$

and $\quad y = r \sin (\theta + \phi) = r \sin \theta \cos \phi + r \cos \theta \sin \phi$
$$= x' \sin \phi + y' \cos \phi.$$

Hence the required formulas for the *rotation of the axes through an angle ϕ* are

$$\begin{aligned} x &= x' \cos \phi - y' \sin \phi \\ y &= x' \sin \phi + y' \cos \phi. \end{aligned} \qquad (97)$$

If we solve equations (97) for x' and y', and simplify, we obtain

$$\begin{aligned} x' &= x \cos \phi + y \sin \phi \\ y' &= - x \sin \phi + y \cos \phi. \end{aligned} \qquad (98)$$

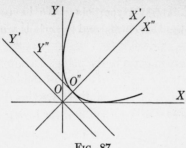

Fig. 87

Example. Find the equation of the parabola $x^2 - 2xy + y^2$ $- 2ax - 2ay + a^2 = 0$ * when the axes are rotated through 45° and reduce the resulting equation by a translation of axes to the standard form.

Since $\sin 45° = \cos 45° = \dfrac{1}{\sqrt{2}}$, equations (97) become, for this rotation,

$$x = \frac{x' - y'}{\sqrt{2}}, \quad y = \frac{x' + y'}{\sqrt{2}}.$$

On substituting these values of x and y in the given equation of the parabola, we obtain

$$\frac{(x' - y')^2}{2} - (x' - y')(x' + y') + \frac{(x' + y')^2}{2} - \sqrt{2}a(x' - y')$$
$$- \sqrt{2}a(x' + y') + a^2 = 0.$$

On expanding and simplifying this equation, we find that it reduces to

$$2y'^2 - 2\sqrt{2}ax' + a^2 = 0.$$

If we now translate the origin to the point $\left(\dfrac{\sqrt{2}a}{4}, 0\right)$, the resulting equation may be reduced to the standard form $y''^2 = \sqrt{2}ax''$ of the equation of a parabola.

---

* In the textbooks on calculus, this equation is usually given in the form $x^{\frac{1}{2}} + y^{\frac{1}{2}} = a^{\frac{1}{2}}$, wherein (contrary to the notation we have adopted) both the positive and the negative values of the square root should be taken in each case. The student should show, by removing the fractional exponents by squaring, that this equation may be reduced to the form given in the text.

65. The Equilateral Hyperbola. We have seen (Art. 58) that the equation of an equilateral hyperbola with center at the origin and foci on the x-axis is

$$x^2 - y^2 = a^2.$$

The asymptotes $y = \pm x$ of this hyperbola make angles of $\pm 45°$ with the x-axis. We shall find the equation of this curve

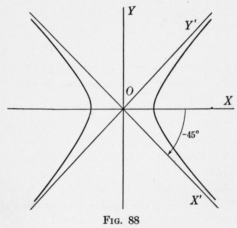

Fig. 88

when the axes are rotated through an angle of $-45°$ so that the asymptote $y = -x$ becomes the new x'-axis and $y = x$ the new y'-axis. Since

$$\sin(-45°) = -\frac{1}{\sqrt{2}}, \quad \text{and} \quad \cos(-45°) = \frac{1}{\sqrt{2}},$$

the equations (97) of the transformation are

$$x = \frac{x' + y'}{\sqrt{2}}, \qquad y = \frac{-x' + y'}{\sqrt{2}}.$$

On substituting these values of x and y in the given equation of the equilateral hyperbola, we have

$$\frac{(x' + y')^2}{2} - \frac{(-x' + y')^2}{2} = a^2,$$

which reduces, on expanding and simplifying, to

$$2x'y' = a^2. \tag{99}$$

This is the equation of the equilateral hyperbola referred to its asymptotes as coördinate axes.

EXERCISES

1. Find the coördinates of the following points when the axes are rotated through 30°.

(a) $(8, 6)$, (b) $(5, 5)$, (c) $(-1, -3)$, (d) $(0, 6)$, (e) $(3\sqrt{3}, 3)$.

2. Solve Ex. 1 when the angle of rotation is 45°.

3. Solve Ex. 1 when the angle of rotation is 90°.

Find the transformed equation when the axes are rotated through the angle indicated.

4. $x + y = 4$,   (a) 45°,   (b) $-45°$.

5. $12x - 5y + 26 = 0$, $\tan^{-1} \frac{12}{5}$.

6. $x^2 + 4xy + y^2 = 9$,   45°.

7. $7x^2 - 6\sqrt{3}xy + 13y^2 = 1$,   30°.

8. Find the equation of the equilateral hyperbola $x^2 - y^2 = a^2$ when the axes are rotated through an angle of 45°.

Derive the equation of each of the following conics from one of the definitions. Then rotate the axes so that the line joining the foci (or through the given focus perpendicular to the given directrix) is the new x-axis.

9. Foci $(2, 1)$ and $(-2, -1)$, $a = 3$.

10. Focus $(2, 2)$, corresponding directrix $x + y - 1 = 0$, $e = 2$.

11. Focus $(0, 0)$, directrix $3x + y - 2 = 0$, $e = 1$.

12. Show that the expression $\sqrt{x^2 + y^2}$ is transformed into $\sqrt{x'^2 + y'^2}$ by a rotation of the axes through any angle ϕ and explain this result geometrically.

CHAPTER VII

THE GENERAL EQUATION OF THE SECOND DEGREE

66. The Conic Sections. Any equation of the form

$$Ax^2 + Bxy + Cy^2 + Dx + Ey + F = 0, \qquad (100)$$

wherein A, B, and C are not all zero, is called an *equation of the second degree* and its locus, if it has one, is a **conic section.**[*]

In this chapter, we shall show how any given equation of the second degree can be reduced to a simple standard form by a suitable rotation and translation of axes.

67. Simplification by Translation. The Types of Conic Sections. If, in equation (100), we have $B = 0$, so that the term in xy does not appear, that equation takes the form

$$Ax^2 + Cy^2 + Dx + Ey + F = 0, \qquad (101)$$

wherein A and C are not both zero. We shall show that such an equation can be simplified by a translation only, without a rotation.

In order to reduce equation (101) to a standard form, we must distinguish a number of cases, according as certain of the coefficients in it are positive, negative, or zero.

Case I. *Neither A nor C is zero.* If we first complete the squares of the terms in x and in y, we may write the given equation in the form

$$A\left(x^2 + \frac{D}{A}x + \frac{D^2}{4A^2}\right) + C\left(y^2 + \frac{E}{C}y + \frac{E^2}{4C^2}\right) = \frac{D^2}{4A} + \frac{E^2}{4C} - F$$

---

[*] This definition of a conic section slightly extends the one given in Art. 40. It includes, for example, two parallel lines; two such lines are sections of a right circular cylinder, but not of a right circular cone.

or $\qquad A\left(x + \dfrac{D}{2A}\right)^2 + C\left(y + \dfrac{E}{2C}\right)^2 = \dfrac{D^2}{4A} + \dfrac{E^2}{4C} - F.$

If we now translate the origin to the point $\left(-\dfrac{D}{2A}, -\dfrac{E}{2C}\right)$, the new equation of the conic is found to be

$$Ax'^2 + Cy'^2 = F', \tag{102}$$

wherein $\qquad F' = \dfrac{D^2}{4A} + \dfrac{E^2}{4C} - F.$

Equation (102) is a standard form of one of the following types:

Type a. If A, C, and F' all have like signs, the curve is an *ellipse*.

Type b. If A and C have like signs and F' is of the opposite sign, there are no points on the graph. Such an equation is said to define an *imaginary ellipse*.

Type c. If A and C have like signs and $F' = 0$, there is just one point, the new origin, on the graph. The equation defines, under these circumstances, a *point ellipse*.

Type d. If A and C have opposite signs and $F' \neq 0$, the locus is a *hyperbola*.

Type e. If A and C have opposite signs and $F' = 0$, the locus consists of *two intersecting lines*.

Case II. *Either $A = 0$ or $C = 0$.* We shall consider only the case in which $A = 0$ and $C \neq 0$. The corresponding treatment of the case in which $C = 0$, $A \neq 0$ can be found by interchanging x and y, and the corresponding coefficients, in the following discussion.

Subcase α: $A = 0$, $C \neq 0$, $D \neq 0$. In this subcase, we translate the origin to the point $\left(\dfrac{E^2 - 4CF}{4CD}, -\dfrac{E}{2C}\right)$. We obtain:

Type f. The equation is

$$Cy'^2 + Dx' = 0.$$

The curve is a *parabola*.

Subcase β: $A = 0$, $C \neq 0$, $D = 0$.   In this subcase, we translate the origin to the point $\left(0, -\dfrac{E}{2C}\right)$.   The new equation is

$$Cy'^2 = F', \quad \text{where} \quad F' = \frac{E^2 - 4CF}{4C}.$$

This equation gives rise to the following three types.

Type g. If C and F' have like signs, the locus is composed of *two parallel lines*.

Type h. If C and F' have unlike signs, there are no points on the locus. The equation is said to define *two imaginary parallel lines*.

Type i. If $F' = 0$, the locus is *the line $y' = 0$, counted twice*.

Example 1. Simplify the equation $3x^2 - 5y^2 + 6x + 20y - 17 = 0$ and state the type of conic defined by this equation.

By completing the square of the terms in x and in y and then translating the origin to the point $(-1, 2)$, we obtain

$$3x'^2 - 5y'^2 = 0.$$

By factoring the left-hand member of this equation, we find that the locus is composed of the two intersecting lines $\sqrt{3}x' - \sqrt{5}y' = 0$ and $\sqrt{3}x' + \sqrt{5}y' = 0$.

Example 2. Simplify the equation $2x^2 - 3y - 12x + 6 = 0$ and name the type of curve defined by the equation.

By completing the square of the terms in x, we find that the given equation may be written in the form $2(x - 3)^2 - 3(y + 4) = 0$. If we now translate the origin to the point $(3, -4)$, this equation reduces to $2x'^2 - 3y' = 0$.

The curve is a parabola, with its axis coinciding with the y'-axis.

EXERCISES

Simplify the following equations by a translation of axes, name the type of curve defined by the equation, draw both sets of axes, and plot the curve when it exists.

1. $2x^2 + 8y^2 - 8x - 16y + 9 = 0$.

2. $4x^2 - 3y^2 + 8x - 12y - 4 = 0$.

3. $x^2 + 5y^2 + 3x - 5y + 7 = 0$.

4. $3y^2 + 7x - 24y + 13 = 0$.

5. $x^2 - 4y^2 + x - 6y - 2 = 0$.

6. $3x^2 + 5y^2 + 18x + 10y + 32 = 0$.

7. $3x^2 - 3y^2 - 12x + 18y + 2 = 0$.

8. $x^2 + 6x + 5y - 9 = 0$.

68. Simplification by Rotation. Removal of the *xy*-term.
We shall show in this article that if, in the general equation of
a conic,

$$Ax^2 + Bxy + Cy^2 + Dx + Ey + F = 0, \qquad (103)$$

the coefficient $B \neq 0$, it is always possible, by rotating the
axes through a suitable angle, to reduce the equation to one
in which the coefficient of the $x'y'$-term is equal to zero.

Let the coördinate axes be rotated through an angle ϕ, so
that x and y are replaced by (Art. 64)

$$x = x' \cos \phi - y' \sin \phi, \qquad y = x' \sin \phi + y' \cos \phi.$$

After this substitution has been effected, equation (103) takes
the form

$$A'x'^2 + B'x'y' + C'y'^2 + D'x' + E'y' + F' = 0. \quad (104)$$

wherein

$$A' = A \cos^2 \phi + B \sin \phi \cos \phi + C \sin^2 \phi,$$
$$B' = 2(C - A) \sin \phi \cos \phi + B(\cos^2 \phi - \sin^2 \phi),$$
$$C' = A \sin^2 \phi - B \sin \phi \cos \phi + C \cos^2 \phi,$$
$$D' = D \cos \phi + E \sin \phi,$$
$$E' = E \cos \phi - D \sin \phi, \quad \text{and} \quad F' = F.$$

The condition that B', the coefficient of the $x'y'$-term,
vanishes is that the angle of rotation, ϕ, is chosen so that

$$B' = 2(C - A) \sin \phi \cos \phi + B(\cos^2 \phi - \sin^2 \phi) = 0.$$

With the aid of the trigonometric formulas for the double angle (Introd., Art. 12), this equation may be reduced to

$$(C - A) \sin 2\phi + B \cos 2\phi = 0,$$

that is, if $C - A \neq 0$, to

$$\tan 2\phi = \frac{B}{A - C}, \tag{105}$$

and if $C - A = 0$, $B \neq 0$, to

$$\cos 2\phi = 0. \tag{105'}$$

Example. Remove the xy-term from $5x^2 + 4xy + 8y^2 = 9$ by a rotation of axes.

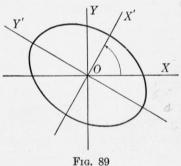

Fig. 89

By (105), we must rotate the axes through an angle ϕ such that

$$\tan 2\phi = \frac{4}{5 - 8} = -\frac{4}{3}.$$

By trigonometry, we have * $\cos 2\phi = -\frac{3}{5}$, and, by the half-angle formulas (Introd., Art. 12), we find

$$\sin \phi = \sqrt{\frac{1 - \cos 2\phi}{2}} = \sqrt{\frac{1 + \frac{3}{5}}{2}} = \frac{2}{\sqrt{5}}$$

$$\cos \phi = \sqrt{\frac{1 + \cos 2\phi}{2}} = \sqrt{\frac{1 - \frac{3}{5}}{2}} = \frac{1}{\sqrt{5}}.$$

---

* In determining 2ϕ by means of (105), we shall suppose, throughout, that $0 \leqq 2\phi < 180°$. With this assumption, $\cos 2\phi$ will always agree in sign with $\tan 2\phi$ and, since $0 \leqq \phi < 90°$, $\sin \phi$ and $\cos \phi$ will always be positive or zero.

On substituting these values of $\sin \phi$ and $\cos \phi$ in (97), we obtain, as the formulas for the required rotation of axes,

$$x = \frac{x' - 2y'}{\sqrt{5}}, \qquad y = \frac{2x' + y'}{\sqrt{5}}.$$

If, in the given equation, we replace x and y by these expressions, and simplify, we find, as the required equation,

$$9x'^2 + 4y'^2 = 9.$$

This is the equation of an ellipse with foci on the y'-axis and with semi-axes of lengths $\frac{3}{2}$ and 1.

EXERCISES

Remove the xy-term from the following equations by a rotation of axes. Draw both sets of axes and the curve.

1. $5x^2 + 6xy - 3y^2 = 3$.   **2.** $4x^2 + 24xy - 3y^2 = 60$.

3. $25x^2 - 30xy + 9y^2 = 5$.   **4.** $2x^2 - 4xy - y^2 = 6$.

5. $5x^2 + 8xy + 5y^2 = 25$.   **6.** $5x^2 - 12xy + 10y^2 = 10$.

7. $7x^2 + 8xy - 8y^2 = 35$.   **8.** $9x^2 - 24xy + 16y^2 = 64$.

69. Reduction of Numerical Equations to a Standard Form.

If the second degree terms in the given equation do not form a perfect square, that is if $B^2 - 4AC \neq 0$, we first translate the origin to the point (h, k), then determine h and k, as in example 1 below, so that the coefficients of x' and y' are zero. We then rotate the axes so as to remove the xy-term.

If the second degree terms do form a perfect square, that is, if $B^2 - 4AC = 0$, we first remove the xy-term by a rotation of axes and then complete the simplification of the equation by a translation, as in example 2 on page 138.

Example 1. Simplify $6x^2 + 24xy - y^2 - 12x + 26y + 11 = 0$.

Since $B^2 - 4AC = 24^2 - 4 \cdot 6(-1) \neq 0$, we first translate the origin to the point (h, k) by putting $x = x' + h$, $y = y' + k$. We have, after collecting the coefficients,

$$6x'^2 + 24x'y' - y'^2 + (12h + 24k - 12)x' + (24h - 2k + 26)y'$$
$$+ 6h^2 + 24hk - k^2 - 12h + 26k + 11 = 0.$$

If we equate to zero the coefficients of x' and y' in this equation, we have

$$12h + 24k - 12 = 0, \qquad 24h - 2k + 26 = 0.$$

By solving these equations as simultaneous, we find $h = -1$,

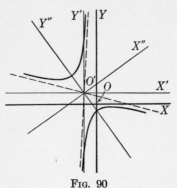

Fig. 90

$k = 1$. If we now substitute these values of h and k in the above equation, we obtain

$$6x'^2 + 24x'y' - y'^2 + 30 = 0.$$

To remove the xy-term, we rotate the axes through an angle ϕ such that $\tan 2\phi = \frac{24}{7}$. Then $\cos 2\phi = \frac{7}{25}$, $\sin \phi = \frac{3}{5}$, $\cos \phi = \frac{4}{5}$, and the equations of the rotation are

$$x' = \frac{4x'' - 3y''}{5}, \qquad y' = \frac{3x'' + 4y''}{5}.$$

On making these substitutions, and simplifying, we obtain, as the required equation of the conic,

$$15x''^2 - 10y''^2 + 30 = 0, \quad \text{or} \quad \frac{y''^2}{3} - \frac{x''^2}{2} = 1.$$

The curve is a hyperbola with center at the new origin and transverse axis on the y''-axis.

Example 2. Simplify $144x^2 - 120xy + 25y^2 - 118x + 190y - 81 = 0$.

Since $B^2 - 4AC = 14400 - 14400 = 0$, we first remove the xy-term by a rotation of axes.

To determine ϕ, we put $\tan 2\phi = -\frac{120}{119}$. Hence $\cos 2\phi = -\frac{119}{169}$, $\sin \phi = \frac{12}{13}$, $\cos \phi = \frac{5}{13}$, and the equations of the required rotation are

$$x = \frac{5x' - 12y'}{13}, \qquad y = \frac{12x' + 5y'}{13}.$$

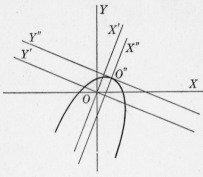

FIG. 91

If we substitute these values of x and y in the given equation, and simplify, we obtain

$$169y'^2 + 130x' + 182y' - 81 = 0.$$

We may write this equation in the form

$$169(y' + \tfrac{7}{13})^2 + 130(x' - 1) = 0.$$

Hence, if we put $x' = x'' + 1$, $y' = y'' - \frac{7}{13}$, the above equation becomes

$$169y''^2 + 130x'' = 0, \quad \text{or} \quad 13y''^2 + 10x'' = 0.$$

The curve is a parabola with vertex at the new origin and axis coinciding with the x''-axis.

EXERCISES

Simplify the following equations, draw all the axes, and draw the curve if it exists.

1. $3x^2 - 6xy - 5y^2 - 6x + 22y + 24 = 0.$
2. $x^2 + 12xy - 4y^2 + 14x + 4y + 5 = 0.$
3. $16x^2 - 24xy + 9y^2 - 14x - 2y + 15 = 0.$

4. $31x^2 + 24xy - 14y^2 - 110x + 32y - 28 = 0.$

5. $3x^2 + 2xy + 3y^2 + 6x - 14y + 19 = 0.$

6. $7x^2 + 8xy + y^2 - 50x - 26y + 88 = 0.$

7. $9x^2 - 12xy + 4y^2 + 30x - 20y - 1 = 0.$

8. $5x^2 + 6xy + 5y^2 - 6x + 22y + 53 = 0.$

9. $3x^2 - 24xy - 4y^2 + 30x - 16y + 18 = 0.$

10. $4x^2 + 12xy + 9y^2 - 4x - 6y + 1 = 0.$

11. $7x^2 - 4xy + 7y^2 - 11x + y + 11 = 0.$

12. $9x^2 - 6xy + y^2 - 22x - 6y + 53 = 0.$

13. $8x^2 + 24xy + y^2 - 32x + 20y - 30 = 0.$

14. $2x^2 + 2xy + 2y^2 - 10x + 4y + 13 = 0.$

Find the equations of the following loci, simplify the equation, and draw the curve.

15. Determine the locus of a point, given that its undirected distance from the origin equals twice its undirected distance from the line $x + y = a$.

16. Find the locus of the vertex of a triangle, given that the ends of the base are $(0, 0)$ and $(a, 0)$ and that the sum of the slopes of the sides is $\frac{7}{12}$.

17. The ends of the base of a triangle are $(0, 0)$ and $(a, 0)$. The base angle at $(a, 0)$ exceeds by $45°$ the base angle at $(0, 0)$. Find the locus of the vertex.

18. The ends of the base of a triangle are $(0, 0)$ and $(a, 0)$. The base angle at $(a, 0)$ is equal to twice the base angle at $(0, 0)$. Find the locus of the vertex.

19. Determine the locus of a point, given that the square of its distance from the origin is equal to the product of its directed distances from the lines $x + 7y + 2 = 0$ and $x + y - 4 = 0$.

SELECTED EXERCISES

1. Show that, if equation (103) is transformed into (104) by rotating the axes through any given angle ϕ, then $A' + C' = A + C$ and $B'^2 - 4A'C' = B^2 - 4AC$.

Note. Because of these equations, the quantities $A + C$ and $B^2 - 4AC$ are said to be *invariants* under rotation.

2. If the axes are rotated so that $B' = 0$, show that A' and C' are the roots of the following quadratic equation in t:

$$t^2 - (A + C)t + AC - \frac{B^2}{4} = 0.$$

3. Show that, if $B^2 - 4AC \neq 0$, the general equation of second degree becomes, after a translation to remove the first degree terms,

$$Ax'^2 + Bx'y' + Cy'^2 = \frac{\Delta}{2(B^2 - 4AC)}, \text{ wherein } \Delta = \begin{vmatrix} 2A & B & D \\ B & 2C & E \\ D & E & 2F \end{vmatrix}$$

Note. The determinant Δ is called the *discriminant* of the given equation.

Hint. First show that the new constant term can be written in the form $\frac{1}{2}[(2Ah + Bk + D)h + (Bh + 2Ck + E)k + (Dh + Ek + 2F)]$ and hence that, if h and k are chosen so that the coefficients of x' and y' are zero, this expression reduces to $\frac{1}{2}(Dh + Ek + 2F)$.

4. Show that, if $B^2 - 4AC = 0$, the general equation of second degree may be reduced, after a rotation of axes to remove the xy-term, to $(A + C)x'^2 + \dfrac{D\sqrt{A} \pm E\sqrt{C}}{\sqrt{A + C}} x' + \dfrac{E\sqrt{A} \mp D\sqrt{C}}{\sqrt{A + C}} y' + F = 0$ wherein the indeterminate sign in the coefficient of x' agrees with, and that in the coefficient of y' is opposite to, the sign of B.

5. Using the results of Ex. 3 and 4, show that the condition that a conic is degenerate, that is, that the left-hand member of its equation can be factored into real or imaginary linear factors, is that $\Delta = 0$.

Hint. In the case in which $B^2 - 4AC = 0$, show that $\Delta = -2(E\sqrt{A} \mp D\sqrt{C})^2$.

Find the equation of the conic that passes through the following five points.

6. $(0, 0)$, $(-2, 0)$, $(0, 3)$, $(1, 1)$, $(-3, 2)$.

7. $(0, 7)$, $(10, 2)$, $(4, -1)$, $(-2, 5)$, $(6, 1)$.

8. $(2, 3)$, $(1, 1)$, $(1, 3)$, $(4, 5)$, $(2, 1)$.

CHAPTER VIII

HIGHER PLANE CURVES

70. Introduction. We have seen that, if the equation of a curve is of first degree in x and y,

$$Ax + By + C = 0,$$

the curve is a line and, if its equation is of the second degree,

$$Ax^2 + Bxy + Cy^2 + Dx + Ey + F = 0,$$

the locus of the equation (if it exists) is a conic section. If the given equation cannot be reduced to either of the above forms, its locus is said to be a **higher plane curve.**

A plane curve is **algebraic** if it can be defined by equating to zero a polynomial in which x and y appear only with positive integral exponents; otherwise, it is **transcendental.** Lines and conics, for example, are algebraic curves, as are also the loci defined by such equations as $x^3 + y^3 + 1 = 0$ or $3xy + x^5 - y^5 = 0$. The curve defined by such an equation as $y = \tan x$ or $y \log x + x^2 = 0$ is transcendental.

In this chapter, we shall point out some of the properties of certain of the higher plane curves that are encountered most frequently in advanced mathematics and we shall discuss some of the methods that may be used to assist in drawing their graphs. The figures that appear in the text will be found useful for reference in the student's later work in mathematics.

I. ALGEBRAIC CURVES

71. Discussion of the Equation. When we have given the equation of a higher plane curve, our first problem in connection with it, before we attempt to draw the curve, is to try to determine, from the form of the given equation, some of the essential properties of the curve. The determination of these outstanding properties is called the *discussion of the equation*.

In this article, we shall show how to determine several important properties that are usually found in the algebraic curves most frequently met with, that can be determined quite readily from the given equations, that are helpful in drawing the graphs, and are of importance in the applications.

(*a*) *Symmetries.* A curve is symmetric with respect to a given line or to a given point if, when $P(x, y)$ is any point on the curve, then its symmetric point with respect to the given line or the given point also lies on the curve.

The point symmetric to $P(x, y)$ with respect to:

(1) the x-axis is $(x, -y)$ (2) the y-axis is $(-x, y)$
(3) the line $y = x$ is (y, x) (4) the origin is $(-x, -y)$.

Hence, an algebraic curve is symmetric to:

(1) the x-axis if y enters its equation only to even powers
(2) the y-axis if x enters its equation only to even powers
(3) the line $y = x$, if its equation remains unchanged when x and y are interchanged in it
(4) the origin, if the equation remains unchanged when x and y are replaced by $-x$ and $-y$, respectively.

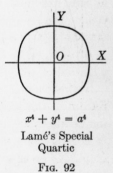

$$x^4 + y^4 = a^4$$

Lamé's Special Quartic

Fig. 92

The curve $x^4 + y^4 = a^4$ (Fig. 92) exhibits all of the above-mentioned symmetries. The student should plot this curve, and the circle $x^2 + y^2 = a^2$, carefully on one set of axes. Are there any points on the curve that lie inside the circle?

(*b*) *Intercepts.* The intercepts on the x-axis are found by putting $y = 0$ in the equation of the curve and solving for x;

and, on the y-axis, by putting $x = 0$ and solving for y. The graph must pass through every point determined in this way and it does not meet either axis in any other point.

Thus, the curve $x^4 + y^4 = a^4$, shown in Fig. 92, meets the x-axis at $(\pm a, 0)$, and the y-axis at $(0, \pm a)$. It has no other point in common with either axis.

(c) *Tangent Lines at the Origin.* If the given curve passes through the origin, we may find its approximate form near that point, since x and y are small, by considering only their smallest powers that appear in the equation, and neglecting all higher powers; that is, *to find the tangent lines to the curve at the origin, equate to zero those terms in its equation for which the sum of the exponents of x and y has the smallest value.*

Thus, for the curve $x^2y^2 + a^2x^2 - a^2y^2 = 0$, the sum of the exponents of x and y in the first term is 4 and in each of the remaining two terms is 2. The tangent lines at the origin are found, by equating these last two terms to zero, to be $x^2 - y^2 = 0$, or $x + y = 0$ and $x - y = 0$.

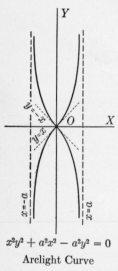

$x^2y^2 + a^2x^2 - a^2y^2 = 0$

Arclight Curve

Fig. 93

(d) *Horizontal and Vertical Asymptotes.* When we were studying, in Art. 54, the graph of the equation $b^2x^2 - a^2y^2 = a^2b^2$ of a hyperbola, we noticed that the curve recedes toward infinity, in any one of the quadrants, in such a way that it approaches a fixed line which we called an asymptote to the hyperbola.

Since many other curves extend out indefinitely far in a similar way, we make the following definition: *If a branch of a curve extends toward infinity in such a way that it approaches indefinitely near to a fixed line, this line is called an asymptote to the curve.*

If an algebraic curve has vertical or horizontal asymptotes, these lines can be determined from the equation of the curve as in the following example.

Example. Find the vertical and the horizontal asymptotes to the curve $xy^2 - a^2y - b^2x = 0$.

In this equation, if we assign to x a fixed value $x_1 \neq 0$, the resulting quadratic equation in y has two roots which are the ordinates of the two intersections of the vertical line $x = x_1$ with the curve.

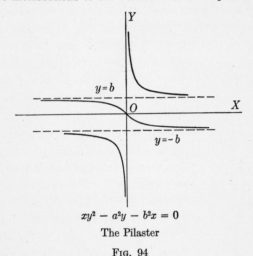

$$xy^2 - a^2y - b^2x = 0$$

The Pilaster

Fig. 94

If we now let x_1 approach indefinitely near to zero, one of the two corresponding values of y increases indefinitely in numerical value and the corresponding point on the curve recedes toward infinity in such a way that it approaches indefinitely near to the line $x = 0$, that is, to the y-axis (Fig. 94). This line is, accordingly, an asymptote.

Similarly, if we arrange the given equation in powers of x,

$$(y^2 - b^2)x - a^2y = 0,$$

and assign to y any value $y_1 \neq \pm b$, the root of the resulting equation in x is the abscissa of the single intersection of the line $y = y_1$ with the curve. If y_1 is now made to approach $+ b$ or

$- b$, the numerical value of x will increase indefinitely and the corresponding point on the curve will approach the asymptote $y = b$ or $y = -b$.

By applying reasoning similar to the foregoing to any given algebraic curve, we deduce the following general rule for finding the vertical and horizontal asymptotes: *To find the vertical asymptotes to an algebraic curve, equate to zero the real, linear factors of the coefficient of the highest power of y in the equation. To find the horizontal asymptotes, equate to zero the real, linear factors of the coefficient of the highest power of x in the equation.*

If the coefficient of the highest power of y (or of x) in the given equation is a constant, or if its linear factors are all imaginary, there are no vertical (or no horizontal) asymptotes. Thus, the curve $y^4 + x^2y^2 + x^2 + 1 = 0$ has no vertical asymptotes since the coefficient of the highest power of y is unity. It has no horizontal asymptotes since the factors of $y^2 + 1$, the coefficient of the highest power of x, are imaginary.

(e) *Excluded Intervals.* If, when the given equation is solved for y, square roots occur in the right-hand member, the values of x throughout certain intervals may cause the quantity under the radical sign to be negative and thus make y imaginary. Since no point can be plotted if either of its coördinates is imaginary, any such interval should be excluded from consideration in drawing the graph.

In the same way, when we solve for x, certain intervals may be found on the y-axis for which the values of x are imaginary. These intervals must also be excluded when we draw the graph.

If, for example, we solve the equation $x^2y^2 - a^2x^2 - a^2y^2 = 0$ for y, we find that $y = \dfrac{\pm\, ax}{\sqrt{x^2 - a^2}}$, which shows that, for all values of x between $x = -a$ and $x = a$, except $x = 0$, y is imaginary. There are, accordingly, no points on the curve except the point $(0, 0)$ within this interval (Fig. 95).

If we now solve the above equation for x, we obtain

$x = \dfrac{\pm\, ay}{\sqrt{y^2 - a^2}}.$ It follows that, for all values of y between $-a$

and a, except $y = 0$, x is imaginary. This interval on the y-axis should also be excluded in drawing the graph.

A point, such as the origin in this example, that lies on the curve, but which has no other points on the curve in its neighborhood, is called a *conjugate* (or *isolated*) *point* on the curve.

72. Graphs of Equations. When it is required to draw the graph of a given equation, we first discuss the equation, as in Art. 71, and note on the figure the information thus obtained. We then plot points on the curve, as we did in Chapter I, taking care, however, always to plot some points on each branch of the locus and to plot the points most numerously at the places

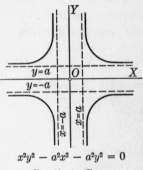

$x^2y^2 - a^2x^2 - a^2y^2 = 0$

Cruciform Curve

Fig. 95

where the curve seems to be changing its direction most rapidly. If a very accurate graph is required, a rather large number of points will need to be plotted in this way.

EXERCISES

Discuss the following equations for: (a) symmetries, (b) intercepts, (c) tangent lines at the origin, (d) vertical and horizontal asymptotes, and (e) excluded intervals. Plot a sufficient number of points on the graph to determine its form, and draw it.

1. $xy - 2x - 2y = 0$
2. $x^2 + 4y^2 = 9$
3. $x^2 + y^2 + 4x + 4y = 0$
4. $y^2 + x - 2 = 0$
5. $xy^2 = 1$
6. $y = x^3 - x$
7. $xy^2 + 4x - 8 = 0$
8. $xy^2 - 4x - 8 = 0$
9. $x^4 - x^2 + y^2 = 0$
10. $x^3 - x^2 + y^2 = 0$
11. $x^2y^2 - 4y^2 - x = 0$
12. $x^2y - x^2 - y - 1 = 0.$

In the following articles, we shall discuss the equations and draw the graphs of some of the more important algebraic higher plane curves.

73. The Witch of Agnesi. The locus of the equation $x^2y + a^2y - a^3 = 0$ is called the *witch of Agnesi* (or, simply, the *witch*) (Fig. 96).

This curve is symmetric with respect to the y-axis which it intersects at $(0, a)$. It has the x-axis as an asymptote and does not intersect it. If we solve the equation for x, we find that $x = \pm a\sqrt{\dfrac{a - y}{y}}.$ Hence x is imaginary if $y < 0$ or $y > a$. If we solve the equation for y, we have $y = \dfrac{a^3}{x^2 + a^2}$, from which it follows that y has its largest value, a, when $x = 0$ and that it decreases continually as the numerical value of x increases. (Why?)

Figure (96) can now be sketched quite accurately by plotting a number of points on the curve and drawing it in such a way that it satisfies the above conditions.

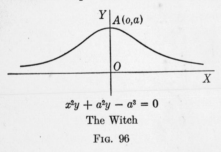

$x^2y + a^2y - a^3 = 0$
The Witch

Fig. 96

Exercise. On the segment OA (Fig. 96) as a diameter, draw a circle and draw the tangent line to this circle at A. Through O draw any line intersecting the circle at a point B and the tangent line at a point C. Through B draw a line parallel to the x-axis and through C one parallel to the y-axis. Show that the locus of the intersection P of these last two lines is the witch.

74. The Strophoid. The name *strophoid* is given to the curve defined by the equation $x^3 + xy^2 + ax^2 - ay^2 = 0$ (Fig. 97).

The curve is symmetric with respect to the x-axis. It intersects the x-axis at the origin and at $(-a, 0)$ and the y-axis at the origin only. The lines $y = \pm x$ are tangent to the curve at the origin and the line $x - a = 0$ is an asymptote. If $x > a$ or if $x < -a$, the values of y are imaginary.

The graph is constructed by plotting points on the locus and drawing through them a smooth curve that satisfies the above conditions.

Exercise. Through $A(-a, 0)$ (Fig. 97) draw any line and denote its intersection with the y-axis by B. On the line through A and B there are two points P and P' such that $PB = P'B = OB$. Show that the locus of the points P and P' is the strophoid.

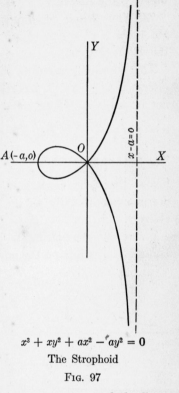

$$x^3 + xy^2 + ax^2 - ay^2 = 0$$

The Strophoid

FIG. 97

75. The Trisectrix of Maclaurin.

This curve is the locus of the equation $x^3 + xy^2 + ay^2 - 3ax^2 = 0$ (Fig. 98).

The graph of this equation is symmetric with respect to the x-axis, passes through the origin, and meets the x-axis again at $(3a, 0)$. The line $x + a = 0$ is an asymptote and the lines $y = \pm \sqrt{3}x$ are tangent to it at the origin. If $x < -a$ or if $x > 3a$, the values of y are imaginary (Fig. 98).

This curve is of interest in connection with the problem of trisecting a given angle,* as may be seen from the following exercise.

------

* The following problems became famous in antiquity because of the unsuccessful efforts of the Greek geometers to solve them by the methods of elementary geometry:

Exercise. Through the origin, draw any line and denote its inclination by α. Through the point $A(2a, 0)$ draw the line having an angle of inclination 3α. Show that the locus of the point of intersection of these lines is composed of the x-axis and a trisectrix of Maclaurin. Hence, show how, given a trisectrix of Maclaurin, any given angle may be trisected.

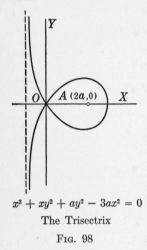

$$x^3 + xy^2 + ay^2 - 3ax^2 = 0$$

The Trisectrix

Fig. 98

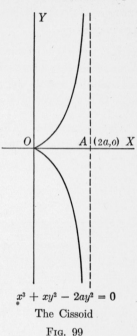

$$x^3 + xy^2 - 2ay^2 = 0$$

The Cissoid

Fig. 99

76. The Cissoid of Diocles. The graph of the equation $x^3 + xy^2 - 2ay^2 = 0$ is called the *cissoid of Diocles* (or, more briefly, the *cissoid*) (Fig. 99).

To trisect a given angle.

To construct a square equal in area to a given circle.

To construct the edge of a cube whose volume is equal to twice the volume of a given cube.

In elementary geometry, it is customary to assume that the only construction instruments that are permitted to be used are: the straightedge to draw lines that pass through two known points and compasses to draw circles of known centers and known radii. It has been proved in modern times that, *under these limitations*, the above constructions are all impossible. They are, however, all possible, and were all actually effected by the Greeks, with the aid of other instruments.

This curve is symmetric with respect to the x-axis. It intersects the axes only at the origin and its tangents at that point are defined by $y^2 = 0$. The line $x - 2a = 0$ is a vertical asymptote. If x is negative, or is greater than $2a$, the values of y are imaginary.

Exercise. On the segment joining $O(0, 0)$ to $A(2a, 0)$ (Fig. 99) as a diameter, draw a circle. Through O draw any line meeting the circle at a point B and the line $x - 2a = 0$ at C. Lay off $\overline{OP} = \overline{BC}$ and show that the locus of P is the cissoid.

77. The Serpentine. The name *serpentine* is given to the curve defined by the equation $x^2y + b^2y - a^2x = 0$ (Fig. 100).

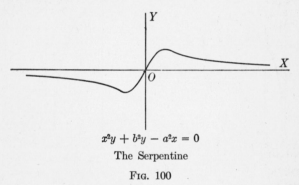

$$x^2y + b^2y - a^2x = 0$$

The Serpentine

Fig. 100

This curve is symmetric with respect to the origin. It touches the line $b^2y - a^2x = 0$ at the origin and does not meet either axis at any other point. The x-axis $(y = 0)$ is an asymptote. If we write the equation in the form $x = \dfrac{a^2 \pm \sqrt{a^4 - 4b^2y^2}}{2y}$, we find that there are no points on the curve outside the interval $y = \pm \dfrac{a^2}{2b}$. (Why?) When y has these limiting values, the corresponding values of x are found to be $x = b$ and $x = -b$.

78. The Bipartite Cubic. The locus of the equation

$$y^2 = x(x - a)(x - b), \qquad 0 < a < b$$

is composed of two entirely separate branches and is called a *bipartite cubic* curve (Fig. 101).

It is symmetric with respect to the x-axis, touches the y-axis at the origin, and intersects the x-axis again at $(a, 0)$ and at $(b, 0)$.

The ordinate y is real only if $0 \leqq x \leqq a$ or if $x > b$. By plotting points carefully on the locus, we find that the branch between $x = 0$ and $x = a$ is an oval, slightly more pointed to the right than to the left, and that the branch for $x \geqq b$ extends to infinity in the first and fourth quadrants without approaching any rectilinear asymptote.

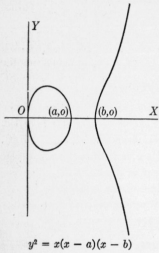

$$y^2 = x(x - a)(x - b)$$

The Bipartite Cubic

Fig. 101

EXERCISES

Determine, for the following curves, the symmetries, intercepts, tangent lines at the origin, asymptotes, and excluded intervals. Plot enough points on the graph to determine its form, and draw the curve.

1. $a^2y = x^3$ *The Cubical Parabola*

2. $ay^2 = x^3$ *The Semi-cubical Parabola*

3. $y = x^n$. Plot on one set of axes for $n = -2, -1, \frac{1}{2}, \frac{5}{2}, 4$, and 5.

4. $xy - 3x + 2y = 0$

5. $x^2 - y^2 + 2x + 4y - 8 = 0$

6. $x^2y - x^2 - 4y = 0$

7. $y = (x^2 - 1)^2$

8. $xy^2 - x - 1 = 0$

9. $y = x(x + 1)^2$

10. $y^3 + 3x^2y + y^2 - x^2 = 0$

11. $xy = (x^2 - 1)(x - 2)$

12. $x^4 + x^2y^2 - y^2 = 0$

13. $y^2 = x^3 - x^2$

14. $xy^2 - x^2 - 1 = 0$

15. $y^2 = x^3 - x$

16. $xy^2 + y^2 - x^2 + x = 0$

17. $x^6 - 4x^4 + y^2 = 0$

18. $x^2y^2 - y^2 + 1 = 0$

19. $x^6 + y^6 = a^6$

20. $x^2y - x^2 - y + 2x = 0$

21. $(x^2 + y^2)^2 = a^2(x^2 - y^2)$ *The Lemniscate*

22. $y^4 - 2ay^3 + a^2x^2 = 0$ *The Top* $a = 2$

23. $(x^2 + y^2)^2 = ax^2y$ *The Bifolium*

24. $(x^2 + 2ay - a^2)^2 - y^2(a^2 - x^2) = 0$ *The Cocked Hat*

25. The locus of a point that moves so that the product of its distances from two fixed points, $(-a, 0)$ and $(a, 0)$, is equal to a constant b^2 is called an *oval of Cassini*. Find the equation of the curve and draw it for $a = \dfrac{b}{2}$, $a = b$, and $a = 2b$.

26. The locus of a point that moves so that its distances from $O(0, 0)$ and $A(a, 0)$ satisfy the relation $AP = \pm\, bOP \pm c$ is called a *Cartesian oval*. Find the equation and draw the curve.

27. If a is the length of the edge of a given cube, show that the parabolas $y^2 = 2ax$ and $x^2 = ay$ intersect in a point whose abscissa is the edge of a cube of twice the volume of the given cube.

28. The force F of gravitational attraction between two bodies is expressed as a function of the distance r between them by the equation $F = \dfrac{k}{r^2}$. Show this relation graphically.

29. The squares of the periods of revolution of the planets about the sun are proportional to the cubes of the major semi-axes of their orbits. Express this relation by an equation, and draw the graph.

30. Equal squares of side x are cut from a square piece of tin of side a and the edges are then folded up so as to form a box with an open top. Express the volume of the box as a function of x, and draw the graph.

II. TRANSCENDENTAL CURVES

79. **The Sine and Cosine Curves.** The sine curve is defined by the equation

$$y = \sin x. \tag{106}$$

It may be plotted by laying off, on the x-axis, the radian measure of the angle (Introd., Art. 7) and, in the y direction, the value of the sine. For angles in the interval $0 \leqq x \leqq 90°$, these values of x and y may be found from the table on page 292. For angles outside of this interval, we add to, or subtract from, the given angle integer multiples of $90°$ $\left(\dfrac{\pi}{2}\ \text{radians}\right)$ and determine the value of the sine with the aid of the trigonometric reduction formulas (Introd., Art. 10).

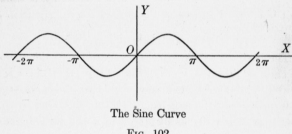

The Sine Curve

Fig. 102

The sine curve is **periodic** (with period 2π), since $\sin\ (x + 2\pi)$ $= \sin x$. It is also symmetric with respect to the origin, since $-\sin\ (-x) = \sin x$. Moreover, since, for all real values of x, $-1 \leqq \sin x \leqq 1$, there are no points on the curve for which $y > 1$ or $y < -1$.

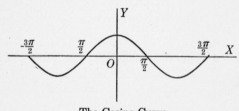

The Cosine Curve

Fig. 103

The cosine curve. By means of the reduction formula $\sin\left(\dfrac{\pi}{2} + x\right) = \cos x$ we find that Fig. 102 may also be used to represent the cosine curve

$$y = \cos x, \tag{107}$$

provided that the origin is moved $\frac{\pi}{2}$ units to the right.   In other words, the sine curve and the cosine curve are identical in size and form.   They differ only in their position with respect to the y-axis.

Since cos $(-x)$ = cos x, the cosine curve is symmetric with respect to the y-axis.

The curves
$$y = a \sin bx \quad \text{and} \quad y = a \cos bx,$$

which occur frequently in the applications, may be derived at once from the sine and cosine curves, respectively, by multiplying the ordinates by a and dividing the abscissas by b.   The number a is called the **amplitude** and b the **periodicity factor** of the resulting curve.

Example.   Draw the curve $y = \frac{3}{2} \sin 2x$ from $x = 0$ to $x = 2\pi$.

We first draw the sine curve for one complete period, and then construct the curve $y = \frac{3}{2} \sin x$ which is obtained from it by multiplying all the ordinates by the amplitude $\frac{3}{2}$.   The required

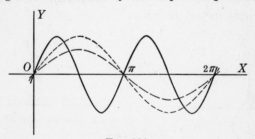

Fig. 104

curve is then obtained by dividing all the abscissas of this curve by the periodicity factor 2, and repeating the figure so obtained as many times as is necessary (Fig. 104).

80. The Tangent Curve.   The graph of the equation
$$y = \tan x \tag{108}$$
is the tangent curve (Fig. 105).   It may be plotted by the aid

of the table on page 292 and the reduction formulas (Introd., Art. 10). Since tan $(x + \pi) = \tan x$ the curve is periodic with period π. It crosses the x-axis at the points $(k\pi, 0)$ (where k is

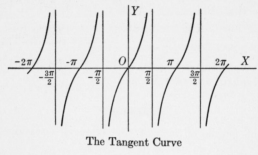

The Tangent Curve

FIG. 105

zero or any positive or negative integer) and has the lines $x = k\pi + \dfrac{\pi}{2}$ as vertical asymptotes. Since $- \tan (- x) = \tan x$, the curve is symmetric with respect to the origin.

81. The Inverse Trigonometric Functions. If we solve the inverse trigonometric equations

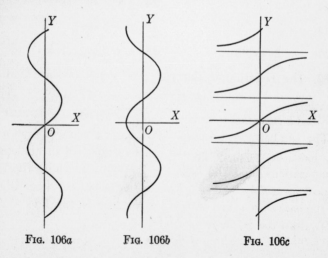

FIG. 106a FIG. 106b FIG. 106c

$$y = \sin^{-1} x, \quad y = \cos^{-1} x, \quad \text{and} \quad y = \tan^{-1} x \qquad (109)$$

for x, we have, respectively,

$$x = \sin y, \quad x = \cos y, \quad \text{and} \quad x = \tan y.$$

It follows that the curves defined by equations (109) are identical in form with the ordinary sine, cosine, and tangent curves and differ from them only in that they are placed on the figure in such a way that their positions with respect to the x- and y-axes are interchanged.

EXERCISES

Draw the graphs of each of the following equations for two periods.

1. $y = \sin \pi x$
2. $y = \text{ctn } x$
3. $y = \sec x$
4. $y = \csc x$
5. $y = \text{ctn}^{-1} x$
6. $y = \sec^{-1} x$
7. $y = \sin (x + 1)$
8. $y = \sin^{-1} (x + 1)$

Hint. In Ex. 7 and 8, first translate the origin to $(-1, 0)$.

9. $y = 3 \sin x$
10. $y = \sin 3x$
11. $y = \tan 2x$
12. $y = \text{ctn } 2x$
13. $y = 2 \sin 3x$
14. $y = \frac{1}{2} \sin 2x$
15. $y = 3 \cos \dfrac{x}{2}$
16. $y = 3 \tan \dfrac{x}{4}$
17. $y = 2 \cos^{-1} 3x$
18. $y = 3 \cos (2x + 4)$

82. The Logarithmic Curves. The graph of the equation

$$y = \log_a x, \qquad a > 1 \qquad (110)$$

is called a *logarithmic curve*.

The number a is the **base**. Two bases are in common use: the base 10, which is the one usually employed in numerical computations, and the base $e = 2.71828^+$, which is the one almost invariably used in advanced mathematics. Logarithms to the base e are called *natural*, or *Naperian*, logarithms.

To draw the graph of

$$y = \log_{10} x,$$

we assign to x a series of values and determine the corresponding values of y with the aid of the table of logarithms on pages 290–1.

Since the logarithms of negative numbers are imaginary, the graph does not extend to the left of the y-axis. The curve intersects the x-axis at $(1, 0)$, since $\log 1 = 0$. If $x > 1, \log_{10} x$

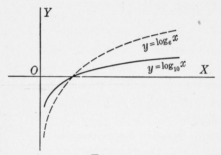

Fig. 107

is positive and the curve lies in the first quadrant. The points on the curve in the interval $0 < x < 1$ are found by using the relation $\log \left(\dfrac{1}{M} \right) = - \log M$ (Introd., Art. 4). The graph approaches the negative end of the y-axis as an asymptote (Fig. 107).

The logarithmic curve $y = \log_a x$, where $a \neq 10$, can be plotted by means of the table on pages 290–1, provided that we also make use of the formula $\log_a x = \dfrac{\log_{10} x}{\log_{10} a}$ (Introd., Art. 4).

For example, since $\log_{10} e = \log_{10} 2.71828 = 0.4343^- = \dfrac{1}{2.303^-}$, we may draw the graph of $y = \log_e x$ by putting

$$y = \log_e x = \frac{\log_{10} x}{\log_{10} e} = 2.303 \log_{10} x.$$

The graph of the equation $y = \log_e x$ may thus be obtained from that of $y = \log_{10} x$ by multiplying all the ordinates of the latter curve by 2.303. The resulting graph is shown in the dotted curve in Fig. 107.

83. The Exponential Curves. The graph of the equation

$$y = a^x, \qquad a > 1 \qquad (111)$$

is called an *exponential curve*.

If we solve equation (111) for x, we have, from the definition of a logarithm (Introd., Art. 4)

$$x = \log_a y. \qquad (112)$$

This is the equation of a logarithmic curve (Art. 82) with x and y interchanged in it; that is, *the exponential curve differs from the logarithmic only in that it is placed on the figure so that its position with reference to the x- and y-axes is interchanged.*

Because of this relation between their graphs, the functions a^x and $\log_a x$ are said to be *inverse functions*.

To draw the graph of equation (111), one usually takes the logarithms to the base 10 of both sides of the equation. One thus obtains

$$\log_{10} y = x \log_{10} a.$$

Values may then be assigned to y and the corresponding values of x determined with the aid of a table of logarithms.

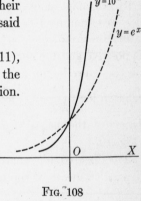

Fig. 108

In the applications, the exponential equation usually appears in the form

$$y = ae^{bx},$$

where a and b are constants the values of which are assigned in the given problem, and $e = 2.71828^+$. The graph of this equation also may be found by taking the logarithms of both sides of the given equation and writing the result in the form

$$\log_{10} y = bx \log_{10} e + \log_{10} a.$$

If a series of values are now assigned to y, the corresponding values of x may be computed by means of this equation.

Example 1. Draw the graph of the exponential equation $y = 1.84 \, e^{0.57x}$.

If we take the logarithms to the base 10 of both sides of this equation, we have

$$\log_{10} y = 0.57x \log_{10} e + \log_{10} 1.84.$$

But $\qquad \log_{10} e = 0.4343$, and $\log_{10} 1.84 = 0.2648$.

If we substitute these values of $\log_{10} e$ and $\log_{10} 1.84$ in the above equation, and simplify, we obtain

$$\log_{10} y = 0.2475x + 0.2648.$$

If we solve this equation for x, we have

$$x = 4.040 \log_{10} y - 1.070.$$

By assigning values to y and computing the corresponding values of x, we obtain the following table of pairs of values of x and y that satisfy the given equation.

x	-3.502	-2.286	-1.575	-1.070	0.146	0.857	1.362	1.754
y	0.25	0.5	0.75	1	2	3	4	5

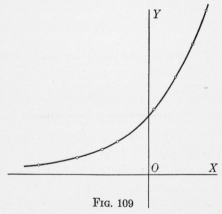

Fig. 109

If we plot these points and draw a smooth curve through them, we obtain Fig. 109.

Example 2. Draw the graph of the logarithmic equation $y = \log_{10} 3(x + 1)^2$.

We first write the given equation in the equivalent form

$$y = 2 \log_{10} (x + 1) + \log_{10} 3.$$

By assigning values to x and computing the corresponding values of y with the aid of the table of logarithms on pages 291–2, we find

x	-0.9	-0.75	-0.5	-0.25	0	0.5	1	2
y	-1.523	-0.727	-0.125	0.227	0.477	0.829	1.079	1.431

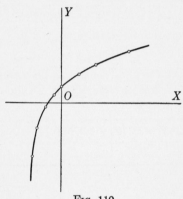

Fig. 110

Fig. 110 is obtained by plotting these points and drawing a smooth curve through them.

84. Applications. The exponential equation appears in many of the applications of mathematics, for example:

The law of variation of the pressure of the atmosphere with the height is exponential.

The rate of increase of the number of bacteria in a culture tends to follow an exponential formula.

The law of cooling of a heated body is exponential.

The rate of decomposition of radium follows an exponential law.

The speed of many chemical reactions varies according to an exponential law.

The rate of decrease of the velocity of an automobile, coasting along a level road, is exponential.

The strength of a physiological stimulus tends to vary as an exponential function of the reaction it produces.

The amount A of a sum of money P, at compound interest at a rate r for n years, is given by the exponential equation $A = P(1 + r)^n$. For this reason, the exponential function is often called "the compound interest law."

★ **85. Damped Vibrations.** If a vibrating body, such as a tuning fork or a swing, is allowed to oscillate subject only to the action of frictional forces, the motion tends to die out in such a way that the displacement, d, of a point of the body from the position of rest varies with the time, t, approximately, according to the law

$$d = ae^{-kt} \cos (\alpha t + \beta). \qquad (113)$$

This equation is said to define a *damped vibration*.

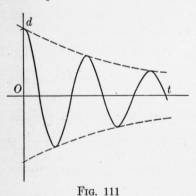

Example. Draw the graph of $d = 2e^{-\frac{t}{4}} \cos \pi t$.

We first draw the curves $d = 2e^{-\frac{t}{4}}$ and $d = -2e^{-\frac{t}{4}}$ which bound the amplitudes of the vibrations.

When $t = 0$, $d = 2$ and the required curve touches the upper boundary curve $d = 2e^{-\frac{t}{4}}$. As t increases to unity, the value of d decreases.

Fig. 111

The graph crosses the t-axis when $t = \frac{1}{2}$ and touches the lower boundary curve when $t = 1$. The value of d now increases, the graph crosses the t-axis at $t = \frac{3}{2}$, and touches the upper boundary curve again at $t = 2$ (Fig. 111).

EXERCISES

Draw the graphs of the following equations, using the table of logarithms on pages 291–2.

1. $y = \log_{10}(-x)$ **2.** $y = \log_{10}(x+3)$

3. $y = \log_{10} 3x$ **4.** $y = \log_{10} x^3$

5. $y = \log_3 x$ **6.** $y = \log_e(x-5)$

7. $y = \log_e(1+x^2)$ **8.** $y^2 = \log_{10} x$

9. $y = \log_{10} 2(x-5)^2$ **10.** $y = \log_{10} 4\sqrt{x+2}$

11. $y = 3^x$ **12.** $y = e^{-x}$

13. $y = -e^x$ **14.** $y = 3e^{2x}$

15. $y = (1.04)^x$ **16.** $5y = e^{\frac{x}{10}}$

17. $y = 0.23e^{1.41x}$ **18.** $y = 2.35(1.83)^x$ $e^{-2.781281}$

19. $y = xe^x$ **20.** $y = e^{-x^2}$. The Probability Curve.

21. Compare the graphs of $y = (\frac{1}{2})^x$ and $y = 2^{-x}$.

22. Draw on one set of axes the graphs expressing the amount of one dollar at interest for n years (a) at 6% compounded annually, and (b) at 8% simple interest. State the meaning of the points of intersection of these curves and find their coördinates approximately.

23. Find approximately, from a figure, the number of years in which one dollar will double at 5%, compound interest.

★ **86. Addition of Ordinates.** Let it be required to draw the graph of the equation

$$y = x + \sin x.$$

To find the value of y corresponding to a given value x_1, of x, the equation tells us to add together the numbers x_1 and $\sin x_1$. Instead of finding this sum by an arithmetic computation, the following geometric device for performing the addition will often be found easier and more satisfactory.

We first draw the curves

$$y = x \quad \text{and} \quad y = \sin x.$$

The values of y for the points on these two curves, when $x = x_1$, are obviously $y = x_1$ and $y = \sin x_1$. Hence, *the algebraic* *sum of the ordinates of the points on the two curves, for $x = x_1$, is the ordinate of the point on the required curve for $x = x_1$.* We

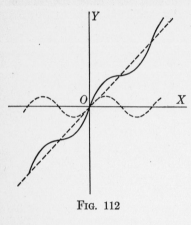

Fig. 112

may locate as many points as we please on the required curve, accordingly, by adding graphically the ordinates of the corresponding points on the component curves; that is, by laying off, in a vertical direction from any point on the line $y = x$, a directed distance equal to the ordinate of the point directly above or below it on the curve $y = \sin x$ (Fig. 112).

As a second example of the method of addition of ordinates, consider the ellipse

$$x^2 + 2xy + 2y^2 - 3x - 8y + 8 = 0.$$

If we solve this equation for y, we have

$$y = \tfrac{1}{2}(- x + 4 \pm \sqrt{- x^2 - 2x}).$$

To draw the graph of this equation, we shall first draw the line

$$y = \frac{- x + 4}{2},$$

and the ellipse

$$y = \pm \frac{\sqrt{- x^2 - 2x}}{2};$$

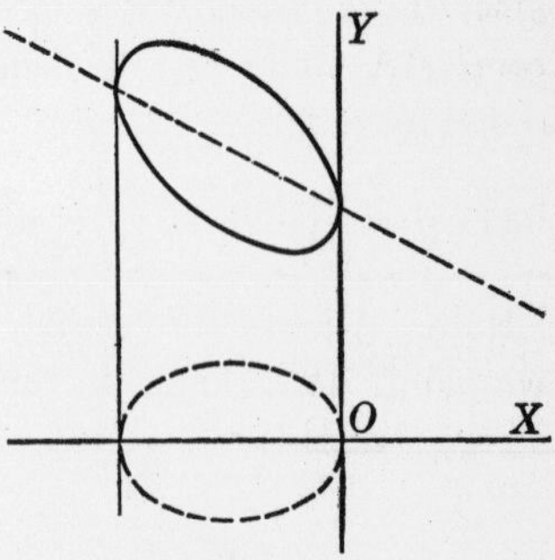

Fig. 113

that is, the ellipse $(x + 1)^2 + 4y^2 = 1$.

If we now add, graphically, the ordinates of corresponding points on these two curves, we determine the corresponding points on the required curve. An ellipse drawn through these points is the graph of the given equation.

EXERCISES

By the method of addition of ordinates, draw the graphs of the following curves.

1. $y = \sin x + \cos x$ **2.** $y = 2 \cos x + \cos 2x$

3. $y = 3 \cos 2x + 2 \sin x$ **4.** $y = \dfrac{x}{2} + \cos x$

5. $y = x + \log_{10} x$ **6.** $y = \sin x + \log_e x$

7. $y = \cos x + e^{\frac{x}{2}}$ **8.** $y = x^2 - \cos x$

9. $y = \sin^2 x$ **10.** $y = \cos^2 x.$

Hint: $\sin^2 x = \frac{1}{2}(1 - \cos 2x),$ and $\cos^2 x = \frac{1}{2}(1 + \cos 2x).$

11. $y = x + 2 \pm \sqrt{x}$

12. $y = 2x - 3 \pm \sqrt{(x-2)(x+2)}$

13. $4x^2 - 4xy + y^2 - x + 2y + 6 = 0$

14. $10x^2 + 6xy + y^2 + 6x + 2y - 2 = 0$

15. $y = \dfrac{e^x - e^{-x}}{2}.$ **16.** $y = \dfrac{e^x + e^{-x}}{2}.$

Note. The right-hand members of Exercises 15 and 16 are called the *hyperbolic sine of x* and the *hyperbolic cosine of x*, respectively. The first is denoted by the symbol sinh x and the second by cosh x.

17. $y = \dfrac{a}{2}\left(e^{\frac{x}{a}} + e^{-\frac{x}{a}}\right) = a \cosh \dfrac{x}{a}.$ *The Catenary.*

Note. A perfectly flexible, inextensible cord, suspended between two points on it, hangs in the form of a catenary.

CHAPTER IX

PARAMETRIC EQUATIONS

87. Introduction. Instead of representing a curve by a single equation connecting x and y, it is sometimes preferable to use two equations which express the coördinates of the points on the curve in terms of a third variable. This third variable is called the **parameter** and the two equations which express x and y in terms of this parameter are the **parametric equations** of the curve.

In the following articles, we shall derive the parametric equations of a number of curves and indicate a few of the uses of such equations.

88. Parametric Equations of the Circle. Let there be given a circle with center at the origin and radius a (Fig. 114). Let $P(x, y)$ be any point on this circle and denote the angle XOP by ϕ. From the figure, we obtain

$$x = a \cos \phi, \quad y = a \sin \phi. \quad (114)$$

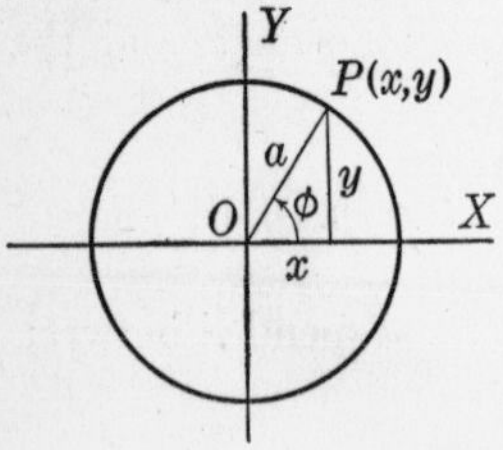

These two equations, which express the coördinates of any point P on the circle in terms of the parameter ϕ, are the *parametric equations of the given circle.*

FIG. 114

If the parametric equations of a curve are given, the rectangular equation may be found by eliminating the parameter between the two given equations. Thus, from (114), if we square both members of each equation, add, and simplify the result, we have

$$x^2 + y^2 = a^2, \quad (115)$$

which is the rectangular equation of the given circle.

If the rectangular equation of the curve is given, however, various parametric equations can be found for it, depending on the choice of the parameter. For the circle (115), for example, we may choose as the parameter the slope m of the line through any point P on the circle and the fixed point $(-a, 0)$. The equation of this line is $y = m(x + a)$. (Why?) Since the coördinates of P satisfy the equation of this line and also the equation (115) of the circle, we find, on solving these two equations for x and y,

$$x = a\,\frac{1 - m^2}{1 + m^2}, \qquad y = a\,\frac{2m}{1 + m^2}. \tag{116}$$

These two equations, also, constitute a pair of parametric equations of the circle (115).

89. Parametric Equations of the Ellipse. Any point whose coördinates satisfy the parametric equations,

$$x = a \cos \phi,$$
$$y = a \sin \phi, \tag{117}$$

wherein ϕ is the parameter, lie on an ellipse. For, if we divide the first equation by a,

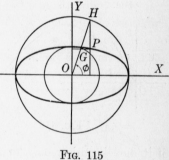

Fig. 115

the second by b, square both members, add, and simplify, we find, as the rectangular equation of the curve,

$$\frac{x^2}{a^2} + \frac{y^2}{b^2} = 1,$$

which is the equation of an ellipse.

From equations (117), one readily derives the construction by points of the ellipse that is given in Art. 52, (2) (b). For, the parametric equations of the major and minor auxiliary circles, that is, the circles with centers at the origin and radii a and b, respectively, are, by Art. 88,

For the major auxiliary circle

$$x = a \cos \phi, \quad y = a \sin \phi,$$

and, for the minor auxiliary circle,

$$x = b \cos \phi, \quad y = b \sin \phi.$$

It follows from these equations, together with (117), that, if P, H, and G are the points defined on the ellipse, the major auxiliary circle, and the minor auxiliary circle, respectively, by a given value of ϕ, then the abscissas of P and H are equal, as are also the ordinates of P and G.

It should be noted further that, in (117), the parameter ϕ is *not* the inclination of the line OP, but of the line through O and the corresponding points G and H on the auxiliary circles.

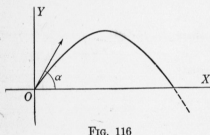

FIG. 116

90. Path of a Projectile. If a projectile is fired from the origin with an initial velocity v_0, in a direction making an angle α with OX, and if it moves subject only to the attraction of gravitation, it is shown in the textbooks on physics that its position at the end of t seconds is given by the equations

$$x = t v_0 \cos \alpha, \qquad y = t v_0 \sin \alpha - \tfrac{1}{2} g t^2,$$

where g is a constant. These two equations constitute the parametric equations of the path of the projectile in terms of the parameter t.

To find the rectangular equation of the path, we solve the first equation for t, substitute in the second equation, and simplify. The result is

$$y = x \tan \alpha - \frac{g x^2}{2 v_0^2} \sec^2 \alpha.$$

This rectangular equation defines the path of the projectile, but it does not state the position of the body at any given time. The parametric equations define not only the path but also the law according to which the projectile traverses its path.

91. Parametric Equations of the Folium of Descartes. If we wish to draw the folium of Descartes, which is defined by the equation

$$x^3 + y^3 - 3axy = 0,$$

we first find, by discussing the equation as in Art. 71, that the curve is symmetric with respect to the line $y = x$, that it

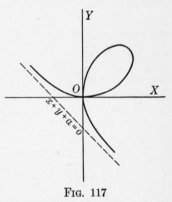

touches both axes at the origin, and that it has no other points in common with either axis.

If we now wish to plot points on the curve by assigning values to x, we find that we have, in each case, to solve a cubic equation in order to determine the corresponding values of y. Instead of doing this, it will be found more convenient to determine a pair of parametric equa-

Fig. 117

tions of the curve and to plot points on the curve from these parametric equations.

To find the required parametric equations, we notice that any line $y = mx$ through the origin intersects the folium at the origin and at the point whose coördinates are

$$x = \frac{3am}{1 + m^3}, \quad y = \frac{3am^2}{1 + m^3}. \tag{118}$$

These equations constitute a pair of parametric equations of the curve in terms of the parameter m.

By assigning to m real values (other than -1) we can now determine as many points as we please on the curve. By drawing a smooth curve through these points (that joins them in the order of the corresponding values of m), we obtain the required graph of the folium (Fig. 117).

If we assign to m the value $m = -1$, we do not obtain a corresponding point on the curve. (Why?) By assigning to m a number of values very near to -1, however, we find that the corresponding points are far from the origin but very close to the line $x + y + a = 0$. This line is thus an asymptote.

1 – 14   Eliminate parameter

EXERCISES

Draw the following curves by assigning values to the parameter, plotting the corresponding points, and drawing a smooth curve through them. Then find the rectangular equation by eliminating the parameter.   *a = 3 b = 2*

1. $x = 3t$, $y = 4 - t$

2. $x = 2t$, $y = \dfrac{2}{t}$

3. $x = 2 \tan \phi$, $y = 2 \cot \phi$

4. $x = \tan^2 \phi$, $y = 3 \tan \phi$

5. $x = at$, $y = \pm b\sqrt{1 - t^2}$

6. $x = a \sec \phi$, $y = b \tan \phi$

7. $x = 2pt^2$, $y = 2pt$

8. $x = t + \dfrac{1}{t}$, $y = t - \dfrac{1}{t}$

9. $x = 3 \cos \phi + 2$, $y = 5 \sin \phi - 3$

10. $x = a \cos \phi - b \sin \phi$, $y = a \sin \phi + b \cos \phi$

11. $x = at$, $y = at^3$

12. $x = at^2$, $y = bt^3$

13. $x = a \cos^4 \phi$, $y = a \sin^4 \phi$

14. $x = a \cos^3 \phi$, $y = a \sin^3 \phi$

15. Show that $x = a + bt$, $y = c + dt$ are parametric equations of a line and find its slope.

16. Find parametric equations of the ellipse $b^2x^2 + a^2y^2 = a^2b^2$ by finding its intersections with the lines $y = m(x + a)$ through the point $(-a, 0)$.

17. Find parametric equations of the strophoid (Art. 74) by finding its intersections with the lines $y = mx$ through the origin.

18. Find parametric equations of the trisectrix of Maclaurin (Art. 75).

19. Find parametric equations of the cissoid (Art. 76).

20. A wheel of radius 8 inches makes 2 revolutions per second about its center which is a fixed point. Find parametric equations of the path of a point on the rim by stating the coördinates of this point at the end of t seconds.

21. A line through the point $K(2, 4)$ intersects the coördinate axes at the points A and B. Find the locus of the midpoint of the segment AB as the line rotates about K.

92. The Cycloid.
The path of a point fixed on the circumference of a circle that rolls along a fixed line is called a **cycloid**.

We shall find the parametric equations of the cycloid when the fixed line on which the circle rolls is taken as the x-axis and any one of the positions at which the tracing point comes in contact with this line is taken as origin.

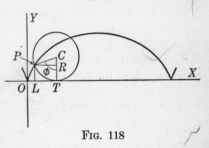

Let a be the radius of the rolling circle, $P(x, y)$ be any position of the tracing point, and let ϕ be the number of *radians* in the

Fig. 118

angle through which the circle has rolled from its position when the tracing point was at the origin.

From the figure

$$x = \overline{OL} = \overline{OT} - \overline{LT}, \tag{119}$$

and

$$y = \overline{LP} = \overline{TR} = \overline{TC} - \overline{RC}. \tag{120}$$

Since the circle has rolled from O to T, $\overline{OT} =$ arc TP, and, since ϕ is measured in radians, we have (Introd., Art. 7) arc $TP = a\phi$. Hence

$$\overline{OT} = \text{arc } TP = a\phi.$$

Also $\overline{LT} = \overline{PR} = a \sin \phi$, $\overline{RC} = a \cos \phi$,   and $\overline{TC} = a$.

If we make these substitutions in (119) and (102), we may write the resulting equations in the form

$$\begin{aligned} x &= a(\phi - \sin \phi) \\ y &= a(1 - \cos \phi) \end{aligned} \tag{121}$$

These are the required parametric equations of the cycloid, in terms of the parameter ϕ.

To find the rectangular equation of the cycloid, we first solve the second of equations (121) for $\cos \phi$. This gives

$$\cos \phi = \frac{a - y}{a}.$$

If we find the values of ϕ and of $\sin \phi$ from this equation and substitute them in the first of equations (121), we obtain, as the required rectangular equation of the curve,

$$x = a \cos^{-1} \frac{a - y}{a} \pm \sqrt{2ay - y^2}.$$

This equation is much less convenient, for most practical purposes, than the parametric equations (121).

EXERCISES

1. Draw the graph of one arch of the cycloid for $a = 10$.

2. Find the length of the base and the coördinates of the highest point of one arch of the cycloid.

3. If the abscissas of two points on the cycloid differ by $2\pi a$, show that their ordinates are equal. Interpret this result geometrically.

4. Find the parametric equations of the cycloid when the origin is translated to the top of an arch.

5. Find the parametric equations of the cycloid when the circle rolls along the under side of the fixed line.

6. If the tracing point lies on a fixed radius (or radius produced) of the rolling circle, at a distance $b \neq a$ from the center, show that the equations of its path are

$$x = a\phi - b \sin \phi \qquad y = a - b \cos \phi$$

This curve is called a **prolate cycloid** if $b > a$ and a **curtate cycloid** if $b < a$. In either case, the curve is also called a **trochoid**.

7. Draw the graph of the curtate cycloid $x = 10\phi - 5 \sin \phi$, $y = 10 - 5 \cos \phi$.

8. Draw the graph of the prolate cycloid $x = 10\phi - 15 \sin \phi$, $y = 10 - 15 \cos \phi$.

9. A circle of radius a feet rolls along a line at the rate of b radians per second. At the instant that a certain radius extends vertically downward, a particle starts from the center along that radius at the rate of c feet per second. Find the path of the particle.

★ **93. The Epicycloid.** The path of a point fixed on the circumference of a circle that rolls tangent externally to a fixed circle is called an **epicycloid**.

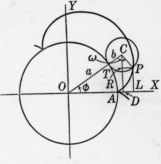

Denote the radius of the fixed circle by a and of the rolling circle by b. Take the center, O, of the fixed circle as origin and the x-axis through a point A where the tracing point is in contact with the fixed circle (Fig. 119).

Let ϕ be the number of radi-ans in the angle XOC which the

FIG. 119

line of centers makes with the x-axis and let ω be the number of radians in the angle OCP through which the radius CP has turned from the line of centers.

From the figure,
$$\text{angle } DCO = \frac{\pi}{2} - \phi,$$

and
$$\text{angle } DCP = \omega - \text{angle } DCO = \omega - \left(\frac{\pi}{2} - \phi\right) = \phi + \omega - \frac{\pi}{2}.$$

Also
$$x = \overline{OL} = \overline{OD} + \overline{DL} = \overline{OD} + \overline{RP},$$

and
$$y = \overline{LP} = \overline{DR} = \overline{DC} - \overline{RC}.$$

Since $OC = a + b$ (Why?), we have, from the definitions of the sine and cosine of an angle,

$$\overline{OD} = (a + b) \cos \phi, \quad \overline{RP} = b \sin (DCP) = -b \cos (\phi + \omega).$$
$$\overline{DC} = (a + b) \sin \phi, \quad \overline{RC} = b \cos (DCP) = b \sin (\phi + \omega).$$

On making these substitutions in the preceding equations for x and y, we have

$$x = (a + b) \cos \phi - b \cos (\phi + \omega)$$
$$y = (a + b) \sin \phi - b \sin (\phi + \omega)$$

Moreover, since the outside circle rolls on the fixed one, we have

$$\text{arc } AT = \text{arc } PT$$

But
$$\text{arc } AT = a\phi \quad \text{and} \quad \text{arc } PT = b\omega$$

Hence
$$a\phi = b\omega \quad \text{or} \quad \omega = \frac{a\phi}{b}$$

On substituting this value of ω in the above equations, we obtain

$$x = (a + b) \cos \phi - b \cos \frac{a + b}{b} \phi$$
$$y = (a + b) \sin \phi - b \sin \frac{a + b}{b} \phi \tag{122}$$

These are the parametric equations of the epicycloid in terms of the parameter ϕ.

★ **94. The Hypocycloid.** The path of a point fixed on the circumference of a circle that rolls tangent internally to a fixed circle is called a **hypocycloid**.

If we denote the radius of the fixed circle by a, of the rolling circle by b, and the angles AOC and TCP (measured in radians) by ϕ and ω respectively, we find, precisely as for the epicycloid, that the equations

$$x = (a - b) \cos \phi + b \cos \frac{a - b}{b} \phi$$
$$y = (a - b) \sin \phi - b \sin \frac{a - b}{b} \phi \tag{123}$$

are the parametric equations of the hypocycloid.

It should be observed that the parametric equations of the epicycloid are reduced to those of the hypocycloid by replacing b by $-b$. The derivation of the equations of the hypocycloid from the figure is left as an exercise for the student.

In Fig. 120, we have taken $b = \dfrac{a}{4}$. This hypocycloid is of special interest and is called the **four-cusped hypocycloid.**

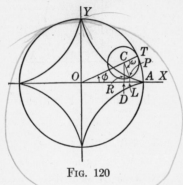

FIG. 120

If we put $b = \dfrac{a}{4}$ in the parametric equations of the hypocycloid and simplify by means of the trigonometric identities

$$\cos 3\phi = 4 \cos^3 \phi - 3 \cos \phi \quad \sin 3\phi = 3 \sin \phi - 4 \sin^3 \phi$$

we obtain $x = a \cos^3 \phi, \qquad y = a \sin^3 \phi$

as the parametric equations of the four-cusped hypocycloid.

By eliminating ϕ from these two equations, we obtain

$$x^{\frac{2}{3}} + y^{\frac{2}{3}} = a^{\frac{2}{3}}$$

as the rectangular equation of this curve.

EXERCISES

1. Plot the epicycloids for which (a) $a = 3b$;   (b) $a = 2b$; (c) $a = b$.

2. Plot the hypocycloids for which (a) $a = 3b$;   (b) $a = 2b$; (c) $2a = b$.

3. If a thread is unwound from around a fixed circle, and is held taut in the plane of the circle, any point fixed on the thread will describe a curve called an *involute of the circle*. Show that the parametric equations of this curve are

$$x = a(\cos \phi + \phi \sin \phi) \qquad y = a(\sin \phi - \phi \cos \phi)$$

Hint. Show that the angle OTP (Fig. 121) is a right angle.

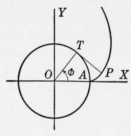

Fig. 121

4. Plot the involute of the circle from $\phi = 0$ to $\phi = 2\pi$.

5. A crank OA, 2 feet long, turns about O. A rod AB, 6 feet long, has one end attached at A while its other end B slides along a line OC through O. Find the path of a point P on AB at a distance k from A.

CHAPTER X

CURVES IN POLAR COÖRDINATES

95. Introduction. In preceding chapters, we have discussed the polar equations of lines, of circles, and of the conic sections. We shall now consider the problem of drawing a higher plane curve when its equation is given to us in polar coördinates.

The problem of drawing the graph of an equation in polar coördinates is complicated by the fact that, for a given point P, we can find infinitely many pairs of polar coördinates (Art. 16). If any one of these pairs of coördinates satisfy the equation, then P lies on the curve. We shall find, in fact, that sometimes only one pair of coördinates of P, and sometimes more than one pair, will satisfy the given equation. For example, if $P(r, \theta)$ is a point on the curve $r = \theta$ (Art. 102), only one pair of coördinates of P satisfy the given equation; but, if P lies on the line $r \cos \theta = 1$, then every pair of coördinates of P satisfy this equation.

Frequently, also, there are two or more different equations that define the same curve. For example, the equations $r = 1$ and $r = -1$ define the same circle. Two equations that define the same curve are said to be *equivalent equations*.

96. Discussion of the Equation. When it is required to plot the curve defined by a given equation in polar coördinates, time will usually be saved, and better results obtained, if, before plotting points on the curve, one tests the curve with respect to the following properties.

(a) *Symmetries*. If the equation of a curve remains unchanged, or is changed to an equivalent equation, when

    (1) θ is replaced by $-\theta$, the curve is symmetric with respect to the initial line.

(2) θ is replaced by $\pi - \theta$, it is symmetric with respect to the 90°-axis.

(3) θ is replaced by $\pi + \theta$, or when r is replaced by $- r$, the curve is symmetric with respect to the origin.

The curve $r^2(2 - \cos^2 \theta) = 8$, for example, exhibits all of the above symmetries. This curve is an ellipse, as may be

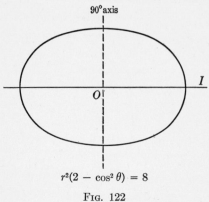

$$r^2(2 - \cos^2 \theta) = 8$$

FIG. 122

seen at once by writing its equation, $x^2 + 2y^2 = 8$, in rectangular coördinates.

(b) *Intercepts.* To find the intercepts on the initial line, one puts $\theta = 0, \pm \pi, \pm 2\pi$, etc., and solves for r. Similarly, the intercepts on the 90°-axis are found by putting $\theta = \pm \dfrac{\pi}{2}, \pm \dfrac{3\pi}{2}$, etc. This method frequently fails to determine the intersections, if there are any, at the origin, but these intersections will be determined under (c).

For example, the points of intersection of the ellipse $r^2(2 - \cos^2 \theta) = 8$ with the initial line are found in this way to be $(2\sqrt{2}, 0)$ and $(2\sqrt{2}, \pi)$ and its intersections with the 90°-axis are found to be $\left(2, \pm \dfrac{\pi}{2}\right)$.

(c) *Tangents at the origin.* If the curve passes through the origin, the angles made by its tangent line, or lines, with the initial line are found by putting $r = 0$ in the equation and solving for θ.

Thus, in the equation
$$r = a \sin 3\theta,$$
if we put $r = 0$, we have $\sin 3\theta = 0$, so that $3\theta = 0, \pm \pi, \pm 2\pi$, etc.

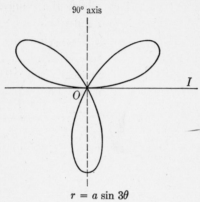

$$r = a \sin 3\theta$$

Three-leaved Rose

Fig. 123

Hence, $\theta = 0, \pm \dfrac{\pi}{3}, \pm \dfrac{2\pi}{3}$, etc. There are thus three tangent lines to this curve at the origin, of inclinations $0, \dfrac{\pi}{3}$, and $\dfrac{2\pi}{3}$, respectively. This curve is called a *three-leaved rose* curve. It belongs to a type that we shall discuss more fully in Art. 101.

(d) *Directions in which the curve extends to infinity.* To determine the directions in which the curve extends to infinity, we equate to zero the coefficient of the highest power of r in the given equation and solve for θ.

For example, to determine the directions in which the curve
$$r^2 \cos^3 \theta = a^2 \sin \theta$$
(Fig. 124) recedes to infinity, we equate to zero the coefficient of r^2. This gives $\cos^3 \theta = 0$, so that $\theta = \pm \dfrac{\pi}{2}, \pm \dfrac{3\pi}{2}$, etc.

This curve thus extends to infinity in the ± 90° directions. It is a cubical parabola (Art. 78, Ex. 1) and has no asymptote.

(e) *Intervals in which one coördinate is imaginary.* It is frequently possible, by using the fact that neither sin θ nor cos θ is ever numerically greater than unity, to assign limits between which the numerical values of r must lie.

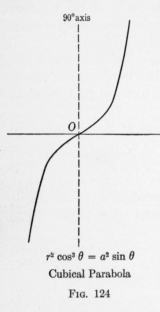

$$r^2 \cos^3 \theta = a^2 \sin \theta$$

Cubical Parabola

Fig. 124

Thus, for the three-leaved rose (Fig. 123), the largest numerical value that r can have is a. This numerical value is attained when sin 3θ = ± 1, that is, when $\theta = \pm \dfrac{\pi}{6}, \pm \dfrac{\pi}{2}, \pm \dfrac{5\pi}{6}$, etc.

Similarly, for the line r cos θ = 5, the smallest numerical value that r can have is 5. This value is reached when cos θ = ± 1, that is, when θ = 0, ± π, ± 2π, etc.

For the ellipse $r^2(2 - \cos^2 \theta)$ = 8 (Fig. 122), we find in a similar way that the largest numerical value that r can have is $2\sqrt{2}$, and the smallest is 2.

Again, if the given equation can be solved for r^2, it may be possible to find values of θ for which r is imaginary. These values of θ must be excluded in drawing the graph. In the case of the cubical parabola, $r^2 \cos^3 \theta = a^2 \sin \theta$ (Fig. 124), for example, r is imaginary if sin θ and cos θ have opposite signs, that is, if θ is in the second or fourth quadrants. There are thus no points on the curve corresponding to these values of θ.

(f) *Transformation to rectangular coördinates.* It frequently happens that the equation of the curve in rectangular coordinates is one with which the student is already familiar, or from which it is easier to determine the properties of the equation than it is from its polar equation. We found that the locus of the equation $r^2(2 - \cos^2 \theta) = 8$, for example, was an ellipse by finding its rectangular equation. Similarly, it is usually easier to recognize that the locus of the equation $r \cos \theta = 5$ (or $r = 5 \sec \theta$) is a line from its rectangular equation $x = 5$ than it is from either of the polar forms.

In any event, any information about the curve that is obtained from the discussion of its equation in rectangular coördinates, or by plotting points on it from its rectangular equation, must hold for the required graph.

Equally, if the equation is given to us in rectangular coördinates, it may be possible to simplify the problem of drawing the curve by finding its equation in polar coördinates. It is thus good practice, when the equation of a curve is given to us either in rectangular or in polar coördinates, to discuss its equation in both systems of coördinates before attempting to draw the graph.

(g) *Use of the laws of variation of the trigonometric functions.* If the given equation defines r as equal to a simple expression in terms of the trigonometric functions of θ, a fairly accurate preliminary sketch of the curve can often be obtained quickly by observing how these functions change as θ increases. For this purpose, the graphs of the trigonometric curves in Arts. 79 and 80 will be found quite helpful. The preliminary sketch obtained in this way may then be corrected by discussing the equation and plotting points on the curve.

Thus, if the given equation is

$$r = a \tan \theta,$$

it is obvious that $r = 0$ when $\theta = 0$, that r increases to a as θ increases to $\frac{\pi}{4}$ and that it then increases indefinitely as θ increases to $\frac{\pi}{2}$. By following the variation of $\tan \theta$ through the four quadrants, a figure somewhat resembling Fig. 125 will thus be obtained. By discussing the given polar equation, and the rectangular equation $x^4 + x^2y^2 = a^2y^2$, of this curve, and plotting a number of points on it, we obtain Fig. 125. The lines $x = \pm a$ are asymptotes.

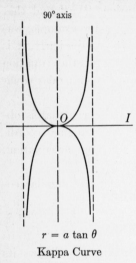

This curve is called the *kappa curve*, from its supposed resemblance to the Greek letter kappa.

$r = a \tan \theta$

Kappa Curve

Fig. 125

In the following articles, we shall discuss the equations and draw the graphs of a number of curves the equations of which are frequently encountered in polar coördinates.

97. The Lemniscate. The locus of the equation $r^2 = a^2 \cos 2\theta$ is called a *lemniscate of Bernoulli* (or, usually, simply a *lemniscate*) (Fig. 126).

This curve is symmetric with respect to both axes and the origin. It intersects the initial line at $(\pm a, 0)$ and these are the points on the curve farthest from the origin. It also passes through the origin and touches, at that point, the lines making angles of $\pm \dfrac{\pi}{4}$ and $\pm \dfrac{3\pi}{4}$ with the initial line. The radius vector r is imaginary if $\cos 2\theta$ is negative, that is, if θ lies in the intervals $\dfrac{\pi}{4} < \theta < \dfrac{3\pi}{4}$, or $\dfrac{5\pi}{4} < \theta < \dfrac{7\pi}{4}$, etc.

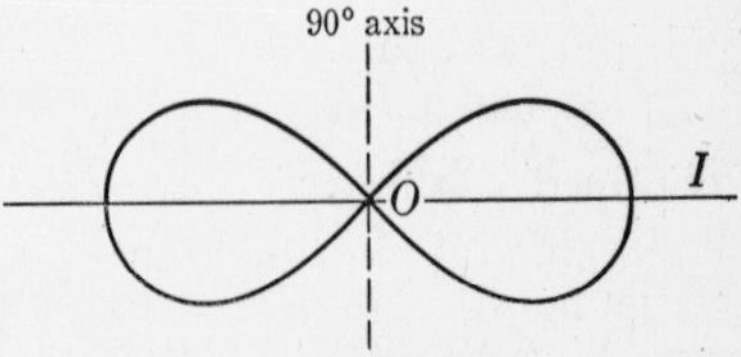

$r^2 = a^2 \cos 2\theta$

Lemniscate

Fig. 126

Exercise 1. Draw the curve $r^2 = a^2 \sin 2\theta$ and show that this curve is a lemniscate.

Exercise 2. Find the rectangular equation of the lemniscate and show that the curve is an oval of Cassini (Art. 78, Ex. 25) for which $a = b$.

98. The Cardioid. The cardioid is the locus of the equation $r = a(1 - \cos \theta)$.

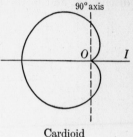

This locus is symmetric with respect to the initial line. It touches the initial line at the origin and intersects it at $(2a, \pi)$. The latter point is the point of the curve that is farthest from the origin. It crosses the 90°-axis at $\left(a, \pm \dfrac{\pi}{2}\right)$. The radius vector increases from 0 at $\theta = 0$ to $2a$ at $\theta = \pi$, then decreases to 0 again at $\theta = 2\pi$.

Cardioid

Fig. 127

99. The Limaçon. The equation $r = a - b \cos \theta$ defines a curve called the *limaçon of Pascal* (or *limaçon*).

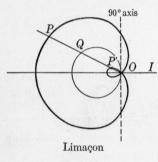

If $a = b$, the limaçon becomes a cardioid. In Fig. 128, we have taken $a < b$. The construction of the figure for $a > b$ is left as an exercise for the student.

The limaçon is frequently constructed by points in the following way: Draw the circle $r = -b \cos \theta$ and let Q be any point on this circle. Draw the line through O and Q and on it lay off, in opposite directions, the segments $QP = QP' = a$. Then the locus of the points P and P' is the limaçon.

Limaçon

Fig. 128

Exercise. Draw the following limaçons and cardioids:

(a) $r = 10 - 5 \cos \theta$ (b) $r = 10 + 5 \cos \theta$
(c) $r = 5(1 + \cos \theta)$ (d) $r = 5 - 10 \cos \theta$
(e) $r = 10 - 5 \sin \theta$ (f) $r = 5 - 10 \sin \theta$
(g) $r = 5(1 - \sin \theta)$ (h) $r = 5(1 + \sin \theta)$.

100. The Conchoid of Nicomedes. The locus of the equation $r = a \csc \theta \pm b$ is the *conchoid of Nicomedes*.

There are three cases according as $a \lesseqgtr b$. In the following discussion, and in the figure, we have taken $a < b$. The dis-

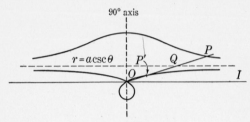

Conchoid of Nicomedes

Fig. 129

cussion of the other two cases is left as an exercise for the student.

The curve is symmetric with respect to the 90°-axis and intersects it at the origin and at the points $r = a \pm b$. It intersects the initial line only at the origin, at which point its tangents make angles $\theta = \csc^{-1}\left(\pm \dfrac{b}{a} \right)$ with the initial line. It extends to infinity in such a way that each of its two branches approaches the horizontal line $r = a \csc \theta$ as an asymptote.

This curve may be constructed by points in the following way: Draw the line $r = a \csc \theta$ and let Q be any point on it. Draw the line through O and Q and on it lay off, in opposite directions, the segments $QP = QP' = b$. Then the locus of the points P and P' is the conchoid.

Exercise. Draw the following conchoids:

(a) $r = 5 \csc \theta \pm 15$ (b) $r = 15 \csc \theta \pm 5$
(c) $r = 5(\csc \theta \pm 1)$ (d) $r = 15 \sec \theta \pm 5$
(e) $r = 5 \sec \theta \pm 15$ (f) $r = 5(\sec \theta \pm 1)$.

101. The Rose Curves. The loci of the equations,

$$r = a \cos n\theta \quad \text{and} \quad r = a \sin n\theta, \tag{124}$$

wherein n is an integer, are called *rose curves*. Each loop extending out from the origin is called a "leaf" of the rose.

The three-leaved rose, $r = a \sin 3\theta$, was shown in Fig. 123.

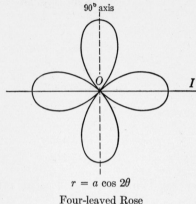

$$r = a \cos 2\theta$$

Four-leaved Rose

Fig. 130

The four-leaved rose, $r = a \cos 2\theta$, appears in Fig. 130. It is symmetric with respect to the origin and to both axes and it intersects the axes at the points $(a, 0)$, $\left(-a, \dfrac{\pi}{2}\right)$, (a, π), and $\left(-a, \dfrac{3\pi}{2}\right)$. Its tangent lines at the origin are defined by $\theta = \pm \dfrac{\pi}{4}, \pm \dfrac{3\pi}{4}$, etc.

Exercise 1. Show that the one-leaved rose, $r = a \cos \theta$, is a circle.

Exercise 2. Draw the following curves.

(a) $r = a \sin 2\theta$ (b) $r = a \sin 4\theta$
(c) $r = a \cos 4\theta$ (d) $r = a \cos 5\theta$.

Exercise 3. In equations (124), show that, if n is an odd integer, the number of leaves is n, but that if n is an even integer, the number of leaves is $2n$.

102. The Spirals. If a curve, or one of its branches, winds infinitely many times about the origin in such a way that r increases (or decreases) continuously as θ increases or decreases continuously, then the curve is called a *spiral*.

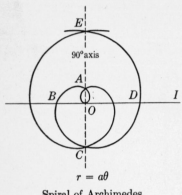

$r = a\theta$

Spiral of Archimedes

Fig. 131

The equation $r = a\theta$ defines a **spiral of Archimedes**.

This curve is symmetric with respect to the 90°-axis since, if a point (r, θ) lies on the curve, so also does $(-r, -\theta)$ and any two such points are symmetric with respect to the 90°-axis. (Why?) It touches the initial line at the origin and the rate of increase of the numerical value of r is proportional to that of θ.

Exercise. Show that the lengths of the successive segments OA, OB, OC, etc. from the origin to the successive intersections of the curve with the axes, as θ increases through positive values, form an arithmetic progression.

The locus of the equation $*\log_e r = a\theta$ is called a **logarithmic spiral**. The equation of this curve is also often written in the equivalent form $r = e^{a\theta}$.

For $\theta = 0$, we have $r = 1$. As θ increases from zero, the value of r increases more and more rapidly and becomes very large as θ approaches $+\infty$. If θ decreases from zero, the value of r decreases slowly and approaches zero as θ approaches $-\infty$.

To plot points on this curve, we take logarithms, to the base 10, of the members of its equation $r = e^{a\theta}$. This gives

---

* The number $e = 2.71828^+$ is the base of the natural system of logarithms (Art. 82).

$$\log_{10} r = a\theta \log_{10} e.$$

We now assign values to r and determine the corresponding values of θ with the aid of a table of logarithms.

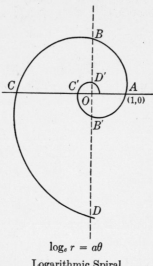

$$\log_e r = a\theta$$

Logarithmic Spiral

Fig. 132

Exercise. Show (a) that the length of the segments OC', OB', OA, OB, etc. from the origin to successive intersections of the curve with the axes form a geometric progression, (b) that the angles $C'B'A$, $B'AB$, ABC, etc. are right angles.

EXERCISES

Discuss the following equations and draw the corresponding curves on polar coördinate paper. State the name of the curve if you know it.

1. $r \sin \theta = a$
2. $r = a \sin \theta$
3. $r^2 \cos 2\theta = a^2$
4. $r^2 \sin 2\theta = a^2$
5. $r^2(1 - e^2 \cos^2 \theta) = b^2$. Three cases: $e < 1$, $e = 1$, $e > 1$
6. $r(1 - \cos \theta) = a$
7. $r = a(1 - \cos \theta)$
8. $r \cos^3 \theta = a \sin^2 \theta$
9. $r^2 \sin^3 \theta = a^2 \cos \theta$

10. $r^2 = a^2 \sin \theta$ **11.** $r = a \cos \left(\dfrac{\theta}{2}\right)$

12. $r^2 = a^2\theta$. *The parabolic spiral.*

13. $r\theta = a$. *The hyperbolic,* or *reciprocal, spiral.*

14. $r^2\theta = a$. *The lituus.*

15. Find the polar equations of the curves in Arts. 73 to 77.

16. Find the rectangular equations of the curves in the text of Arts. 97 to 100.

★ **103. Intersections of Curves in Polar Coördinates.** We have seen (Art. 16) that any given point in the plane has infinitely many pairs of polar coördinates and it has been pointed out (in Art. 95) that not all of these pairs need to satisfy the given polar equation of the curve. This fact introduces difficulties into the problem of finding the coördinates of the intersections of two curves whose polar equations are given. For, at a given intersection P, the pair of coördinates of P that satisfy the first equation may not be the pair that satisfy the second one. They may, instead, satisfy only an equation that is equivalent (Art. 95) to the given second equation.

Again, at the origin, $r = 0$ but θ may have any value whatever. The origin may therefore lie on both curves although the values of θ that make $r = 0$ may be entirely different for the two equations.

It is, accordingly, usually best, when one wishes to find the intersections of two curves from their polar equations, to plot both curves on one set of axes, and then to determine the intersections indicated on the figure by considering, if necessary, not only the given equations but also the equations equivalent to them.

The following examples will illustrate how the above-mentioned difficulties may arise, and how they may be met.

Example 1. Find the points of intersection of the curves $r = 3\theta$ and $r = \pi$.

From the figure, it is seen that these curves intersect in two points, one in the first quadrant and one in the second. The solution of the two given equations, however, determines only the intersection $P_1\left(\pi, \dfrac{\pi}{3}\right)$. To find the second intersection P_2, we replace the second equation by the equivalent equation $r = -\pi$. This, together with $r = 3\theta$, determines $P_2\left(-\pi, -\dfrac{\pi}{3}\right)$.

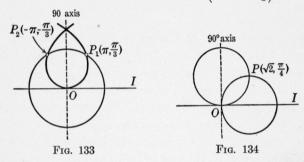

FIG. 133   FIG. 134

Example 2. Find the points of intersection of the circles

$$r = 2 \sin \theta \quad \text{and} \quad r = 2 \cos \theta.$$

If we eliminate r between these equations, we have

$$2 \sin \theta = 2 \cos \theta, \text{ or } \tan \theta = 1,$$

so that $\theta = \dfrac{\pi}{4}, \dfrac{5\pi}{4}$, etc. On substituting back in both given equations, we find that $P_1\left(\sqrt{2}, \dfrac{\pi}{4}\right)$ is one of the required intersections.

The two circles also intersect at the origin since $(0, 0)$ satisfies one of the given equations and $\left(0, \dfrac{\pi}{2}\right)$ satisfies the other. Hence, the origin is the second required intersection of the two circles.

EXERCISES

Draw the following pairs of curves on one set of axes and find the coördinates of their points of intersection.

1. $r \sin \theta = 4$ **2.** $r = 4 \sin \theta$
    $r = 8$ $r \sin \theta = 3$

3. $r = 2 \cos \theta$
$r = 2 \cos 2\theta$

4. $r = 4(1 + \cos \theta)$
$r(1 - \cos \theta) = 3$

5. $r \cos \theta = 2 \sin^2 \theta$
$r = 2 \cos \theta$

6. $r = 1 - 2 \cos \theta$
$r = \sin \theta$

7. $r^2 = \cos 2\theta$
$3r = \sqrt{6} \cos \theta$

8. $r^2 = 2 \sin \theta$
$r = 1$

9. $r^2 = \theta$
$r = 1$

10. $r\theta = 4$
$r = 2.$

CHAPTER XI

TANGENTS, NORMALS, DIAMETERS, POLES, AND POLARS

104. Definitions. Before we attempt to find the equation of the tangent line to a curve at a point on it, we must set up a working definition of a tangent line. The following definition is the one customarily employed in calculus, and throughout advanced mathematics.

Let P_1 be a given point on a given curve C. It is required to define the tangent line to C at P_1.

Let P_2 be another point on C and draw the secant line P_1P_2. If we now hold P_1 fixed and let P_2 move along C and approach P_1, the secant line P_1P_2 will turn around P_1. *The limiting position of the line P_1P_2, as P_2 approaches P_1 as a limit, along the curve, is the* **tangent line** *to C at P_1.*

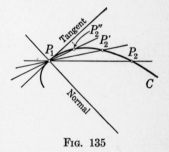

The line through P_1 perpendicular to the tangent is the **normal line** to C at P_1.

In the following sections, we shall derive the equations of the

Fig. 135

tangent and normal lines to the conic sections according to the foregoing definitions. The principles we shall employ are those of differential calculus, and the discussion should be thought of as preparatory to that subject.

105. Tangent and Normal to a Parabola. Let $P_1(x_1, y_1)$ be a given point on the parabola $y^2 = 2px$. It is required to find the equations of the tangent and normal lines to this parabola at P_1.

Since P_1 lies on the required tangent line P_1T, we can find the equation of this line if we can find its slope m, for

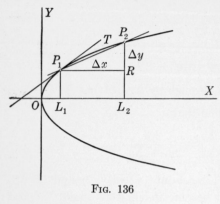

FIG. 136

we can then substitute this value of m in the point slope form $y - y_1 = m(x - x_1)$ of the equation of a line through $P_1(x_1, y_1)$.

To find the slope m of the tangent line, we must, by the definition of Art. 104, first find the slope of the secant line P_1P_2 and then find the limiting value of this slope as P_2 approaches P_1 along the curve.

Denote the coördinates of P_2 by $(x_1 + \Delta x, y_1 + \Delta y)$.* From the figure, the slope, m', of the secant line P_1P_2 is found to be

$$m' = \frac{y_1 + \Delta y - y_1}{x_1 + \Delta x - x_1} = \frac{\Delta y}{\Delta x}. \tag{125}$$

The limit of this value of m' as P_2 approaches P_1 along the curve, that is, as Δy and Δx approach zero, is the required slope of the tangent line.†

Since P_2 lies on the parabola, we have

$$(y_1 + \Delta y)^2 = 2p(x_1 + \Delta x) \qquad \text{(Why?)}$$

---

* The symbol Δx is read "delta x." It means simply the difference between the abscissas of P_1 and P_2, that is, it is the length $\overline{P_1R}$ in Fig. 136. Similarly, Δy (read "delta y") is the difference $\overline{RP_2}$ between the the ordinates of P_1 and P_2.

† The limiting value of $\dfrac{\Delta y}{\Delta x}$ as Δy and Δx approach zero is called, in calculus, "the derivative of y with respect to x" and is denoted by the symbol $\dfrac{dy}{dx}$. The study of the properties of this limit is the fundamental problem of differential calculus.

or $\qquad y_1^2 + 2y_1\Delta y + (\Delta y)^2 = 2px_1 + 2p\Delta x.$

Since P_1 also lies on the parabola, we have

$$y_1^2 = 2px_1. \tag{126}$$

From the last two equations, we obtain by subtraction

$$2y_1\Delta y + (\Delta y)^2 = 2p\Delta x.$$

By dividing this equation through by Δx, solving for $\dfrac{\Delta y}{\Delta x}$, and substituting in (125), we find that

$$m' = \frac{\Delta y}{\Delta x} = \frac{2p}{2y_1 + \Delta y}.$$

Now let P_2 approach P_1 as a limit. Clearly, $2p$ and $2y_1$ will remain fixed and Δy will become indefinitely small. Hence, $\dfrac{\Delta y}{\Delta x}$, or m', will approach $\dfrac{2p}{2y_1}$, or $\dfrac{p}{y_1}$. But this limit which m' approaches is m, the slope of the tangent line at P_1, that is,

$$m = \frac{p}{y_1}.$$

On substituting this value of m in the point slope equation of a line (Art. 20), we obtain, as the required equation of the tangent line to the parabola at P_1,

$$y - y_1 = \frac{p}{y_1}(x - x_1).$$

This equation can be simplified. Multiply by y_1, giving

$$y_1y - y_1^2 = px - px_1.$$

Now replace y_1^2 by its value from (126) and simplify. The result is

$$\boldsymbol{y_1y = p(x + x_1).} \tag{127}$$

This is the equation of the tangent line to the given parabola at $P_1(x_1, y_1)$.

The slope of the normal line at $P_1(x_1, y_1)$ is the negative reciprocal of the slope of the tangent at that point (Why?), or $-\dfrac{y_1}{p}$. Hence

$$y - y_1 = \frac{-y_1}{p}(x - x_1),$$

or $\qquad\qquad p(y - y_1) + y_1(x - x_1) = 0, \qquad\qquad (128)$

is the equation of the normal line to the parabola at $P_1(x_1, y_1)$.

106. Tangent and Normal to the Ellipse. To find the tangent and normal lines to the ellipse $b^2x^2 + a^2y^2 = a^2b^2$ at a point

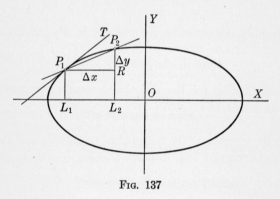

Fig. 137

$P_1(x_1, y_1)$ on it, we follow the same line of reasoning that we used for the parabola.

Let $P_2(x_1 + \Delta x, y_1 + \Delta y)$ be any point other than P_1 on the ellipse. Then we have

$$b^2(x_1 + \Delta x)^2 + a^2(y_1 + \Delta y)^2 = a^2b^2,$$

or

$$b^2x_1^2 + 2b^2x_1\Delta x + b^2(\Delta x)^2 + a^2y_1^2 + 2a^2y_1\Delta y + a^2(\Delta y)^2 = a^2b^2.$$

We have also, since $P_1(x_1, y_1)$ lies on the ellipse,

$$b^2x_1^2 + a^2y_1^2 = a^2b^2. \qquad\qquad (129)$$

By subtraction, we obtain from the last two equations,

$$2b^2x_1\Delta x + b^2(\Delta x)^2 + 2a^2y_1\Delta y + a^2(\Delta y)^2 = 0,$$

or

$$m' = \frac{\Delta y}{\Delta x} = -\frac{2b^2x_1 + b^2\Delta x}{2a^2y_1 + a^2\Delta y}.$$

As P_2 approaches P_1, Δx and Δy approach zero and m' approaches $-\dfrac{b^2x_1}{a^2y_1}$, which is the slope, m, of the tangent at $P_1(x_1, y_1)$. The equation of this tangent is, accordingly,

$$y - y_1 = -\frac{b^2x_1}{a^2y_1}(x - x_1).$$

To simplify this equation, we multiply by a^2y_1, and rearrange, giving

$$b^2x_1x + a^2y_1y = b^2x_1{}^2 + a^2y_1{}^2.$$

On substituting for the right-hand member its value from (129), we have
$$b^2x_1x + a^2y_1y = a^2b^2, \tag{130}$$

which is the equation of the tangent line to the ellipse at $P_1(x_1, y_1)$.

Since the normal line is perpendicular to the tangent, its slope is $\dfrac{a^2y_1}{b^2x_1}$, and its equation reduces to

$$b^2x_1(y - y_1) = a^2y_1(x - x_1). \tag{131}$$

This is the equation of the normal line to the ellipse at $P_1(x_1, y_1)$.

107. Tangent and Normal to the Hyperbola. For the equations of the tangent and normal lines to the hyperbola

$$b^2x^2 - a^2y^2 = a^2b^2,$$

at a point $P_1(x_1, y_1)$ on it, we have, respectively,

$$b^2x_1x - a^2y_1y = a^2b^2, \tag{132}$$

which is the equation of the tangent line at P_1;

and
$$b^2x_1(y - y_1) + a^2y_1(x - x_1) = 0, \tag{133}$$

which is the equation of the normal line at P_1.

The derivation of these equations, which differs but little from that given in Art. 106 for the ellipse, is left as an exercise for the student.

EXERCISES

Find the equations of the tangent and normal lines to the following curves at the point indicated.

1. $y^2 = 8x$ (18, 12)   2. $9x^2 + 4y^2 = 72$ (2, -3)
3. $2x^2 - 3y^2 = 5$ (4, 3)   4. $x^2 = 12y$ (-6, 3)
5. $x^2 - y^2 = 9$ (5, 4)   6. $x^2 + y^2 - 10x = 0$ (8, 4)
7. $y^2 = 10x + 6$ (3, 6)   8. $xy = 8$ (2, 4)
9. $y = x^3$ (2, 8)   10. $y^2 = x^3$ (4, 8)
11. $y = x^2 + x^3$ (1, 2)   12. $x^3 + y^3 - 3xy = 0$ $(\tfrac{2}{3}, \tfrac{4}{3})$
13. $y = ax^2 + bx + c$ (x_1, y_1)
14. $Ax^2 + Bxy + Cy^2 + Dx + Ey + F = 0$ (x_1, y_1)

15. Show analytically that the normal line to a circle at any point on it passes through the center of the circle.

16. Show that the tangent lines to the parabola at the ends of the latus rectum are perpendicular to each other.

17. If P_1 is any point on the parabola $y^2 = 2px$, show that P_1, the focus, and the point of intersection of the tangent line at P_1 with the x-axis are vertices of an isosceles triangle.

18. By the angle between two curves at a point of intersection, one means the angle between their tangent lines at that point. Find the acute angle between the following pairs of curves at their point of intersection that lies in the first quadrant.

(a) $x^2 + y^2 = 17$ (b) $x^2 - 2y^2 = 1$
     $y^2 = 10x + 6$ $xy = 6$
(c) $x^2 + y^2 = 25$ (d) $y = x^3$
     $x^2 - y^2 = 7$ $y = 3x^2$.

19. If an ellipse and a hyperbola have the same foci, show that the tangent lines at their points of intersection are perpendicular to each other.

20. Find the condition that the tangent lines to the circles $x^2 + y^2 + Dx + Ey + F = 0$ and $x^2 + y^2 + D'x + E'y + F' = 0$ at their points of intersection are perpendicular to each other.

21. Let the tangent and normal to a curve at a point P_1 on it intersect the x-axis at T and N, respectively (Fig. 138), and let L be the foot of the perpendicular from P_1 to the x-axis. Then we define, at the point P_1:

$P_1 T$ as the *length of the tangent*,

$P_1 N$ as the *length of the normal*,

$L T$ as the *length of the subtangent*,

and $\qquad\qquad L N$ as the *length of the subnormal*.

Find these lengths (a) for the parabola $y^2 = 2px$, (b) for the ellipse $b^2x^2 + a^2y^2 = a^2b^2$, and (c) for the hyperbola $b^2x^2 - a^2y^2 = a^2b^2$, at the point $P_1(x_1, y_1)$.

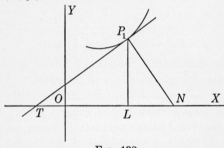

Fig. 138

108. Tangents Having a Given Slope. If we are given, instead of the point of tangency, the slope m of a tangent line to a conic, we can find the equation of this tangent line in the following way:

(a) *The parabola.* To find the line of slope m that is tangent to the parabola

$$y^2 = 2px,$$

we consider, first, a secant line

$$y = mx + k \qquad\qquad (134)$$

that has the given slope m and that meets the parabola in two points P' and P'' (Fig. 139). If, by holding m constant and varying k, we move this line parallel to its original position until it becomes tangent to the parabola, its intersections P' and P'' will move into coincidence at the point of tangency P_1.

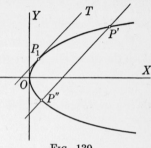

To make the line (134) tangent to the parabola, we must thus impose on k the condition that the two intersections of this line with the parabola coincide.

Substitute the value of y from (134) in the equation of the parabola. The roots of the resulting equation

Fig. 139

$$(mx + k)^2 = 2px,$$
or
$$m^2x^2 + 2(mk - p)x + k^2 = 0, \qquad (135)$$

are the abscissas of the points of intersection of the line (134) with the parabola. (Why?)

The condition that the two intersections coincide is, consequently, that the two roots of (135) are equal. The roots are (Introd., Art. 1)

$$x = \frac{p - mk \pm \sqrt{(mk - p)^2 - m^2k^2}}{m^2}$$

and the condition that these two roots are equal is that the quantity under the radical sign is equal to zero, that is,

$$(mk - p)^2 - m^2k^2 = 0,$$
or
$$k = \frac{p}{2m}.$$

By substituting this value of k in (134), we obtain

$$y = mx + \frac{p}{2m} \qquad (136)$$

as the equation of the tangent line of slope m to the parabola

$$y^2 = 2px.$$

(b) *The ellipse.* To find the lines of slope m that are tangent
to the ellipse

$$b^2x^2 + a^2y^2 = a^2b^2,$$

we proceed as we did for the parabola.

The abscissas of the two intersections of the line $y = mx + k$
with the given ellipse are the roots of the equation

$$b^2x^2 + a^2(mx + k)^2 = a^2b^2,$$

or $\qquad (b^2 + a^2m^2)x^2 + 2a^2mkx + a^2(k^2 - b^2) = 0.$

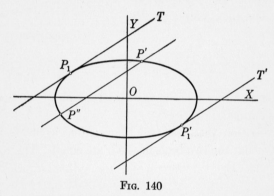

Fɪɢ. 140

If we solve this equation for x, and impose the condition that
the two roots are equal, we obtain

$$4a^4m^2k^2 - 4a^2(b^2 + a^2m^2)(k^2 - b^2) = 0,$$

so that $\qquad k = \pm\sqrt{a^2m^2 + b^2}.$

If we substitute these values of k in the equation $y = mx + k$
of the line, we have

$$y = mx \pm \sqrt{a^2m^2 + b^2} \qquad (137)$$

as the equations of the lines of slope m that are tangent to the
given ellipse. There are two such lines, as is shown in Fig. 140.

(c) *The hyperbola.* For the hyperbola

$$b^2x^2 - a^2y^2 = a^2b^2,$$

we find in the same way that the equations of the tangent lines of slope m are

$$y = mx \pm \sqrt{a^2m^2 - b^2} \tag{138}$$

The details of the derivation of this equation should be carried out by the student.

EXERCISES

1. Find the line of slope m that is tangent to the parabola $y^2 = 6x$.

2. Find two lines that are tangent to the ellipse $4x^2 + 6y^2 = 24$ and are (a) parallel and (b) perpendicular to the line $y = 4x + 7$.

3. Find the equations of the lines through $(4, 3)$ that are tangent to the hyperbola $7x^2 - 8y^2 = 56$.

4. Find the lines that are tangent to the hyperbola $4x^2 - 25y^2 = 100$ and are parallel to the line through $(1, 2)$ and $(5, 4)$.

5. Show that the product of the distances to the foci from a tangent line (a) to an ellipse, (b) to a hyperbola, is a constant.

6. Find the equation of the normal line of slope m to the parabola $y^2 = 2px$.

Hint. Find the point of tangency of a tangent line of slope $-\dfrac{1}{m}$. Through this point, find the line of slope m.

7. Show that the locus of the point of intersection of two tangents of a parabola that are perpendicular to each other is the directrix.

8. Find the locus of the point of intersection of two perpendicular tangents (a) to an ellipse, (b) to a hyperbola.

9. Find the locus of the foot of the perpendicular from the vertex of a parabola on a tangent line.

10. By the methods of this article, find the equations of the tangent lines of slope m to the hyperbola $2xy = a^2$.

11. Find the equations of the tangent lines of slope m to:

(a) the parabola $(y - k)^2 = 2p(x - h)$;
(b) the ellipse $b^2(x - h)^2 + a^2(y - k)^2 = a^2b^2$;
(c) the hyperbola $b^2(x - h)^2 - a^2(y - k)^2 = a^2b^2$.

109. Diameters. We shall show that *the midpoints of any family of parallel chords to a conic lie on a line.* Such a line is called a **diameter** of the conic.

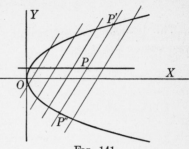

(*a*) *The parabola.* Let the equation of the given parabola be

$$y^2 = 2px$$

and let

$$y = mx + k \quad (139)$$

be the equation of a chord of slope *m*, with end points P'

Fig. 141

and P'' (Fig. 141). For the equations of the chords parallel to $P'P''$, *m* will remain fixed but *k* will vary from chord to chord.

Since $P'(x', y')$ and $P''(x'', y'')$ lie on the given line and on the parabola, their coördinates are found, by solving the preceding equations as simultaneous, to be

$$x' = \frac{p - mk + \sqrt{p^2 - 2mkp}}{m^2}, \qquad y' = \frac{p + \sqrt{p^2 - 2mkp}}{m};$$

and

$$x'' = \frac{p - mk - \sqrt{p^2 - 2mkp}}{m^2}, \qquad y'' = \frac{p - \sqrt{p^2 - 2mkp}}{m}.$$

The coördinates of the point $P(x, y)$ midway between P' and P'' are, by Art. 9, $\left(\dfrac{x' + x''}{2}, \ \dfrac{y' + y''}{2}\right)$ or, on substituting the values we have found for these coördinates,

$$x = \frac{p - mk}{m^2}, \qquad y = \frac{p}{m}. \tag{140}$$

Since the equations of the chords parallel to $P'P''$ are obtained from (139) by holding *m* fixed and allowing *k* to vary, it follows from (140) that the abscissa of the midpoint will vary with *k* but that the ordinate will retain the fixed value $\dfrac{p}{m}$; that is, that the midpoints of all the chords of slope m to the parabola lie on the line

$$y = \frac{p}{m}. \tag{141}$$

This line is thus the diameter of the parabola that bisects all the chords of slope m.

Exercise. Show (*a*) that every diameter is parallel to the axis of the parabola and (*b*) that every line parallel to the axis is a diameter.

(*b*) *The ellipse.* To find the diameter of the ellipse

$$b^2x^2 + a^2y^2 = a^2b^2$$

that bisects the chords of slope m, we first find the coördinates of the points $P'(x', y')$ and $P''(x'', y'')$ of intersection with the ellipse of the line

$$y = mx + k$$

on which such a chord lies. The results are

$$x' = \frac{-a^2mk + \sqrt{\Delta}}{a^2m^2 + b^2}, \qquad y' = \frac{b^2k + m\sqrt{\Delta}}{a^2m^2 + b^2},$$

and $\quad x'' = \dfrac{-a^2mk - \sqrt{\Delta}}{a^2m^2 + b^2}, \qquad y'' = \dfrac{b^2k - m\sqrt{\Delta}}{a^2m^2 + b^2},$

wherein $\quad \Delta = a^4m^2k^2 - a^2(a^2m^2 + b^2)(k^2 - b^2).$

Since these points are the ends of a chord of slope m, the midpoint $P(x, y)$ of this chord is $\left(\dfrac{x' + x''}{2}, \ \dfrac{y' + y''}{2}\right)$ or, on substituting the values we have found for these coördinates,

$$x = \frac{-a^2mk}{a^2m^2 + b^2}, \qquad y = \frac{b^2k}{a^2m^2 + b^2}.$$

By eliminating k between these two equations, we find that, for all chords of slope m, this midpoint lies on the line

$$y = \frac{-b^2x}{a^2m}, \tag{142}$$

since its coördinates satisfy this equation for all values of k. Hence, (142) is the equation of the diameter of the ellipse that bisects the chords of slope m.

(c) *The hyperbola.* For the hyperbola

$$b^2x^2 - a^2y^2 = a^2b^2$$

the student may verify in the same way that the line defined by the equation

$$y = \frac{b^2x}{a^2m} \tag{143}$$

is the diameter that bisects the chords of slope m.

Exercise. Show (a) that every diameter of an ellipse or a hyperbola passes through its center and (b) that every line through the center is a diameter.

110. Conjugate Diameters. Two diameters of an ellipse or a hyperbola are called **conjugate diameters** if each bisects the chords of the given ellipse or hyperbola that are parallel to the other.

From (142), the condition that the line $y = m_2x$ is the diameter that bisects the chords of the ellipse $b^2x^2 + a^2y^2 = a^2b^2$ that are parallel to the line $y = m_1x$ is that

$$m_2 = \frac{-b^2}{a^2m_1}. \tag{144}$$

For, if this condition is satisfied, the line $y = m_2x$ coincides with the diameter (142) for the chords of slope m_1.

Moreover, equation (144) may also be written in the form $m_1 = \dfrac{-b^2}{a^2m_2}$, from which it follows that, if (144) is satisfied, the line $y = m_1x$ bisects the chords parallel to $y = m_2x$.

Hence, equation (144) is the condition that the lines $y = m_1x$ and $y = m_2x$ are conjugate diameters of the given ellipse. If we multiply it through by m_1, we obtain this condition in the form

$$m_1m_2 = \frac{-b^2}{a^2}. \tag{145}$$

By similar reasoning, we find that, for the hyperbola $b^2x^2 - a^2y^2 = a^2b^2$,

$$m_1 m_2 = \frac{b^2}{a^2} \qquad (146)$$

is the condition that the diameters $y = m_1 x$ and $y = m_2 x$ are conjugate diameters to the hyperbola.

EXERCISES

1. Find the diameter of the parabola $y^2 = 12x$ that bisects the chords (a) of slope $m = 3$, (b) of slope $m = \frac{1}{2}$.

2. Find the diameter of the ellipse $2x^2 + 3y^2 = 6$ that bisects the chords parallel to the line through the origin and the point $(-5, -10)$.

3. Find the diameter of the hyperbola $5x^2 - y^2 = 10$ that bisects the chords perpendicular to the line $6x + 5y = 9$.

4. Find the pair of conjugate diameters of the ellipse $5x^2 + 6y^2 = 30$ of which one bisects the chords of slope $m = 2$.

5. Find two conjugate diameters of the hyperbola $8x^2 - 3y^2 = 5$ of which one bisects the chord whose end points are $(1, 1)$ and $(2, 3)$.

6. Show that the sides of any parallelogram inscribed in an ellipse are parallel to a pair of conjugate diameters.

7. Show that the lines joining any point on an ellipse or a hyperbola to the points of intersection of a diameter with the curve are parallel to a pair of conjugate diameters.

★ 111. Poles and Polar Lines.

It was shown in Art. 105 that, if the point $P_1(x_1, y_1)$ lies on the parabola $y^2 = 2px$, then the line

$$y_1 y = p(x + x_1) \qquad (147)$$

is the tangent line to the parabola at P_1.

Now let P_1 be any point whatever in the plane (lying on the parabola or not lying on it). Equation (147) still defines a line. This line is called the **polar line** of P_1, and P_1 is called the **pole** of the line with respect to the parabola $y^2 = 2px$.

Similarly, if $P_1(x_1, y_1)$ is any point in the plane except the origin, the equation

$$b^2x_1x + a^2y_1y = a^2b^2 \qquad (148)$$

defines a line called the **polar line** of P_1 with respect to the ellipse $b^2x^2 + a^2y^2 = a^2b^2$, and

$$b^2x_1x - a^2y_1y = a^2b^2 \qquad (149)$$

defines the **polar line** of P_1 with respect to the hyperbola $b^2x^2 - a^2y^2 = a^2b^2$. In each case, P_1 is the **pole** of the line with respect to the curve.

It follows from the above definitions and the results of Arts. 105 to 107, that *the polar line of a point P_1 with respect to a parabola, an ellipse, or a hyperbola is the tangent line to the conic at P_1 if, and only if, the point P_1 lies on the conic.*

We shall prove the following theorem for the parabola only. The theorem is true for the ellipse and the hyperbola also but the proof is left as an exercise for the student.

Theorem I. *If a point P_2 lies on the polar line of P_1, then P_1 lies on the polar line of P_2.*

The condition that P_2 lies on the polar line of P_1 is that its coördinates satisfy (147), that is, that

$$y_1y_2 = p(x_2 + x_1).$$

But this is precisely that condition that P_1 lies on the line

$$y_2y = p(x + x_2),$$

that is, that P_1 lies on the polar line of P_2.

Two points, such as P_1 and P_2 in theorem I, that are situated so that each lies on the polar line of the other are called **conjugate points** with respect to the given conic.

From theorem I, we readily obtain:

Theorem II. *If the polar line of P_1 intersects the conic at P_2' and P_2'', then P_1 is the point of intersection of the tangent lines at P_2' and P_2''.*

For, by theorem I, P_1 lies on the polar lines of P_2' and P_2''. But, since P_2' and P_2'' lie on the conic, these polar lines are the tangent lines, at P_2' and P_2'', to the conic.

EXERCISES

Find the polar line, with respect to the given conic, of the point indicated. Determine which of these polar lines are tangent lines.

1. $y^2 = 6x$ $(-2, 3)$ 2. $3x^2 + 4y^2 = 12$ $(2, 1)$
3. $4x^2 + 25y^2 = 100$ $(3, -\frac{8}{5})$ 4. $y^2 = 5x$ $(5, -2)$
5. $2x^2 - 9y^2 = 18$ $(3, 1)$ 6. $2x^2 - y^2 = 7$ $(4, 5)$
7. $y^2 = 18x$ $(2, 6)$ 8. $2x^2 - 7y^2 = 35$ $(2, 6)$
9. $x^2 + 9y^2 = 18$ $(-3, -1)$ 10. $11x^2 + y^2 = 2$ $(2, -3)$

Find the pole, with respect to the given conic, of the line indicated.

11. $y^2 = 12x$ $3x + 4y + 6 = 0$
12. $4x^2 + 9y^2 = 36$ $8x - 9y + 36 = 0$
13. $4x^2 - y^2 = 4$ $3x - y - 2 = 0$
14. $y^2 = 6x$ $5x + 2y - 6 = 0$.

Show that the two given points are conjugate points with respect to the given conic.

15. $3x^2 - 7y^2 = 21$ $(7, 1), (2, 3)$ 16. $y^2 = 16x$ $(-2, 5), (7, 8)$

17. In Ex. 5, find the points of intersection of the polar line of the given point with the given hyperbola. Find the tangent lines to the hyperbola at these points and show that they intersect at $(3, 1)$.

18. Find the point of intersection of the tangent lines to the hyperbola $8x^2 - 3y^2 = 5$ at $(2, 3)$ and $(1, 1)$. Show that this point of intersection is the pole of the line through the two given points.

CHAPTER XII

EMPIRICAL EQUATIONS

112. Equations Derived from Experimental Data. The student is familiar with many pairs of variables whose values are known to be connected by an equation. The relation between the distance traversed by a freely falling body and the time, between the radius of a circle and its area, or between the length of a pendulum and its period, are examples of such equations. In scientific work it is often necessary to determine equations of this sort by finding experimentally a number of pairs of values of the two variables and then setting up a law connecting the variation of the two quantities as shown by this experimental data. An equation connecting two variables, determined in this way, is called an **empirical equation.**

In this chapter we shall show how empirical equations of certain types can be set up to fit given sets of data. Among the types of such equations that are most frequently used in scientific work are the following:

(1) $y = mx + b$ Linear type

(2) $y = ax^n$ Parabolic type if $n > 0$; hyperbolic, if $n < 0$

(3) $y = a10^{kx}$ Exponential type

(4) $y = a + bx + cx^2 + \cdots + lx^n$ Polynomial type

We shall limit our discussion to these four types, but the methods we shall use can readily be extended to equations of various other kinds.

113. Selecting the Type of Equation. The general form of the required equation may be known from theoretical considerations, or it may be prescribed for us for reasons outside of the given data. If not, we first consider the given pairs of values of the variables as coördinates of points and plot them on a diagram. If the points so plotted tend definitely to lie along a line, we use an equation of type (1). If they do not, we may try plotting them on logarithmic paper (Art. 117). If, when plotted in this way, the points tend to lie on a line, an equation of type (2) may be used. Similarly, if the points tend to lie on a line when they are plotted on semi-logarithmic paper (Art. 118), an equation of type (3) is suggested. If none of these types seems to fit the data satisfactorily, we shall seek an equation of type (4), of as low a degree n as possible, that will fit the data with sufficient accuracy.

Since data determined by measurement is always subject to experimental errors, the required curve is not expected actually to pass through all of the given points. It may not, and in fact usually does not, pass through any of them, but it should not depart from them by an amount greater than the experimental error, and it should show clearly the *trend* of the given data.

When we have settled upon the type of equation to be used, we must next determine the values of the coefficients. We shall discuss this problem for each of the various types of curves separately.

114. Linear Type by the Method of Averages. The determination of the coefficients in an empirical equation by the method of averages, which we shall illustrate in this article, while not as accurate as by the method of least squares which will be discussed in Art. 115, is shorter than that method and easier to carry out. The method of averages consists, essentially, in dividing the given points into two groups and determining the line which passes through an average point for each group, as in the following example.

Example. The maximum osmotic pressure P, in meters, of a sugar solution was found by experiment to vary with the concentration C, in per cent, according to the following table. Express P in terms of C.

C	1	2	3	4	5	6	7
P	0.4	1.1	1.5	2.2	2.6	3.1	3.8

If we plot the pairs of values of C and P on a diagram, we obtain the points shown in Fig. 142. Since these points tend clearly to lie along a line, a linear type equation is suggested. As a check on the accuracy of the computations, the line defined by the answer to the problem should be drawn on the figure and compared with the trend of the plotted points.

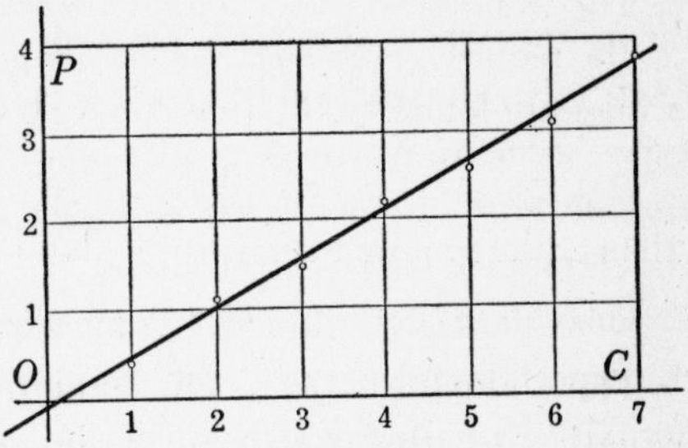

FIG. 142

If we substitute the pairs of values of P and C from the table in the assumed equation of linear type

$$P = mC + b \tag{150}$$

and group together the first four and the last three of the resulting equations, we have the following two sets of equations:

$$0.4 = m + b \qquad\qquad 2.6 = 5m + b$$
$$1.1 = 2m + b \qquad\qquad 3.1 = 6m + b$$
$$1.5 = 3m + b \qquad\qquad 3.8 = 7m + b$$
$$2.2 = 4m + b$$

These seven equations are called the **observational equations** for the given data. They are not consistent with one another since the given points do not all lie on a line. If, however, we add together the members of the equations in each group, we obtain the following two equations:

$$5.2 = 10m + 4b \qquad\qquad 9.5 = 18m + 3b. \tag{151}$$

These two equations are the conditions that the required line (150) passes through the points $\left(\dfrac{10}{4}, \dfrac{5.2}{4}\right)$ and $\left(\dfrac{18}{3}, \dfrac{9.5}{3}\right)$. The first of these points $\left(\dfrac{10}{4}, \dfrac{5.2}{4}\right)$ is the *average point* for the first four of the given points. It is determined by adding together the abscissas, and the ordinates, of these four points and dividing each sum by the number of points. Similarly, $\left(\dfrac{18}{3}, \dfrac{9.5}{3}\right)$ is the average point for the last three of the given points.

The values of m and b found by solving equations (151) are taken as the required coefficients in the empirical equation (150). These values are found to be, approximately,

$$m = 0.53 \qquad\qquad b = -\,0.03.$$

Hence, the required empirical equation is

$$P = 0.53C - 0.03$$

The values of the coefficients obtained for the empirical equation by the method of averages depend on the way the given points are grouped together. In the above problem, for example, if we group together the first three points, and the last four, we obtain, as the empirical equation

$$P = 0.55C - 0.10$$

115. Linear Type by the Method of Least Squares. In accurate scientific work, the values of the coefficients in the formula expressing y in terms of x are found by the method of least squares. In this article, we shall show by an example how the equations to determine m and b are actually set up, leaving the theoretical derivation of these equations to be discussed in the next article (Art. 116).

Example. Find by the method of least squares, for the data given in Art. 114, an equation expressing P in terms of C.

We write down two sets of equations. The equations of the first set are the seven observational equations formed, just as in Art. 114, by substituting the pairs of values of P and C from the table into the assumed equation

$$P = mC + b.$$

The equations of the second set are formed by multiplying each equation of the first set by the coefficient of m in it; thus

$$0.4 = \ m + b \qquad\qquad 0.4 = \ \ m + \ b$$
$$1.1 = 2m + b \qquad\qquad 2.2 = \ \ 4m + 2b$$
$$1.5 = 3m + b \qquad\qquad 4.5 = \ \ 9m + 3b$$
$$2.2 = 4m + b \qquad\qquad 8.8 = 16m + 4b$$
$$2.6 = 5m + b \qquad\qquad 13.0 = 25m + 5b$$
$$3.1 = 6m + b \qquad\qquad 18.6 = 36m + 6b$$
$$3.8 = 7m + b \qquad\qquad 26.6 = 49m + 7b$$

If we add the members of the equations in each of these two sets, we obtain the following two equations

$$14.7 = 28m + 7b \qquad\qquad 74.1 = 140m + 28b.$$

The values of m and b are found by solving these equations as simultaneous. The results are, approximately,

$$m = 0.55 \qquad\qquad b = -0.09.$$

The required formula is, accordingly, by this method,

$$P = 0.55C - 0.09.$$

When, as in this example, the points representing the given data lie nearly on a line, the results obtained by the method of averages and by the method of least squares usually differ but little. When the plotted points are rather widely scattered, the results obtained by the two methods may differ considerably.

In practice, in determining empirical equations, labor can be saved, and more accurate results can usually be obtained, by moving the origin to some convenient point near the middle of the diagram. Thus, in the above example, the computations could have been shortened by putting $C = C' + 4$, $P = P' + 2$, finding the equation expressing P' in terms of C', and then replacing P' and C' by their values in terms of P and C.

★ **116. Derivation of the Formulas for the Method of Least Squares.** Let (x_1, y_1), (x_2, y_2), (x_3, y_3), . . . (x_n, y_n) be the tabulated pairs of values of the variables. It is required to find, by the method of least squares, two equations from which to determine the values of m and b in a linear type equation

$$y = mx + b \qquad (152)$$

which expresses the value of y in terms of that of x.

Let x_k be any one of the values of x in the given table. Then the value of y corresponding to this value of x, as computed from equation (152), is $mx_k + b$, whereas the corresponding value of y, as given by the table, is y_k. The difference between these two values of y is denoted by r_k, that is

$$r_k = y_k - (mx_k + b) \qquad (153)$$

The number r_k is called the **residual** of the point (x_k, y_k) with respect to equation (152). There are n residuals; one for each of the n points (x_1, y_1), (x_2, y_2), . . . (x_n, y_n). The values of these residuals depend on the values assigned to m and b.

Let us form the sum of the squares of the n residuals. We shall denote this sum by Σr^2.* The method of least squares depends essentially on the following **Principle**: *The values of m and b determined by the method of least squares are those that make the sum of the squares of the residuals, Σr^2, as small as possible.*

If we write out the n equations (153) obtained by giving k the successive values 1, 2, 3, . . . n, and square both sides of each equation, we obtain

$$r_1{}^2 = y_1{}^2 - 2my_1x_1 - 2y_1b + m^2x_1{}^2 + 2mx_1b + b^2$$
$$r_2{}^2 = y_2{}^2 - 2my_2x_2 - 2y_2b + m^2x_2{}^2 + 2mx_2b + b^2$$

. . . .

. . . .

. . . .

$$r_n{}^2 = y_n{}^2 - 2mx_ny_n - 2y_nb + m^2x_n{}^2 + 2mx_nb + b^2$$

* The symbol Σr^2 is read "sigma r square." By definition
$$\Sigma r^2 = r_1{}^2 + r_2{}^2 + r_3{}^2 + \cdots \cdots + r_n{}^2$$
Similarly, we shall put
$$\Sigma x = x_1 + x_2 + x_3 \cdots \cdots + x_n$$
$$\text{etc.}$$

If we add the members of these equations and arrange the right-hand member of the sum in powers of b, we have

$$\Sigma r^2 = nb^2 + 2b(m\Sigma x - \Sigma y) + m^2\Sigma x^2 - 2m\Sigma xy + \Sigma y^2. \quad (154)$$

The right-hand member of (154) is a quadratic function of b, and the coefficient of b^2 is positive. Hence, by Art. 63, the value that must be assigned to b in order to make the value of this function as small as possible must satisfy the equation

$$nb + m\Sigma x - \Sigma y = 0. \quad (155)$$

If we rearrange the right-hand member of (154) in powers of m, we obtain

$$\Sigma r^2 = m^2\Sigma x^2 + 2m(b\Sigma x - \Sigma xy) + \Sigma y^2 - 2b\Sigma y + nb^2.$$

Since the right-hand member is a quadratic in m, and the coefficient of m^2 is positive, it follows once more from Art. 63 that the value of m that makes the right-hand member as small as possible must satisfy the equation

$$m\Sigma x^2 + b\Sigma x - \Sigma xy = 0. \quad (156)$$

The values of m and b that make Σr^2 as small as possible must satisfy equations (155) and (156). If we solve these two equations for m and b and substitute in (152), we obtain the required linear type equation by the method of least squares.

To determine equations (155) and (156) for a given problem, we first write out the two sets of equations called for in Art. 115, that is,

$$y_1 = mx_1 + b \qquad x_1y_1 = mx_1{}^2 + bx_1$$
$$y_2 = mx_2 + b \qquad x_2y_2 = mx_2{}^2 + bx_2$$
$$\cdot \quad \cdot \quad \cdot \quad \cdot \qquad \cdot \quad \cdot \quad \cdot \quad \cdot \quad \cdot \quad \cdot$$
$$\cdot \quad \cdot \quad \cdot \quad \cdot \qquad \cdot \quad \cdot \quad \cdot \quad \cdot \quad \cdot \quad \cdot$$
$$\cdot \quad \cdot \quad \cdot \quad \cdot \qquad \cdot \quad \cdot \quad \cdot \quad \cdot \quad \cdot \quad \cdot$$
$$y_n = mx_n + b \qquad x_ny_n = mx_n{}^2 + bx_n$$

If we add the members of each of these two sets of n equations each, we obtain, respectively,

$$\Sigma y = m\Sigma x + bn \qquad \Sigma xy = m\Sigma x^2 + b\Sigma x.$$

The first of these equations is equivalent to (155) and the second to (156). Hence, the values of m and b determined from them are the values which make Σr^2 as small as possible. They are thus the values of m and b in the empirical equation

$$y = mx + b$$

as determined by the method of least squares.

EXERCISES

Plot the points determined by the data in each of the following exercises and find a linear equation connecting the variables (a) by the method of averages and (b) by the method of least squares. Under (a), if the number of observational equations is even, put the first half of them in one group. If the number is odd, group the middle one with those that precede it.

1. Express y in terms of x, given:

x	-3	-2	-1	0	1	2	3
y	8	4	1	-3	-5	-6	-8

2. Express y in terms of x, given:

x	0	1	2	3	4	5	6
y	.088	.094	.099	.102	.106	.111	.118

3. Express y in terms of x, given:

x	2	5	7	12	15	23
y	14	23	26	38	48	69

4. Express y in terms of x, given:

x	1	3	6	9	11	12
y	2	9	22	23	33	37

5. Find the length l, in inches, of a spiral spring, in terms of the weight w, in pounds, suspended from it, given:

w	2	4	6	8	10	12
l	7.41	7.62	7.91	8.13	8.37	8.62

6. The force f, in pounds, that will just lift a weight of w pounds by a certain lifting device is given by the following table. Express f in terms of w.

w	200	400	600	800	1000	1200
f	21	32	45	57	71	86

7. Express R, the resistance of a wire in ohms, in terms of the centigrade temperature C, given:

C	10	20	30	40	50	60
R	5.72	5.84	6.01	6.18	6.39	6.51

8. Express the current i, in amperes, in a certain electric circuit, in terms of the electromotive force e, in volts, given:

e	4.9	8.8	11.7	17.2	19.8
i	6.6	11.8	15.7	23.2	26.1

9. The pressure P, in centimeters of mercury, of a certain quantity of gas was found to vary with the centigrade temperature C, when its volume was held constant, according to the following table. Express P in terms of C.

C	21	44	61	83	92
P	58.9	62.5	66.4	70.6	72.5

10. Find the latent heat of vaporization of water, in calories, in terms of the temperature from the following data:

C	60	80	100	120	140	160
L	564	552	537	524	508	497

11. Express the length of an iron bar in terms of the temperature from the following data:

C	0	50	100	150	200	250
l	1.0000	1.0005	1.0012	1.0016	1.0025	1.0033

12. The following pairs of values of two variables were obtained in an experiment on the index of refraction of a prism. Express M in terms of L.

L	30	33	41	53	61
M	0.649	0.651	0.658	0.669	0.686

117. Parabolic and Hyperbolic Types. If we wish to determine, for a given set of data, an empirical equation of the form

$$y = ax^n \qquad (157)$$

we first take the logarithms (to the base 10) of both sides of the equation. We thus obtain

$$\log y = n \log x + \log a.$$

Let u and v be two new variables, such that

$$u = \log x \qquad v = \log y$$

If we substitute these values for $\log x$ and $\log y$ in the preceding equation, we have

$$v = nu + \log a.$$

This is an equation of linear type connecting u and v. Hence, if we make a new table, formed by taking the logarithms of the entries in the given table, and if we denote the entries for $\log x$ by u, and for $\log y$ by v, our problem reduces to the determination of a linear relation connecting u and v and may be solved by the method of Art. 114 or of Art. 115.

It follows that, to determine whether an equation of the type of equation (157) is applicable to a given set of data, we may plot, on ordinary coördinate paper, the logarithms, u and v, of the numbers in the given table. If the points so plotted tend to lie on a line, an equation of this type may be used to express y in terms of x.

We may, however, when we are trying to decide whether an equation (157) is applicable to a given set of data, save the inconvenience of looking up the logarithms of all the numbers in the given table by plotting the given values of x and y directly on **logarithmic paper**. This paper (Fig. 143) has rulings, both horizontal and vertical, which are spaced at distances equal to the logarithms of the numbers 1, 2, 3, . . . 10, 20,

30, . . . In order that an equation of the type of equation (157) may be applicable to the data, its points must tend to lie on a line when they are plotted on logarithmic paper.

Example. Derive a formula for the air resistance R, in pounds per square foot of projecting area, against an automobile traveling V miles per hour, given

V	10	20	30	40	50	60
R	0.32	1.26	3.06	5.42	8.34	11.6

When we plot this data on logarithmic paper, as in Fig. 143, we find that the points tend to lie on a line. Hence, an equation of the

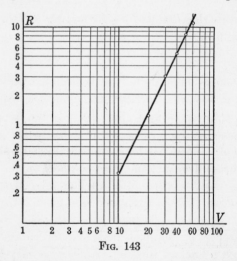

Fig. 143

type $R = aV^n$ may be used to express the required formula. We shall determine the values of a and n by the method of least squares.

From the table of logarithms on pages 290–1, we have

$u = \log V$	1.0000	1.3010	1.4771	1.6021	1.6990	1.7782
$v = \log R$	-0.4949	0.1004	0.4857	0.7340	0.9212	1.0645

To simplify the computations, we put $u' = u - 1.5$ and $v' = v - 0.5$ and determine the empirical equation $v' = mu' + b$, where $b = \log a$. We have

$$-.9949 = -.5000m + b \qquad .4975 = .2500m - .5000b$$
$$-.3996 = -.1990m + b \qquad .0795 = .0396m - .1990b$$
$$-.0143 = -.0229m + b \qquad .0003 = .0005m - .0229b$$
$$.2340 = .1021m + b \qquad .0239 = .0104m + .1021b$$
$$.4212 = .1990m + b \qquad .0838 = .0396m + .1990b$$
$$.5645 = .2782m + b \qquad .1570 = .0774m + .2782b$$

If we add the members of the equations of each of these two sets, we obtain

$$-.1891 = -.1426m + 6b \quad \text{and} \quad .8420 = .4175m - .1426b.$$

Hence, $m = 2.02$, $b = 0.0165$, so that $v' = 2.02u' + 0.0165$, that is,

$$\log R - 0.5 = 2.02(\log V - 1.5) + 0.0165$$

or $$\log R = 2.02 \log V - 2.5135$$

Since $-2.5135 = 7.4865 - 10 = \log 0.00307$, our required equation is

$$R = 0.00307 V^{2.02}.$$

EXERCISES

Show graphically that the data in each of the following exercises can be represented approximately by an equation of the form $y = ax^n$. Find this equation for the data of the first three exercises by the method of averages, and, for the others, by the method of least squares.

1. Find y in terms of x, given:

x	2	4	6	8	10	12	14
y	123	33	14	8	5	4	3

2. Find y in terms of x, given:

x	3.1	3.6	4.5	5.2	6.1	6.5
y	24	36	62	88	132	155

3. Express the coal consumption C of a locomotive, in tons per hour, in terms of its velocity v, in miles per hour, according to the following data:

v	30	35	40	45	50	55
C	2.0	2.7	3.6	4.5	5.6	6.7

4. Express the heating effect H of an electric circuit in terms of the current i, in amperes, given:

i	1	2	3	4	5
H	2.5	11	24	39	63

5. Express the horsepower H of a mill wheel in terms of the head of water h, in feet, from the following data:

h	3	4	5	6	7
H	59	94	127	173	210

6. Find the force of attraction f between two magnetic poles in terms of the distance d, in centimeters, between them, given:

d	0.5	1.0	1.5	2.0	2.5
f	15.5	3.3	1.8	0.83	0.63

7. Determine the pressure p, of a gas expanding adiabatically, in terms of the volume v, from the following data:

v	1.1	1.8	2.3	3.6	5.0
p	649	323	228	122	76

8. For water flowing in a pipe with a velocity of v feet per second, find the loss of pressure L, per thousand feet, from the following data:

v	1.7	2.2	3.5	4.3	5.4
L	1.7	2.8	7.4	11.0	17.0

9. The following table gives, for the six planets nearest the sun, the major semi-axis a of the orbit and the period of revolution T. Find an expression for T in terms of a.

	Mercury	Venus	Earth	Mars	Jupiter	Saturn
a	0.39	0.72	1.00	1.52	5.20	9.54
T	0.24	0.62	1.00	1.88	11.86	29.46

10. A fixed weight attached at the end of a beam of given cross section, but of variable length l, produces a deflection d. Find d in terms of l, given:

l	10	15	20	22	24	26
d	0.025	0.09	0.20	0.29	0.35	0.47

118. Exponential Type. If we wish to express the required formula by an exponential equation

$$y = a\,10^{kx}$$

we again take the logarithms of both sides of the equation. This gives

$$\log y = kx + \log a$$

If we now put $\log y = v$, this equation becomes a linear relation

$$v = kx + \log a$$

between x and v and may be solved by the methods of the preceding articles.

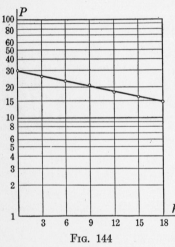

FIG. 144

To determine the suitability of an equation of the exponential type for expressing a given set of data, we may either plot on ordinary coördinate paper the values of x and $\log y$, or we may plot the given data on **semi-logarithmic paper,** that is, on paper that is ruled with equal spaces in one direction and like logarithmic paper in the other (Fig. 144). An exponential equation may be used to represent the required relationship if the points, when plotted in this way, tend to lie on a line.

Example. Find the atmospheric pressure p, in inches of mercury, in terms of the height above sea level h, in thousands of feet, from the following data:

h	0	3	6	9	12	15	18
p	29.9	26.7	23.5	21.2	18.6	16.8	14.7

By plotting the pairs of values of h and p on semi-logarithmic paper (Fig. 144), we find that, within the limits of experimental error, the points lie on a line so that we may represent p in terms of h by an exponential equation. By the method of least squares, we find that

$$\log p = -0.017h + 1.4762$$

or

$$p = 29.9 \, (10^{-.017h})$$

It is often preferable to write an exponential equation in the form $y = ae^{kx}$, where $e = 2.71828^+$ is the base of the natural system of logarithms (Art. 82). Since $10 = e^{2.303}$ approximately, we have, in this example,

$$p = 29.9(e^{2.303})^{-.017h} = 29.9 \, e^{-.039h}$$

EXERCISES

Show graphically that the data of each of the following exercises can be represented approximately by an equation of the form $y = a\,10^{kx}$. Find this equation for the data of exercises 1 to 4 by the method of averages and, for the others, by the method of least squares.

1. Express y in terms of x, given:

x	31	33	35	37	39	41
y	2.1	3.9	5.7	10.2	15.5	26.9

2. Express y in terms of x, given:

x	2	3	5	7	10	15
y	250	166	70	30	8	1

3. In a physiological experiment, the strength of the reaction S was found to vary with the intensity of the stimulus I according to the following table. Find I in terms of S.

S	1	2	3	4	5	6
I	1	2.5	6.4	15	40	100

4. A thermometer was heated in a vessel of water, then taken out and allowed to cool. From the results in the following table, express the Fahrenheit temperature F in terms of the time in minutes.

t	0	0.5	1	2	3	4
F	127	103	93	86	80	76

5. Determine the vapor pressure of water P, in centimeters of mercury, in terms of the centigrade temperature C, using the following table.

C	0	20	40	60	80	100
P	0.5	1.7	5.4	15	35	76

6. A pendulum was set vibrating and allowed to come to rest through the action of friction and the resistance of the air. Find the amplitude of the vibration A, in inches, in terms of the time t, in minutes, given:

t	0	1	2	3	4	5
A	12.0	6.9	4.0	2.6	1.5	0.9

7. The number N of bacteria per unit of volume in a culture, at the end of t hours, is given by the following table. Determine N in terms of t.

t	1	2	3	4	5	6	7
N	73	91	112	131	163	190	241

8. From the following table, which expresses the population of the United States in millions, in terms of the time, find an expression for P in terms of t in the form $P = a\,10^{k(t-1900)}$.

t	1870	1880	1890	1900	1910	1920	1930
P	39	50	63	76	92	106	123

9. A rotating flywheel was allowed to come to rest under the action of frictional forces. Find its rate of rotation R as a function of the time t, given:

t	0	5	10	15	20	25	30
R	1500	921	564	332	196	118	69

10. In a certain chemical reaction, the percentage p of a substance remaining at the end of t minutes is given by the following table. Find p in terms of t.

t	0	2	5	10	15	20	30
p	100	91	82	71	59	47	32

119. Polynomial Type. If none of the preceding types of equations adequately express the trend of the data, an equation of the polynomial type

$$y = a + bx + cx^2 + \cdots + lx^n$$

is frequently used.

The value of n should first be determined graphically in such a way that an equation of the given degree will satisfactorily express the behavior of the data. The values of the coefficients may then be determined as in the following example.

Example. Find a formula of the polynomial type, with $n = 2$,

$$y = a + bx + cx^2 \tag{158}$$

to represent the relation between the variables as given in the following table:

x	-3	-2	-1	0	1	2	3	4	5
y	10	4	1	-1	-3	-4	-2	1	3

a. Solution by the method of averages. We divide the tabulated data into three groups, each of which we shall take, in this example, to consist of three consecutive pairs of values of x and y, and form the observational equations for each group by substituting these pairs of values in equation (158). The resulting equations are

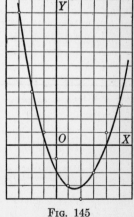

$$10 = a - 3b + 9c$$
$$4 = a - 2b + 4c$$
$$1 = a - b + c$$

$$-1 = a + 0b + 0c$$
$$-3 = a + b + c$$
$$-4 = a + 2b + 4c$$

$$-2 = a + 3b + 9c$$
$$1 = a + 4b + 16c$$
$$3 = a + 5b + 25c$$

Fig. 145

By adding the members of the equations in each of these groups,

we obtain the following three equations from which to determine a, b, and c:

$$15 = 3a - 6b + 14c$$
$$-8 = 3a + 3b + 5c$$
$$2 = 3a + 12b + 50c$$

On solving these equations, we find that

$$a = -1.74 \qquad b = -1.94 \qquad c = 0.611$$

The required equation, by the method of averages is, accordingly,

$$y = -1.74 - 1.94x + 0.611x^2.$$

As in Art. 114, the result obtained by the method of averages depends on the way the points are grouped together.

b. *Solution by the method of least squares.* We form the following three sets of equations: (1) the nine observational equations formed by substituting the pairs of values of x and y from the table in (158), (2) the equations formed by multiplying each observational equation by the coefficient of b in it, and (3) the equations formed by multiplying each observational equation by the coefficient of c in it. We obtain in this way the following sets of equations:

$$10 = a - 3b + 9c \qquad\qquad -30 = -3a + 9b - 27c$$
$$4 = a - 2b + 4c \qquad\qquad -8 = -2a + 4b - 8c$$
$$1 = a - b + c \qquad\qquad -1 = - a + b - c$$
$$-1 = a + 0b + 0c \qquad\qquad 0 = 0a + 0b + 0c$$
$$-3 = a + b + c \qquad\qquad -3 = a + b + c$$
$$-4 = a + 2b + 4c \qquad\qquad -8 = 2a + 4b + 8c$$
$$-2 = a + 3b + 9c \qquad\qquad -6 = 3a + 9b + 27c$$
$$1 = a + 4b + 16c \qquad\qquad 4 = 4a + 16b + 64c$$
$$3 = a + 5b + 25c \qquad\qquad 15 = 5a + 25b + 125c$$

$$90 = 9a - 27b + 81c$$
$$16 = 4a - 8b + 16c$$
$$1 = a - b + c$$
$$0 = 0a + 0b + 0c$$
$$-3 = a + b + c$$
$$-16 = 4a + 8b + 16c$$
$$-18 = 9a + 27b + 81c$$
$$16 = 16a + 64b + 256c$$
$$75 = 25a + 125b + 625c$$

If we add the members of each of these three sets of equations, we have

$$9 = \quad 9a + \quad 9b + \quad 69c$$
$$-37 = \quad 9a + \quad 69b + \quad 189c$$
$$161 = 69a + 189b + 1077c$$

Hence, $a = -1.62$ $b = -1.96$ $c = 0.60$

and the required equation, by the method of least squares, is

$$y = -1.62 - 1.96x + 0.60x^2$$

EXERCISES

In exercises 1 to 8, express y in terms of x by means of an equation of the form $y = a + bx + cx^2$. Use the method of averages in exercises 1 to 4, and the method of least squares in exercises 5 to 8.

1. Find y in terms of x, given:

x	0	1	2	3	4	5	6	7	8
y	0	2	4	5	3	1	0	-1	-5

2. Find y in terms of x, given:

x	5	7	9	11	13	15	17	19	21
y	-5	3	8	10	13	15	16	16	14

3. Express the melting point C, on the centigrade scale, of an alloy of lead and zinc in terms of the percentage p of zinc, given:

p	15	25	35	45	55	65
C	289	263	237	215	195	177

4. Find the specific heat s of diamond in terms of the centigrade temperature C according to the following table:

C	0	40	80	120	160	200
s	0.095	0.134	0.172	0.209	0.245	0.279

5. The Fahrenheit temperature F in a well, at a depth h, in hundreds of feet, is given in the following table. Express F in terms of h.

h	5	10	15	20	25	30	35	40	45
F	59	64	68	73	77	80	84	87	90

6. When 10 liters of water, at $0°C$, is heated, the increase in volume i, in cubic centimeters, is given by the following table. Express i in terms of C.

C	0	2	4	6	8	10	12	14	16
i	0	-1.0	-1.3	-1.0	-0.2	1.2	3.2	5.7	8.7

7. Express the velocity v, in miles per hour, of the flow of a river, in terms of the fraction x of the total depth from the surface, given:

x	0.0	0.1	0.2	0.3	0.4	0.5	0.6	0.7	0.8	0.9
v	2.81	2.84	2.86	2.87	2.86	2.84	2.80	2.76	2.71	2.65

8. The difference d between the Fahrenheit temperature of boiling water and $212°$ is found to vary with the altitude h, in feet, above sea level according to the following table. Find h in terms of d.

d	2	4	6	8	10	12	14	16
h	1110	2230	3350	4490	5620	6770	7910	9070

9. Express y in terms of x by an equation of the form $y = a + bx + cx^2 + dx^3$, by both methods, given:

x	0	1	2	3	4	5	6	7
y	-4	1	2	2	1	0	-1	6

10. Fit an equation of the form $y = a + \dfrac{b}{x^2}$ to the following data, by both methods, by putting $\dfrac{1}{x^2} = u$ and expressing y linearly in terms of u.

x	1	2	3	4	5	6
y	50	15	8.5	6.1	5.0	4.4

11. Fit an equation of the form $x = axy + by$ to the following data, by both methods. Put $\dfrac{1}{x} = u, \dfrac{1}{y} = v$, and express v linearly in terms of u.

x	1	2	3	4	5	6
y	2	3	4	5	5.5	6

SOLID ANALYTIC GEOMETRY

CHAPTER XIII

FUNDAMENTAL DEFINITIONS AND THEOREMS

In plane analytic geometry, we saw that the position of a point in the plane could be fixed by means of directed distances measured on two mutually perpendicular lines. We shall now show how a similar method may be used to fix the position of any point in space.

120. Rectangular Coördinates. Through a fixed point O, the **origin,** in space, let there be given three directed lines, the **x-axis,** the **y-axis,** and the **z-axis,** each per-

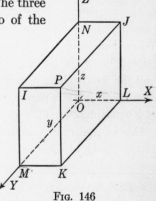

Fig. 146

pendicular to both of the others. The three planes, each of which contains two of the axes, are the **coördinate planes.** They are named, from the two axes that they contain, the **xy-plane, the yz-plane,** and the **zx-plane,** respectively.

Let P be any given point in space. To define the coördinates of P, we pass planes through P parallel to the three coördinate planes and denote the points of intersection of these planes with the x-, y-, and z-axes by L, M, and N, respectively. Then the directed lengths

$$x = \overline{OL}, \quad y = \overline{OM}, \quad z = \overline{ON},$$

are the **coördinates of the point P.**

Conversely, if the coördinates (x, y, z) of the point P are given, we can locate this point P in the following way: measure off from the origin, on the x-axis, the directed distance $\overline{OL} = x$; from L measure off, on a line through L parallel to the y-axis, a distance $\overline{LK} = y$; and finally, from K, on a line parallel to the z-axis, lay off $\overline{KP} = z$. The point P so determined is the point whose coördinates are (x, y, z).

The three coördinate planes divide space into eight parts, called **octants,** which may be distinguished by the signs of the coördinates of the points in them. In particular, the octant in which all the coördinates of a point are positive is known as the *first octant*.

121. Figures. To represent a figure in space on a plane, we shall use what is known as a parallel projection. In this projection, we represent the x- and z-axes by two mutually perpendicular lines and the y-axis by a line that makes an angle of $135°$ with each of the other two (Fig. 146). Distances parallel to the xz-plane are represented correctly to scale but distances parallel to the y-axis are foreshortened in the ratio $\sqrt{2}$ to 2. When this projection is used to draw figures on coördinate paper, the x- and z-axes should be represented along the rulings and the y-axis along a diagonal. Equal lengths along the three axes will then be represented by the sides of a square and a half of its diagonal.

One of the serious difficulties that the student will encounter in the study of solid analytic geometry is the visualization of the actual figure in space. The representation of it on a plane is only a makeshift, and he must assure himself from the beginning that he understands clearly the properties of the three-dimensional figure with which he is dealing. For this purpose, it is often convenient to visualize this figure in space with reference to the floor and two adjacent walls of the room in which the student is sitting, as coördinate planes.

As in plane analytic geometry, the first step in the solution of a problem in solid analytic geometry should consist in the construction of an accurate figure.

EXERCISES

Plot the following point to scale on coördinate paper.

1. $(2, 0, 0)$, $(3, 0, 5)$, $(1, 1, 1)$, $(4, 2, 3)$, $(-4, -2, -3)$, $(-3, -2, 1)$, $(4, 4, -1)$.

2. $(0, -2, 0)$, $(3, 2, 0)$, $(4, 2, -1)$, $(-4, -1, 3)$, $(-2, 4, 3)$, $(3, -3, 4)$, $(-2, -4, 3)$.

3. Find the coördinates of the feet of the perpendiculars from the point (x, y, z) to (a) the coördinate planes and (b) the coördinate axes.

4. Show that the figure $O-LJIM-P$ (Fig. 146) is a rectangular parallelopiped (or box-shaped figure) and find the lengths of all of its edges.

5. Find the length of the segments LP, MP, and NP (Fig. 146) in terms of the coördinates of P.

6. In Fig. 146, find the length of the segment OP.

7. What is the locus of a point for which $x = 0$? for which $y = 0$? for which $z = 0$?

8. What is the locus of a point for which $x = 0$, $y = 0$?

9. What is the locus of a point for which $x = 2$?

10. What is the locus of a point for which $x = 3$, $y = 4$?

11. A cube of side a has one vertex at the origin and three of its edges extending in the positive direction along the axes. Find the coördinates of its vertices.

12. Solve Ex. 11 when the center of the cube is at the origin and its edges are parallel to the coördinate axes.

13. Describe the position in space of the octant for which the signs of the coördinates are $(+, -, -)$.

14. Two points are *symmetric* with respect to a plane if the segment joining them is perpendicular to the plane and is bisected by it. Find the points symmetric to (x, y, z) with respect to the coördinate planes.

15. Find the points symmetric to (x, y, z) with respect to (a) the coördinate axes, (b) the origin.

122. Distance between Two Points. To find the distance between two given points $P_1(x_1, y_1, z_1)$ and $P_2(x_2, y_2, z_2)$, we construct a box-shaped figure by passing planes through P_1 and P_2 parallel to the coördinate planes (Fig. 147). The required distance $d = P_1P_2$ is the length of the diagonal of this

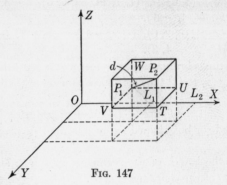

Fig. 147

box and the lengths of the sides of the box are given by the numerical values of P_1U, P_1V, and P_1W.

From Fig. 147, we have

$$\overline{P_1U} = \overline{L_1L_2} = \overline{OL_2} - \overline{OL_1} = x_2 - x_1,$$
$$\overline{P_1V} = y_2 - y_1, \text{ and } \overline{P_1W} = z_2 - z_1. \tag{159}$$

By elementary geometry,

$$P_1P_2{}^2 = P_1T^2 + TP_2{}^2 = P_1U^2 + UT^2 + TP_2{}^2 = P_1U^2 + P_1V^2 + P_1W^2.$$

If we put $P_1P_2 = d$, we have, from (159),

$$d^2 = (x_2 - x_1)^2 + (y_2 - y_1)^2 + (z_2 - z_1)^2.$$

Hence

$$d = \sqrt{(x_2 - x_1)^2 + (y_2 - y_1)^2 + (z_2 - z_1)^2}. \tag{160}$$

This is the formula for the distance between the points

$$P_1(x_1, y_1, z_1) \text{ and } P_2(x_2, y_2, z_2).$$

EXERCISES

1. Find the distance between the following pairs of points.

(a) $(0, 0, 0)$ and $(6, -6, 7)$ (b) $(2, 1, 5)$ and $(6, 4, -7)$

   (c) (4, 3, − 1) and (2, 6, 5)   (d) (5, 1, 2) and (3, 2, 4)

   (e) (4, 2, − 3) and (5, 7, 1)   (f) (− 1, 3, 4) and (3, 1, − 2).

2. Show that (3, 4, − 1), (4, 6, 2), and (6, 3, 1) are the vertices of an equilateral triangle.

3. Show that (− 2, 3, − 6), (3, 4, − 2), and (− 3, 7, − 1) are the vertices of an isosceles triangle.

4. Show that (6, 3, 7), (2, 5, 5), and (3, − 6, 4) are the vertices of a right triangle.

5. Show that (3, 7, 5), (1, − 1, 3), (9, 1, 5), and (3, 1, 11) are the vertices of a regular tetrahedron, that is, of a tetrahedron (or triangular pyramid) whose edges are all equal in length.

6. Find the equation of the locus of a point that moves so that its distance from (2, 5, − 1) is always equal to 3. What locus is defined by this equation?

7. Find the equation of the locus of a point that moves so that its distances from (2, 1, 3) and (4, 2, 1) are always equal. What locus is defined by this equation?

123. Direction Cosines of a Line. Let $P_1(x_1, y_1, z_1)$ be any point on a given directed line l in space. Through P_1 draw the lines P_1A, P_1B, and P_1C, having the same directions as the

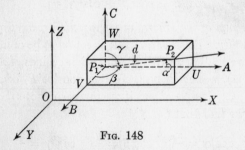

FIG. 148

x-, y-, and z-axes, respectively. Then the angles α, β, and γ, which the positive direction on l makes with the positive direction on P_1A, P_1B, and P_1C, respectively, are called the **direction angles** of l.

We shall usually deal, not with the direction angles α, β,

and γ themselves, but with their cosines. These three cosines, $\cos \alpha$, $\cos \beta$, and $\cos \gamma$, are the **direction cosines** of the line l.

Let $P_2(x_2, y_2, z_2)$ be any point on l in the positive direction from P_1 and let U, V, and W be the points in which the planes through P_2 perpendicular to the x-, y-, and z-axes intersect P_1A, P_1B, and P_1C, respectively. Since the triangles P_1UP_2, P_1VP_2, and P_1WP_2 are right triangles (Why?), we now have, from the definition of the cosine of an angle,

$$\cos \alpha = \frac{\overline{P_1U}}{\overline{P_1P_2}}, \quad \cos \beta = \frac{\overline{P_1V}}{\overline{P_1P_2}}, \quad \text{and} \quad \cos \gamma = \frac{\overline{P_1W}}{\overline{P_1P_2}}.$$

If we now put $P_1P_2 = d$, and substitute for $\overline{P_1U}$, $\overline{P_1V}$, and $\overline{P_1W}$ their values from (159), we have

$$\cos \alpha = \frac{x_2 - x_1}{d}, \cos \beta = \frac{y_2 - y_1}{d}, \quad \text{and} \quad \cos \gamma = \frac{z_2 - z_1}{d}, \quad (161)$$

wherein

$$d = \sqrt{(x_2 - x_1)^2 + (y_2 - y_1)^2 + (z_2 - z_1)^2}.$$

If we square the members of equations (161), add, and substitute for d its value, we find that

$$\cos^2 \alpha + \cos^2 \beta + \cos^2 \gamma = 1 \qquad (162)$$

that is, *the sum of the squares of the direction cosines of any line is equal to unity*. This relation will be found to be of importance whenever we shall deal with the direction cosines of a line.

If, in (161), we let P_1 be the origin and let P_2 be any other point $P(x, y, z)$ in space, and if we further denote the distance OP by ρ, we find that

$$\cos \alpha = \frac{x}{\rho}, \quad \cos \beta = \frac{y}{\rho}, \quad \cos \gamma = \frac{z}{\rho}, \qquad (163)$$

are the direction cosines of the line through the origin and the point P and directed from O toward P.

124. Direction Numbers of a Line. Any three real numbers a, b, and c, not all zero, are called the direction numbers of a line l if they are proportional to the direction cosines of l, that is, if

$$\frac{a}{\cos \alpha} = \frac{b}{\cos \beta} = \frac{c}{\cos \gamma}, \qquad (164)$$

wherein $\cos \alpha$, $\cos \beta$, and $\cos \gamma$ are the direction cosines of l.

To find the direction cosines of a line when its direction numbers a, b, and c are given, we set each of the above fractions equal to k and solve for a, b, and c. The resulting equations are

$$a = k \cos \alpha, \quad b = k \cos \beta, \quad \text{and} \quad c = k \cos \gamma. \qquad (165)$$

By squaring the members of these equations, adding, and simplifying by means of equation (162), we obtain

$$a^2 + b^2 + c^2 = k^2(\cos^2 \alpha + \cos^2 \beta + \cos^2 \gamma) = k^2.$$

Hence, $\qquad\qquad k = \pm \sqrt{a^2 + b^2 + c^2}.$

If we substitute this expression for k in equations (165), and solve, we obtain, as the direction cosines of a line whose direction numbers are a, b, and c,

$$\cos \alpha = \frac{a}{\pm \sqrt{a^2 + b^2 + c^2}}, \quad \cos \beta = \frac{b}{\pm \sqrt{a^2 + b^2 + c^2}},$$

$$\cos \gamma = \frac{c}{\pm \sqrt{a^2 + b^2 + c^2}}. \qquad (166)$$

The sign in the denominator is to be taken as positive throughout, or as negative throughout, according as one direction on the line, or the other, is to be taken as the positive direction on the line (see example 2, p. 236).

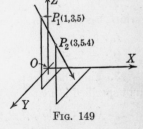

Example 1. Find the direction cosines of the line through $P_1(1, 3, 5)$ and $P_2(3, 5, 4)$.

The distance between these points is

$$d = \sqrt{(3 - 1)^2 + (5 - 3)^2 + (4 - 5)^2} = 3.$$

Fig. 149

Hence, from (161), the direction cosines of this line (directed from P_1 toward P_2) are

$$\cos \alpha = \tfrac{2}{3}, \quad \cos \beta = \tfrac{2}{3}, \quad \cos \gamma = -\tfrac{1}{3}.$$

Example 2. The direction numbers of a line are 6, 2, -3 and the positive direction is chosen on the line so that the angle γ is acute. Find the direction cosines of the line.

On substituting these values of a, b, and c in equations (166), we have

$$\cos \alpha = \frac{6}{\pm \sqrt{36 + 4 + 9}} = \frac{6}{\pm 7}, \quad \cos \beta = \frac{2}{\pm 7}, \quad \cos \gamma = \frac{-3}{\pm 7}.$$

Since the angle γ is acute, its cosine is positive. Hence, from the last of the above equations, the sign in the denominator is negative and we have

$$\cos \alpha = -\tfrac{6}{7}, \quad \cos \beta = -\tfrac{2}{7}, \quad \cos \gamma = \tfrac{3}{7}.$$

EXERCISES

1. Find the direction cosines of the line through P_1 and P_2, given that the line is directed from P_1 toward P_2 and that

(a) $P_1(0, 0, 0)$, $P_2(4, -8, 1)$
(b) $P_1(2, 4, -5)$, $P_2(4, -2, 4)$
(c) $P_1(4, -5, 2)$, $P_2(7, -1, -10)$
(d) $P_1(6, 1, -1)$, $P_2(2, 5, -3)$
(e) $P_1(7, 1, 3)$, $P_2(4, 2, 5)$
(f) $P_1(1, 11, -2)$, $P_2(3, 8, -5)$.

2. Find the direction cosines of a line for which α is acute and which has for its direction numbers:

(a) $3, 2, -6$ (b) $-8, 12, -9$ (c) $14, -5, -2$
(d) $-9, -6, 2$ (e) $1, -2, 3$ (f) $-2, -4, 7$

3. Find the direction cosines of the following lines if the angle not specified is acute:

(a) $\alpha = 45°, \beta = 60°$ (b) $\beta = 120°, \gamma = 90°$

(c) $\alpha = \dfrac{2\pi}{3}, \gamma = \dfrac{\pi}{3}$ (d) $\alpha = \dfrac{2\pi}{3}, \beta = \dfrac{3\pi}{4}$

4. What is known about the direction of a line if (a) $\cos \alpha = 0$, (b) $\cos \alpha = 0$, $\cos \beta = 0$, (c) $\cos \alpha = 1$?

5. Find the direction cosines of each of the coördinate axes.

6. A line through the origin is directed into the first octant and makes equal angles with the coördinate axes. Find its direction cosines.

7. Find the coördinates of P_2, given that the coördinates of P_1 are $(4, 1, 7)$, the length of the segment P_1P_2 is 9, and the direction cosines of the line directed from P_1 toward P_2 are $\frac{2}{3}$, $-\frac{1}{3}$, $\frac{2}{3}$.

8. Show that the direction cosines of the line through $P_1(-3, 4, 1)$ and $P_2(-1, 5, -2)$ are respectively equal to those of the line through P_2 and $P_3(3, 7, -8)$. How are these points situated?

9. Show by means of direction cosines that the points $(5, 4, -3)$, $(2, 5, -1)$, and $(-7, 8, 5)$ lie on a line.

10. Show that the point $(4, 1, 6)$ lies on the line through $(6, 3, 2)$ and $(2, -1, 10)$ and is equally distant from them.

11. Show that any three real numbers a, b, and c (not all zero) are the direction numbers of the line that passes through the origin and the point whose coördinates are (a, b, c).

12. If two given lines, l_1 and l_2, are parallel and have the same positive directions, show that

$$\cos \alpha_1 = \cos \alpha_2, \quad \cos \beta_1 = \cos \beta_2, \quad \cos \gamma_1 = \cos \gamma_2.$$

If they are parallel and have opposite positive directions, show that

$$\cos \alpha_1 = -\cos \alpha_2, \quad \cos \beta_1 = -\cos \beta_2, \quad \cos \gamma_1 = -\cos \gamma_2.$$

125. The Angle between Two Directed Lines.

If we draw two lines at random in space, these two lines, usually, will not intersect. In order that we may speak of the angle between two such lines, we make the following definition: *The angle between two directed lines in space that do not meet is equal to the angle between the positive directions of two intersecting lines having the same directions as the given lines.*

In particular, if the given lines are parallel, the angle between them is zero or π according as their positive directions are the same or opposite.

Let l_1 and l_2 (Fig. 150) be two given directed lines and let ϕ be the angle between them. It is required to express $\cos \phi$ in terms of the direction cosines of l_1 and l_2.

Through the origin O, draw the lines OP_1 and OP_2, having the same directions as l_1, and l_2, respectively. Then, from the

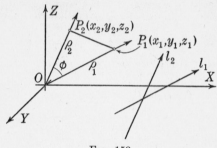

Fig. 150

above definition of the angle between two directed lines, we have

$$\text{angle } P_1OP_2 = \phi.$$

Let the coördinates of P_1 be (x_1, y_1, z_1) and of P_2 be (x_2, y_2, z_2). Let the length of the segment $OP_1 = \rho_1$ and of $OP_2 = \rho_2$. Draw P_1P_2 and apply the law of cosines (Introd., Art. 13) to the triangle P_1OP_2. We have

$$P_1P_2{}^2 = \rho_1{}^2 + \rho_2{}^2 - 2\rho_1\rho_2 \cos \phi$$

or
$$\cos \phi = \frac{\rho_1{}^2 + \rho_2{}^2 - P_1P_2{}^2}{2\rho_1\rho_2}. \tag{167}$$

But $\rho_1{}^2 = x_1{}^2 + y_1{}^2 + z_1{}^2$ and $\rho_2{}^2 = x_2{}^2 + y_2{}^2 + z_2{}^2$

and $P_1P_2{}^2 = (x_2 - x_1)^2 + (y_2 - y_1)^2 + (z_2 - z_1)^2.$

On making these substitutions in the numerator of (167), and simplifying, we obtain

$$\cos \phi = \frac{x_1x_2 + y_1y_2 + z_1z_2}{\rho_1\rho_2}. \tag{168}$$

From (163), we have

$$\cos \alpha_1 = \frac{x_1}{\rho_1}, \quad \cos \beta_1 = \frac{y_1}{\rho_1}, \quad \cos \gamma_1 = \frac{z_1}{\rho_1},$$

and $\qquad \cos \alpha_2 = \dfrac{x_2}{\rho_2}, \qquad \cos \beta_2 = \dfrac{y_2}{\rho_2}, \qquad \cos \gamma_2 = \dfrac{z_2}{\rho_2}.$

On making these substitutions in (168), we have the equation,

$$\cos \phi = \cos \alpha_1 \cos \alpha_2 + \cos \beta_1 \cos \beta_2 + \cos \gamma_1 \cos \gamma_2, \quad (169)$$

which expresses *the cosine of ϕ, the angle between l_1 and l_2, in terms of the direction cosines of l_1 and l_2.*

In particular, the condition that l_1 and l_2 are perpendicular to each other is that $\phi = \dfrac{\pi}{2}$, so that $\cos \phi = 0$. On substituting this value of $\cos \phi$ in (169), we obtain

$$\cos \alpha_1 \cos \alpha_2 + \cos \beta_1 \cos \beta_2 + \cos \gamma_1 \cos \gamma_2 = 0 \quad (170)$$

as *the condition that the lines l_1 and l_2 are perpendicular.*

If, instead of the direction cosines of l_1 and l_2, we have their direction numbers a_1, b_1, c_1 and a_2, b_2, c_2, respectively, we first find the direction cosines of l_1 and l_2 from (166), then substitute these values in (169). This gives

$$\cos \phi = \pm \frac{a_1 a_2 + b_1 b_2 + c_1 c_2}{\sqrt{a_1{}^2 + b_1{}^2 + c_1{}^2}\,\sqrt{a_2{}^2 + b_2{}^2 + c_2{}^2}} \quad (171)$$

as *the value of $\cos \phi$ in terms of the direction numbers of l_1 and l_2.*

Since l_1 and l_2 are perpendicular if, and only if, $\cos \phi = 0$, it follows that

$$a_1 a_2 + b_1 b_2 + c_1 c_2 = 0 \quad (172)$$

is the condition that l_1 and l_2 are perpendicular.

Example 1. Find the angle between the line through $P_1(1, -2, 4)$ and $P_2(3, 8, -7)$ and the line through $P_1'(1, 5, -2)$ and $P_2'(7, -2, 4)$.

From (161), the direction cosines of the first of these lines are $\frac{2}{15}$, $\frac{10}{15}$, and $-\frac{11}{15}$; and those of the second are $\frac{6}{11}$, $-\frac{7}{11}$, and $\frac{6}{11}$.

On substituting these values of the direction cosines of the given lines in (169), we have

$$\cos \phi = \frac{2 \cdot 6 + 10 \cdot (-7) - 11 \cdot 6}{15 \cdot 11} = \frac{-124}{165} = -0.7515.$$

From the tables, by the aid of the reduction formulas, we find that $\phi = 139°$.

Example 2. Find direction numbers of a line that is perpendicular to each of two lines for which the direction numbers are 4, 1, 3 and 6, 3, 5, respectively.

Denote the required direction numbers by a, b, c. We have, from (172),

$$4a + b + 3c = 0$$

and

$$6a + 3b + 5c = 0.$$

If we solve these equations for a and b in terms of c, we have $a = -\dfrac{2c}{3}$ and $b = -\dfrac{c}{3}$. Since only the ratios of these numbers are significant, we may give c any value, except zero, that we please. If we put $c = -3$, we obtain 2, 1, -3 as the required direction numbers.

EXERCISES

1. Find the cosine of the angle between two lines for which the direction cosines are:

(a) $\dfrac{2}{7}, \dfrac{3}{7}, \dfrac{-6}{7}; \quad \dfrac{6}{7}, \dfrac{2}{7}, \dfrac{3}{7}$

(b) $\dfrac{2}{3}, \dfrac{2}{3}, \dfrac{-1}{3}; \quad \dfrac{8}{9}, \dfrac{-4}{9}, \dfrac{1}{9}$

(c) $\dfrac{12}{13}, \dfrac{-3}{13}, \dfrac{4}{13}; \quad \dfrac{2}{11}, \dfrac{-9}{11}, \dfrac{-6}{11}$

(d) $\dfrac{1}{\sqrt{14}}, \dfrac{-3}{\sqrt{14}}, \dfrac{2}{\sqrt{14}}; \quad \dfrac{1}{\sqrt{6}}, \dfrac{2}{\sqrt{6}}, \dfrac{1}{\sqrt{6}}.$

2. Find the cosine of the angle between the lines for which the direction numbers are:

(a) 10, -11, 2; 6, -2, 9   (b) 1, 1, 1; 1, -2, 1

(c) 3, 5, -2; 2, 1, -2 (d) 1, 3, -2; 1, -1, -2.

3. Show by means of direction cosines that the following points are the vertices of a right triangle:

(a) (4, 10, 1), (1, 4, -1), (6, 7, 7)

(b) (2, 2, 3), (1, 4, 0), (-6, -1, -1).

4. Show that the points $(-1, 2, 3)$, $(5, -1, 5)$, $(2, 8, -3)$, and $(8, 5, -1)$ are the vertices of a parallelogram and find its acute angle.

5. Show that the points $(1, 5, 2)$, $(7, -2, 1)$, $(5, 2, 4)$, and $(3, 1, -1)$ are the vertices of a rhombus and find its acute angle.

6. Show that the points $(3, 5, 3)$, $(3, -4, 2)$, $(-1, -1, 4)$, and $(7, 2, 1)$ are the vertices of a rectangle.

7. Show that the points $(4, 3, 5)$, $(-2, 1, 2)$, $(1, 9, 7)$, and $(-5, 7, 4)$ are the vertices of a square and find its area.

8. Show that the three pairs of opposite edges of the tetrahedron (or triangular pyramid) whose vertices are $(1, 6, 3)$, $(5, 2, 5)$, $(8, 2, 8)$, and $(14, -1, -10)$ are perpendicular to each other.

9. Find the direction numbers of a line that is perpendicular to each of two lines whose direction numbers are

(a) $4, 1, 3$; $6, 1, 4$
(b) $-1, 3, 2$; $1, 2, 1$.

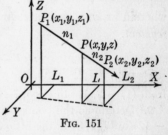

Fig. 151

★ 126. Point Dividing a Segment in a Given Ratio. Let $P_1(x_1, y_1, z_1)$ and $P_2(x_2, y_2, z_2)$ be the end points of the given segment. It is required to find the coördinates of the point $P(x, y, z)$ on the segment such that

$$\frac{\overline{P_1 P}}{\overline{P P_2}} = \frac{n_1}{n_2},$$

where $\dfrac{n_1}{n_2}$ is the given ratio.

Let $\cos \alpha$, $\cos \beta$, and $\cos \gamma$ be the direction cosines of the given segment (directed from P_1 toward P_2). From (161), we have

$$\overline{P_1 P} \cos \alpha = \overline{L_1 L} = x - x_1 \quad \text{and} \quad \overline{P P_2} \cos \alpha = \overline{L L_2} = x_2 - x.$$

Hence

$$\frac{\overline{P_1 P}}{\overline{P P_2}} = \frac{\overline{P_1 P} \cos \alpha}{\overline{P P_2} \cos \alpha} = \frac{x - x_1}{x_2 - x} = \frac{n_1}{n_2}.$$

On solving the last equation of this series for x, we have

$$x = \frac{n_2 x_1 + n_1 x_2}{n_1 + n_2}. \tag{173}$$

By similar reasoning, using $\cos \beta$ and $\cos \gamma$, we obtain

$$y = \frac{n_2 y_1 + n_1 y_2}{n_1 + n_2}, \qquad z = \frac{n_2 z_1 + n_1 z_2}{n_1 + n_2}. \tag{173'}$$

In particular, if P is the midpoint of the segment, then $n_1 = n_2$, and the above equations may be simplified to

$$x = \frac{x_1 + x_2}{2}, \qquad y = \frac{y_1 + y_2}{2}, \qquad z = \frac{z_1 + z_2}{2}, \tag{174}$$

wherein (x, y, z) *are the coördinates of the midpoint of the given segment.*

EXERCISES

1. Find the coördinates of the points of trisection of the segment from $(1, -2, 11)$ to $(-5, 7, -1)$.

2. Determine the point that divides the segment from $(8, 14, -12)$ to $(3, 4, 8)$ in the ratio $3 : 7$.

3. In what ratio does the point $(-2, 8, 11)$ divide the segment from $(2, 6, 5)$ to $(-12, 13, 26)$?

4. Find the lengths of the medians of the triangle whose vertices are the points $(7, 4, 3)$, $(1, 6, 9)$, and $(-5, 2, 15)$.

5. Find the point of intersection of the medians of the triangle in Ex. 4.

6. Show that the lines joining successively the midpoints of the sides of any quadrilateral form a parallelogram.

7. Show that the three lines that join the midpoints of opposite edges of a tetrahedron meet in a point that bisects each of them. This point is called the *center of gravity* of the tetrahedron.

8. Show that the line joining any vertex of a tetrahedron to the point of intersection of the medians of the opposite face passes through the center of gravity (Ex. 7) of the tetrahedron and is divided in the ratio $3 : 1$ at that point.

127. Cylindrical Coördinates. In this article and the following one, we shall describe two systems of coördinates in space, each of which bears some resemblance to polar coördinates in the plane. Both of these systems have been found useful in the applications of analytic geometry.

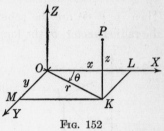

Fɪɢ. 152

Let P be any point in space with rectangular coördinates (x, y, z) and let $K(x, y, 0)$ be the foot of the perpendicular from P on the xy-plane. Let (r, θ) be the polar coördinates in the xy-plane of the point K when O is taken as the origin and OX as the initial line. Then the three numbers (r, θ, z) are called the *cylindrical coördinates* of P.

From Art. 17, we have at once for the values of x, y, and z in terms of the cylindrical coördinates

$$x = r \cos \theta, \quad y = r \sin \theta, \quad z = z. \tag{175}$$

Similarly, for the values of r, θ, and z in terms of the rectangular coördinates of P, we have

$$r = \sqrt{x^2 + y^2}, \quad \theta = \tan^{-1}\frac{y}{x}, \quad z = z, \tag{176}$$

wherein the quadrant in which the angle θ lies is to be determined by plotting the given point on the figure, as in Art. 17.

128. Spherical Coördinates. If the distance ρ of a point P from the origin is known, then P lies on a sphere with center at the origin and radius ρ. We have learned from the study of geography that the position of a point on the surface of a sphere can be determined by two angles (its longitude and latitude). The spherical coördinates of a point consist, accordingly, of a distance and two angles, which we shall define in the following way.

Let $P(x, y, z)$ be any point in space and let $K(x, y, 0)$ be the foot of the perpendicular from P on the xy-plane. Draw OP, OK, and KP. Let

$$\overline{OP} = \rho \qquad \text{angle } XOK = \theta \quad \text{and} \quad \text{angle } ZOP = \phi.$$

Then (ρ, θ, ϕ) are the **spherical coördinates** of P. We call ρ the **radius vector**, θ, the **longitude**, and ϕ, the **co-latitude** of P.

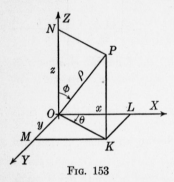

FIG. 153

To find the values of (x, y, z) in terms of (ρ, θ, ϕ), we note that angle $KOP = 90° - \phi$, so that

$$\overline{OK} = \rho \cos KOP = \rho \sin \phi.$$

From the right triangles OLK and ONP, we now have

$$x = \rho \sin \phi \cos \theta,$$
$$y = \rho \sin \phi \sin \theta,$$
$$z = \rho \cos \phi, \qquad (177)$$

as the equations expressing x, y, and z in terms of ρ, θ, and ϕ.

If we solve these equations for ρ, θ, and ϕ, we obtain

$$\rho = \sqrt{x^2 + y^2 + z^2}, \; \theta = \tan^{-1} \frac{y}{x}, \; \phi = \cos^{-1} \frac{z}{\sqrt{x^2 + y^2 + z^2}} \quad (178)$$

as the equations expressing ρ, θ, and ϕ in terms of x, y, and z.

EXERCISES

1. Plot the point and find its rectangular coördinates, given that its cylindrical coördinates are:

(a) $(4, 45°, 3)$ (b) $(2, 120°, -1)$

(c) $\left(1, -\dfrac{\pi}{2}, 2\right)$ (d) $\left(6, \dfrac{7\pi}{6}, -3\right).$

2. Plot the point and find its cylindrical coördinates, given that its rectangular coördinates are:

(a) $(2, 2, 5)$ (b) $(0, 4, -2)$ (c) $(1, \sqrt{3}, 4)$ (d) $(-4, -4, 5).$

3. Plot the point and find its rectangular coördinates, given that its spherical coördinates are:

(a) $(4, 45°, 30°)$ (b) $(3, 90°, 90°)$

(c) $\left(8, \dfrac{\pi}{3}, \dfrac{2\pi}{3}\right)$ (d) $\left(6, \dfrac{4\pi}{3}, \dfrac{3\pi}{4}\right).$

4. Plot the point and find its spherical coördinates, given that its rectangular coördinates are:

(a) $(-3, 0, 0)$ (b) $(0, \sqrt{3}, 1)$

(c) $(4, 4, 2)$ (d) $(-1, -1, -1).$

5. Describe the surfaces defined by the following equations in cylindrical coördinates and find their equations in rectangular coördinates.

(a) $r = 2$ (b) $\theta = 45°$ (c) $r = 3 \cos \theta$ (d) $r = z.$

6. Proceed as in Ex. 5 for the following equations in spherical coördinates:

(a) $\rho = 2$ (b) $\phi = 60°$ (c) $\rho \sin \phi \cos \theta = 6$ (d) $\rho = 4 \cos \phi.$

7. Write each of the following equations in cylindrical and in spherical coördinates:

(a) $x^2 + y^2 + z^2 = 9$ (b) $x^2 + y^2 = 16$
(c) $4(x^2 + y^2) + 9z^2 = 36$ (d) $y = 5.$

8. Assuming that the earth is a sphere of radius 4000 miles, set up a suitable set of coördinate axes and find the spherical and the rectangular coördinates of the following cities:

New York, Long. 74° W., Lat. 41° N.
Tokio, Long. 140° E., Lat. 36° N.
Buenos Aires, Long. 58° W., Lat. 35° S.
Cape Town, Long. 18° E., Lat. 34° S.

9. Find the equations connecting the spherical and the cylindrical coördinates of a point. Find the spherical coördinates of the points in Ex. 1 and the cylindrical coördinates of those in Ex. 3.

10. Find the direction cosines of the line from the origin to the point whose spherical coördinates are (ρ, θ, ϕ).

MISCELLANEOUS EXERCISES

1. Show in two ways that $(3, 1, 2)$, $(7, 4, 6)$, and $(2, 2, 5)$ are the vertices of a right triangle.

2. Show in two ways that $(5, 4, 6)$, $(7, 9, 1)$, and $(1, 2, -3)$ are the vertices of an isosceles triangle.

3. Show that $(5, 7, 3)$, $(7, 4, 2)$, $(2, 5, 4)$, and $(4, 2, 3)$ are the vertices of a rhombus and find the lengths of its diagonals.

4. Find y, given that the line joining $P(2, -3, -2)$ to $(4, y, 1)$ is perpendicular to the line joining P to $(7, -5, 2)$.

5. Find a point in the xy-plane that is equidistant from $(5, 3, -1)$, $(1, 2, 2)$, and $(-1, 1, -1)$.

6. Show that the points $(1, 3, -2)$ and $(3, 9, -6)$ lie on a line that passes through the origin.

7. Show that the tetrahedron whose vertices are $(a, 0, 0)$, $(0, a, 0)$, $(0, 0, a)$, and (a, a, a) is regular; that is, that its sides are all equal in length.

8. Find the angle between two opposite edges of the tetrahedron in Ex. 7.

9. Find the point equidistant from the vertices of the tetrahedron in Ex. 7.

10. Find the angles of the triangle whose vertices are $(6, 3, 2)$, $(5, 1, 4)$, and $(-3, 5, -4)$.

11. Find the direction cosines of a line perpendicular to the three sides of the triangle in Ex. 10.

SELECTED EXERCISES

1. Find the direction numbers of a line that is perpendicular to two given non-parallel lines.

2. Discuss Ex. 1 when the lines are parallel.

3. Find the condition that there exists a line perpendicular to three given lines.

4. Find an expression for the sine of the angle between two lines whose direction cosines are given.

5. The vertices of a triangle are $P_1(x_1, y_1, z_1)$, $P_2(x_2, y_2, z_2)$, and $P_3(x_3, y_3, z_3)$. Find the direction cosines of a line perpendicular to the three sides of this triangle.

6. Show that the area of the triangle in Ex. 5 is

$$\frac{1}{2}\sqrt{\begin{vmatrix} y_1 & z_1 & 1 \\ y_2 & z_2 & 1 \\ y_3 & z_3 & 1 \end{vmatrix}^2 + \begin{vmatrix} z_1 & x_1 & 1 \\ z_2 & x_2 & 1 \\ z_3 & x_3 & 1 \end{vmatrix}^2 + \begin{vmatrix} x_1 & y_1 & 1 \\ x_2 & y_2 & 1 \\ x_3 & y_3 & 1 \end{vmatrix}^2}$$

7. If two pairs of opposite edges of a tetrahedron are perpendicular, show that the third pair is also perpendicular.

8. Using the data of Ex. 8, page 245, find the distance in miles, along a great circle, from New York to Buenos Aires.

CHAPTER XIV

PLANES AND LINES

129. Normal Equation of a Plane. Let ABC (Fig. 154) be the given plane and let N be the foot of the perpendicular from the origin to the plane. Draw the directed line segment $\overline{ON}$, denote its length by p and its direction cosines by $\cos \alpha$, $\cos \beta$, and $\cos \gamma$.

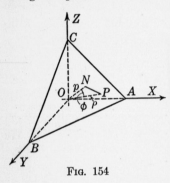

Let $P(x, y, z)$ be any point in the plane. Draw $\overline{OP}$, and denote the length of $\overline{OP}$ by ρ and its direction cosines by $\cos \alpha'$, $\cos \beta'$, and $\cos \gamma'$. Denote also the angle NOP by ϕ.

FIG. 154

Since ON is perpendicular to the plane and N and P lie in the plane, the angle ONP is a right angle. (Why?) Hence, $\cos \phi = \dfrac{p}{\rho}$, or

$$p = \rho \cos \phi. \tag{179}$$

From equation (169), we have

$$\cos \phi = \cos \alpha' \cos \alpha + \cos \beta' \cos \beta + \cos \gamma' \cos \gamma.$$

On substituting this value of $\cos \phi$ in (179) and multiplying through by ρ, we find that

$$p = \rho \cos \alpha' \cos \alpha + \rho \cos \beta' \cos \beta + \rho \cos \gamma' \cos \gamma. \tag{180}$$

From equations (163), we have

$$\rho \cos \alpha' = x, \quad \rho \cos \beta' = y, \quad \rho \cos \gamma' = z.$$

If we make these substitutions in (180), we obtain the result

$$x \cos \alpha + y \cos \beta + z \cos \gamma - p = 0, \qquad (181)$$

which is the required *equation of the plane in the normal form*.

Exercise. If the point $P(x, y, z)$ does not lie in the given plane, show that the foot of the perpendicular from P on the line ON is a point N' distinct from N and hence that the coördinates of P do not satisfy equation (181).

130. General Form of the Equation of a Plane. The normal form (181) of the equation of a plane is of the first degree in x, y, and z with real coefficients. We shall now show, conversely, that *the locus of any equation of the first degree in x, y, and z with real coefficients,*

$$Ax + By + Cz + D = 0, \qquad (182)$$

wherein A, B, and C are not all zero, is a plane.

The locus of equation (182) is not changed if we divide each of its terms by the non-zero constant $\pm \sqrt{A^2 + B^2 + C^2}$. We thus obtain

$$\frac{A}{\pm \sqrt{A^2 + B^2 + C^2}} x + \frac{B}{\pm \sqrt{A^2 + B^2 + C^2}} y + \frac{C}{\pm \sqrt{A^2 + B^2 + C^2}} z$$
$$+ \frac{D}{\pm \sqrt{A^2 + B^2 + C^2}} = 0. \quad (183)$$

By Art. 123, the coefficients of x, y, and z in (183) are the direction cosines of a line, so that we may put

$$\frac{A}{\pm \sqrt{A^2 + B^2 + C^2}} = \cos \alpha$$

$$\frac{B}{\pm \sqrt{A^2 + B^2 + C^2}} = \cos \beta \qquad (184)$$

$$\frac{C}{\pm \sqrt{A^2 + B^2 + C^2}} = \cos \gamma$$

If we substitute these values of the coefficients of x, y, and z in (183), and compare the result with equation (181), we find that equation (183), and hence equation (182) which has the same locus, is the equation of a plane. It follows, moreover, from the comparison with (181), that this plane is perpendicular to the line whose direction cosines are given by (184) and that it lies at a distance from the origin equal to

$$p = \frac{-D}{\pm \sqrt{A^2 + B^2 + C^2}}. \qquad (185)$$

Equation (182) is called the **general form** of the equation of a plane. To reduce it to the normal form (183), we divide each of its terms by $\pm \sqrt{A^2 + B^2 + C^2}$. In order to fix the sign of the radical by which we divide each term of (182) to get (183), *we shall take the sign to agree with that of C if $C \neq 0$, to agree with that of B if $C = 0$, and to agree with that of A if $B = 0$ and $C = 0$.*

Of frequent importance in the applications is the following theorem which follows at once from the foregoing discussion: *the coefficients of x, y, and z in the equation of a plane are the direction numbers of a line perpendicular to the plane.*

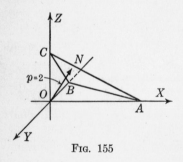

FIG. 155

The lines in which a given plane intersects the coördinate planes are called its **traces** on those planes. A plane is usually represented on the figure by means of its traces on the coördinate planes, as in Fig. 154.

Example. Reduce the equation of the plane $x - 2y + 2z - 6 = 0$ to the normal form. Find the direction cosines of the normal and the distance of the plane from the origin. Determine its traces on the coördinate planes.

To reduce the equation of the plane to the normal form, we divide through by $\sqrt{1^2 + (-1)^2 + 2^2} = 3$. The result is $\frac{1}{3}x - \frac{2}{3}y + \frac{2}{3}z - 2 = 0$.

The direction cosines of the normal to the plane are found, by comparing this equation with (181), to be $\frac{1}{3}$, $-\frac{2}{3}$, $\frac{2}{3}$ and the distance of the plane from the origin is similarly found to be 2.

The equations of the traces of the given plane on the coördinate planes are:

On the xy-plane $x - 2y - 6 = 0$, $z = 0$;
On the xz-plane $x + 2z - 6 = 0$, $y = 0$;
On the yz-plane $- 2y + 2z - 6 = 0$, $x = 0$.

EXERCISES

1. Find the equation of a plane for which

(a) $\alpha = 60°$ $\beta = 45°$ $\gamma = 60°$ $p = 3$

(b) $\alpha = 45°$ $\beta = 90°$ $\gamma = 135°$ $p = 6$

(c) $\alpha = \dfrac{\pi}{3}$ $\beta = \dfrac{2\pi}{3}$ $\gamma = \dfrac{5\pi}{4}$ $p = 5$

(d) $\alpha = \dfrac{\pi}{6}$ $\beta = \dfrac{4\pi}{3}$ $\gamma = \dfrac{\pi}{2}$ $p = 8$.

2. Find the equation of a plane, given that the direction numbers of its normal and its distance from the origin are:

(a) $2, 6, 3$; $p = 1$ (b) $6, 2, 9$; $p = \frac{2}{11}$
(c) $6, - 3, - 2$; $p = 3$ (d) $7, 6, - 6$; $p = 3$
(e) $2, - 1, 6$; $p = 4$ (f) $4, - 1, - 1$; $p = 5$.

3. Find the equation of a plane, given that the coördinates of the foot of the perpendicular from the origin on it are:

(a) $(6, 3, - 6)$ (b) $(12, - 4, - 3)$
(c) $(9, 2, 6)$ (d) $(- 3, - 5, 6)$.

4. Reduce the equations of the following planes to the normal form. Find the direction cosines of the normal to the plane and its distance from the origin. Determine the traces of the plane on the coördinate planes.

(a) $6x - 2y - 3z + 14 = 0$ (b) $4x - 8y + z - 45 = 0$
(c) $9x - 6y + 2z - 12 = 0$ (d) $7x - 6y - 6z + 44 = 0$
(e) $8x - 4y - z + 3 = 0$ (f) $3x - 2y + 5z - 7 = 0$
(g) $4x + 3y - 15 = 0$ (h) $z - 5 = 0$.

5. Show analytically that the locus of a point that moves so that its distances from the points $(3, 1, 4)$ and $(1, - 5, 6)$ are always equal, is a plane. Show also that this plane is perpendicular to the line joining the given points.

6. Find two values of k such that the distance of the plane $4x + ky + z - 27 = 0$ from the origin is numerically equal to 3.

7. Find the point of intersection of the planes

$$x + y + z = 5 \qquad 2x - y + 2z = 1 \qquad x - 2y + 3z = 6$$

131. Angle between Two Planes. It is proved, in elementary geometry, that the magnitudes of the four dihedral angles formed by two intersecting planes are numerically equal, respectively, to the four corresponding angles formed by the two lines that can be drawn through any point in space perpendicular to the given planes (Fig. 156). It is by means of this theorem that the angles between two planes are usually measured in advanced mathematics.

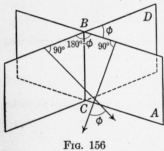

FIG. 156

If positive directions are assigned to the two perpendiculars, we shall choose, as **the angle between the planes,** a dihedral angle formed by them that is equal in magnitude to *the angle between the positive directions of these perpendiculars.*

Thus, if the equations of the planes are given in the normal form

$$x \cos \alpha_1 + y \cos \beta_1 + z \cos \gamma_1 - p_1 = 0,$$

and

$$x \cos \alpha_2 + y \cos \beta_2 + z \cos \gamma_2 - p_2 = 0,$$

then, by Art. 129, the direction cosines of the normals to the planes are $\cos \alpha_1$, $\cos \beta_1$, $\cos \gamma_1$, and $\cos \alpha_2$, $\cos \beta_2$, $\cos \gamma_2$, respectively, and the angle between the planes, being equal in magnitude to the angle between the positive directions of the normals, is found, from equation (169), to be

$$\cos \phi = \cos \alpha_1 \cos \alpha_2 + \cos \beta_1 \cos \beta_2 + \cos \gamma_1 \cos \gamma_2, \quad (186)$$

wherein ϕ is the angle between the planes and α_1, β_1, γ_1 and α_2, β_2, γ_2 are the direction angles of the normals to the planes.

Similarly, if the equations of the planes are given in the general form

$$A_1x + B_1y + C_1z + D_1 = 0$$

and

$$A_2x + B_2y + C_2z + D_2 = 0,$$

then A_1, B_1, C_1 and A_2, B_2, C_2 are the direction numbers of the normals to the planes and the angle between the planes is found, from equation (171), to be

$$\cos \phi = \pm \frac{A_1A_2 + B_1B_2 + C_1C_2}{\sqrt{A_1^2 + B_1^2 + C_1^2}\,\sqrt{A_2^2 + B_2^2 + C_2^2}}. \quad (187)$$

In particular, the condition that the planes are perpendicular is that $\cos \phi = 0$, so that

$$A_1A_2 + B_1B_2 + C_1C_2 = 0. \quad (188)$$

If the given planes are parallel, they are both perpendicular to the same line, and we have

$$\frac{A_1}{A_2} = \frac{B_1}{B_2} = \frac{C_1}{C_2}. \quad (189)$$

132. Plane through a Given Point Perpendicular to a Given Line. Let $P_1(x_1, y_1, z_1)$ be the given point and let a, b, c be the direction numbers of the given line.

From the last theorem of Art. 130, it is seen that the plane

$$ax + by + cz + D = 0 \quad (190)$$

is perpendicular to the given line for all values of D.

We determine D from the condition that the plane (190) passes through P_1. This condition is

$$ax_1 + by_1 + cz_1 + D = 0.$$

If we substitute the value of D from this equation in (190), and collect terms, we have

$$a(x - x_1) + b(y - y_1) + c(z - z_1) = 0 \quad (191)$$

which is the required equation of the plane through $P_1(x_1, y_1, z_1)$ perpendicular to the line whose direction numbers are a, b, and c.

This is a form of the equation of a plane that is much used in the applications of analytic geometry.

133. Distance from a Plane to a Point. Let $P_1(x_1, y_1, z_1)$ be the given point and let the equation of the given plane be

$$Ax + By + Cz + D = 0. \tag{192}$$

From (191), the equation of a plane through P_1 parallel to the given plane (192) is

$$A(x - x_1) + B(y - y_1) + C(z - z_1) = 0. \tag{193}$$

The directed distances from the origin to the planes (192) and (193) are, by (185),

$$p_1 = \frac{-D}{\pm \sqrt{A^2 + B^2 + C^2}} \quad \text{and} \quad p_2 = \frac{Ax_1 + By_1 + Cz_1}{\pm \sqrt{A^2 + B^2 + C^2}}.$$

The difference

$$d = p_2 - p_1$$

between these distances is equal to the required distance from the plane (192) to the given point P_1, that is,

$$d = \frac{Ax_1 + By_1 + Cz_1 + D}{\pm \sqrt{A^2 + B^2 + C^2}}, \tag{194}$$

wherein the sign in the denominator is fixed by the rule given in Art. 130.

The value of d, as found from this equation, is a directed distance. It is positive or negative according as the segment of the perpendicular, measured from the plane to the point P_1, is in the positive or the negative direction along the normal.

EXERCISES

1. Find the cosine of the angle between the planes

(a) $2x - y - 2z - 4 = 0$ $4x - 8y - z - 2 = 0$

(b) $5x - y + z + 5 = 0$ $x - y - z - 3 = 0$

   (c) $3x - y + 5z - 6 = 0$ $2x + y - z + 3 = 0$

   (d) $x + y - 7 = 0$ $x + z + 5 = 0.$

2. Find the distance to the point $(3, -2, -6)$ from each of the planes in Ex. 1.

3. Write the equation of a plane through $(2, 1, -4)$ parallel to each of the planes in Ex. 1.

4. Which of the points $(4, 3, 1)$, $(1, -4, 3)$, $(-1, 3, -2)$, and $(4, 5, 6)$ lie on the same side of the plane $5x - 2y - 3z + 4 = 0$ as the point $(1, 6, -3)$?

5. Write the equation of a plane through $(4, 2, 7)$ perpendicular to the line whose direction numbers are

   (a) $7, 6, -6$ (b) $6, -2, 3$ (c) $4, 1, -1$ (d) $2, 7, -3$

6. Find the equation of a plane through $(-2, 1, 5)$ perpendicular to the line joining $(3, 4, -6)$ to $(1, 6, -2)$.

7. Show that the planes $2x - y + z + 3 = 0$, $x - y + 4z + 1 = 0$, $3x + y - 2z + 8 = 0$, $4x - 2y + 2z - 5 = 0$, $9x + 3y - 6z - 7 = 0$, and $7x - 7y + 28z - 16 = 0$ bound a parallelopiped.

8. Determine k so that the planes $2x + ky + 4z + 6 = 0$ and $3x - 2y - 2z + 4 = 0$ will be perpendicular.

9. Find the distance between the parallel planes

   (a) $2x - 3y + 6z - 5 = 0$, $2x - 3y + 6z - 19 = 0$

   (b) $9x + 2y - 6z - 4 = 0$, $18x + 4y - 12z + 33 = 0.$

10. Find two planes parallel to $2x - 2y - z - 5 = 0$ whose distances from $(1, 3, -5)$ are numerically equal to 4.

11. Show that the condition that the plane $Ax + By + Cz + D = 0$ is perpendicular to the yz-plane is $A = 0$. What is the condition that it is perpendicular to the xz-plane? to the xy-plane?

12. Show that the equation $2x - 3y - 6z + k = 0$, wherein k is a parameter, defines a family of planes. Find the direction cosines of a line perpendicular to the planes of this family.

134. Planes Satisfying Three Conditions.

The position of a plane is usually fixed by assigning three conditions that it must satisfy. For example, we may require it to pass through three given points, or to pass through a given point and be perpendicular to each of two given planes, and so forth.

The method of determining the equation of a plane that satisfies three such conditions is illustrated by the following examples.

Example 1. Find the equation of the plane that passes through the points $(3, 2, -3)$, $(-1, 3, 5)$, and $(5, 4, -2)$.

The condition that any one of these points lies in the plane

$$Ax + By + Cz + D = 0$$

is that its coördinates satisfy the equation of the plane. If we substitute the coördinates of the given points successively in the equation of the plane, we obtain the three equations

$$3A + 2B - 3C + D = 0$$
$$-A + 3B + 5C + D = 0$$
$$5A + 4B - 2C + D = 0.$$

If we solve these three equations for B, C, and D in terms of A, we obtain $B = -\frac{4}{3}A$, $C = \frac{2}{3}A$, $D = \frac{5}{3}A$.

We may now assign to A *any value we please except zero.* To avoid fractions, we put $A = 3$; then $B = -4, C = 2$, and $D = 5$. The required equation of the plane is, accordingly,

$$3x - 4y + 2z + 5 = 0.$$

As a check, the student should verify that the coördinates of each of the given points satisfy this equation.

Example 2. Find the equation of the plane that passes through the points $(6, 1, 2)$ and $(3, 4, 4)$ and is perpendicular to the plane $x + 3y + 2z - 7 = 0$.

The conditions that the plane $Ax + By + Cz + D = 0$ passes through the given points are found, by substituting the coördinates of the points in the equation of the plane, to be

$$6A + B + 2C + D = 0$$
$$3A + 4B + 4C + D = 0.$$

The condition that it is perpendicular to the given plane is

$$A + 3B + 2C = 0.$$

We cannot solve these equations for B, C, and D in terms of A since the resulting equations are incompatible. We can, however, solve for A, C, and D in terms of B. The results are $A = 0$, $C = -\frac{3}{2}B$, $D = 2B$.

If we put $B = 2$ we have $C = -3$ and $D = 4$. The required equation is, accordingly, $2y - 3z + 4 = 0$.

135. Intercept Equation of a Plane. The directed distances from the origin to the points of intersection of a plane with the coördinate axes are called the **intercepts** of the plane on those axes.

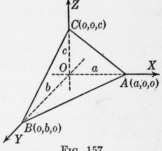

Let a, b, and c (which, we shall suppose, are all different from zero) be the intercepts of the plane

$$Ax + By + Cz + D = 0 \quad (195)$$

on the x-, y-, and z-axis, respectively.

Fig. 157

To find the equation of this plane in terms of its intercepts, we first observe that it passes through the points $A(a, 0, 0)$, $B(0, b, 0)$, and $C(0, 0, c)$ (Fig. 157). Hence the coördinates of each of these points satisfy the equation of the plane, and we have

$$Aa + D = 0, \quad Bb + D = 0, \quad Cc + D = 0.$$

If we solve these equations for A, B, and C in terms of D, and then put $D = -1$, we have

$$A = \frac{1}{a}, \quad B = \frac{1}{b}, \quad C = \frac{1}{c}, \quad D = -1.$$

On substituting these values of A, B, C, and D in (195), we obtain

$$\frac{x}{a} + \frac{y}{b} + \frac{z}{c} = 1 \quad (196)$$

as the *intercept form of the equation of a plane*.

EXERCISES

1. Find the intercepts of the following planes and write their equations in the intercept form:

(a) $3x + 2y + z - 6 = 0$

(b) $2x + 4y - 5z + 20 = 0$

(c) $4x - 3y + 5z - 11 = 0$.

2. Find the equation of the plane that passes through the following points:

(a) $(5, 0, 0), (0, 2, 0), (0, 0, -3)$

(b) $(2, 3, -4), (1, 2, -5), (-5, 2, 4)$

(c) $(3, 0, 1), (2, -3, 2), (3, -1, 4)$

(d) $(1, 1, 4), (2, -3, 1), (-1, 3, -2)$.

3. Find the equation of the plane that passes through the points $(3, 2, -5)$ and $(5, -1, 3)$ and has its x-intercept equal to twice its y-intercept.

4. Find the equation of the plane through the following points that is perpendicular to the given plane:

(a) $(7, 1, 2), (-1, 3, 6); \ 4x - 3y + 6z - 9 = 0$

(b) $(4, 6, -3), (2, 8, -1); \ 5x - 3y + 15z + 11 = 0$

(c) $(3, 1, 4), (5, -2, 2); \ 4x + y + 3z - 5 = 0$.

5. Find the equation of the plane that passes through the given point and is perpendicular to each of the given planes:

(a) $(2, 1, 3); \ 5x + y - z + 3 = 0, \ x + y - 5z + 5 = 0$

(b) $(5, -1, 4); \ 6x - 3y + 2z + 7 = 0, \ 2x + 5y - 2z + 4 = 0$

(c) $(7, 4, 1); \ 3x + 4y + z - 6 = 0, \ x + 3y + z + 2 = 0$.

6. Find the equation of the plane that passes through the points $(3, 1, 1)$ and $(1, -6, -3)$ and has its x-intercept equal to 2.

7. Find the equation of the plane that passes through the point $(2, -4, -11)$, is perpendicular to the plane $x + 2y + z + 5 = 0$, and has its z-intercept equal to 3.

8. Find the equations of two planes through the points $(-1, 1, 2)$ and $(1, 2, 4)$ making an angle of $45°$ with the plane $x - 4y + z - 2 = 0$.

THE LINE IN SPACE

136. Surfaces and Curves. We have seen, in Art. 130, that a single linear equation in x, y, and z, with real coefficients,

$$Ax + By + Cz + D = 0,$$

defines a plane. When we wish to fix the position of a *line* in space, we shall take simultaneously the two equations

$$A_1x + B_1y + C_1z + D_1 = 0 \qquad A_2x + B_2y + C_2z + D_2 = 0$$

of two planes that have this line as their line of intersection. The condition that a point lies on this line is, then, that its coördinates satisfy *both* of these equations.

The discussion in the preceding paragraph is of importance in that it constitutes an elementary illustration of a very general and fundamental principle in the analytic geometry of space. When we wish to study analytically a *surface* in space, we shall think of its position as fixed by a single equation,

$$f(x, y, z) = 0,$$

just as, when we studied the plane, we fixed the position of our plane in space by a single linear equation. When, on the other hand, we wish to fix the position of a *curve* in space, we shall use two equations,

$$f(x, y, z) = 0, \qquad F(x, y, z) = 0,$$

such that each of these equations, taken by itself, is the equation of a surface that contains the curve under consideration. The points that lie on this curve will then possess the property that their coördinates will satisfy the equations of both of these surfaces.

In the articles that follow, we shall deal with the two equations of a line. We shall write these equations in several forms depending on the information that is given us about the line or on the uses to which we intend to put these equations.

137. Line through a Given Point Having a Given Direction. The Symmetric Form. Let $P_1(x_1, y_1, z_1)$ be the given point and let $\cos \alpha$, $\cos \beta$, and $\cos \gamma$ be the direction cosines of the given line.

Let $P(x, y, z)$ be any point on the given line and let $d = \overline{P_1P}$ be the length of the directed segment from P_1 to P. From equations (161), we have

$$x - x_1 = d \cos \alpha \quad y - y_1 = d \cos \beta \quad z - z_1 = d \cos \gamma.$$

If we solve these three equations for d, and equate the values for d so obtained, we have, as the equation of the line,

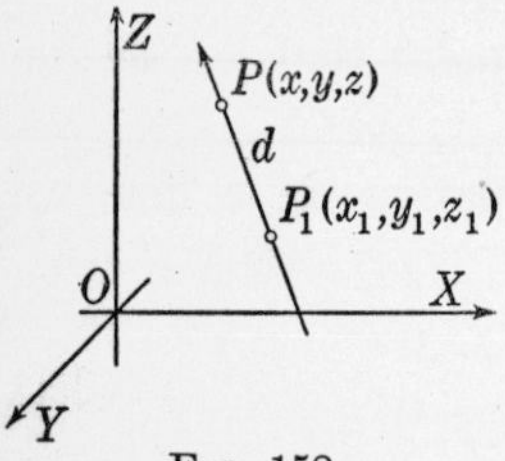

$$\frac{x - x_1}{\cos \alpha} = \frac{y - y_1}{\cos \beta} = \frac{z - z_1}{\cos \gamma}. \quad (197)$$

Fig. 158

These equations constitute the **symmetric form** of the equations of a line.

If, in (197), we multiply all the denominators by any non-zero constant that we please, the equalities still hold. The denominators now become, not the direction cosines, but the direction numbers of the line. If we denote these direction numbers by a, b, and c, we may write the resulting equations of the line in the form

$$\frac{x - x_1}{a} = \frac{y - y_1}{b} = \frac{z - z_1}{c}. \quad (198)$$

These equations are frequently more convenient to use than equations (197) which involve the actual direction cosines.

138. The Two-Point Form. Let $P_1(x_1, y_1, z_1)$ and $P_2(x_2, y_2, z_2)$ be any two fixed points on the line. Since, by equations (161), the numbers $x_2 - x_1$, $y_2 - y_1$, and $z_2 - z_1$ are proportional to the direction cosines of this line, we may use them, in (198), as the direction numbers a, b, and c of the line. The resulting equations are

$$\frac{x - x_1}{x_2 - x_1} = \frac{y - y_1}{y_2 - y_1} = \frac{z - z_1}{z_2 - z_1}. \tag{199}$$

These equations constitute the **two-point form** of the equations of the line.

139. The Parametric Form. If, in equations (198), we equate each of the equal fractions to k and solve for x, y, and z, we obtain

$$x = x_1 + ak \quad y = y_1 + bk \quad z = z_1 + ck. \tag{200}$$

These three equations are the **parametric equations** of the line in terms of the parameter k. The point determined by assigning to k any value we please is a point that lies on the line.

140. The General Form. As the equations of a line, we may take simultaneously the equations

$$\begin{aligned} A_1x + B_1y + C_1z + D_1 &= 0 \\ \text{and} \qquad A_2x + B_2y + C_2z + D_2 &= 0 \end{aligned} \tag{201}$$

of any two planes whatever that have this line as their line of intersection. Any point whose coördinates satisfy both of these equations lies in both planes and thus lies on the given line.

To reduce the general form (201) of the equations of a line to the two-point form and to the symmetric form, we may proceed as in the following example.

Example. Write the equations of the line of intersection of the planes $3x + 3y - 4z + 7 = 0$ and $x + 6y + 2z - 6 = 0$ in the two-point form and in the symmetric form and find its direction cosines.

To fix a point on the line, we may assume for one of its coördinates any value we please and determine its other two coördinates by means of the given equations. For example, if we put $z = 1$, the equations to determine x and y are

$$3x + 3y + 3 = 0, \quad x + 6y - 4 = 0.$$

On solving these equations, we find that $x = -2$, $y = 1$. Hence, $(-2, 1, 1)$ is a point that lies on the line. Similarly, by putting $z = 4$, we find that $(4, -1, 4)$ is a second point on the line.

Since we now know the coördinates of two points on the line, we may substitute these in equation (199) and obtain

$$\frac{x + 2}{4 - (-2)} = \frac{y - 1}{-1 - 1} = \frac{z - 1}{4 - 1}$$

as the two-point form of the equation of this line.

It was pointed out in Art. 138 that the values 6, -2, and 3 of the denominators in these equations are the direction numbers of the line. We may, accordingly, write at once equations (198) for this line. The results are

$$\frac{x + 2}{6} = \frac{y - 1}{-2} = \frac{z - 1}{3}.$$

To reduce these equations to the symmetric form (197), we first determine the direction cosines of the line by dividing each of the direction numbers by $\pm \sqrt{6^2 + (-2)^2 + 3^2} = \pm 7$, the sign being chosen according as one direction on the line, or the other, is taken as the positive direction. The symmetric equations of the line are, accordingly,

$$\frac{x + 2}{\pm \frac{6}{7}} = \frac{y - 1}{\mp \frac{2}{7}} = \frac{z - 1}{\pm \frac{3}{7}}.$$

From the denominators of these expressions, it is seen at once that the direction cosines of the line are $\pm \frac{6}{7}$, $\mp \frac{2}{7}$, and $\pm \frac{3}{7}$.

141. Family of Planes through a Line. Projecting Planes. All of the planes of the family

$$A_1x + B_1y + C_1z + D_1 + k(A_2x + B_2y + C_2z + D_2) = 0, \quad (202)$$

wherein k is the parameter, contain the line defined by equations (201). For, if $P_1(x_1, y_1, z_1)$ is any point on this line, its coördinates satisfy both of the equations (201) and thus, when substituted in (202), reduce this equation to $0 + k(0) = 0$, which is true for all values of k.

By assigning a suitable value to k in equation (202), we can determine a plane that passes through the line (201) and satisfies one additional condition; for example, we can make it pass through a given point not on the line or we can make it be perpendicular to a given plane.

The planes through a line that are perpendicular to the xy-, yz-, and zx-planes, respectively, are called the **projecting planes** of the line on these coördinate planes. The equations of the projecting planes of a given line may be found as in the following example 1.

Example 1. Find the projecting planes of the line $4x - 2y + 3z + 1 = 0$, $5x + 3y + 2z - 3 = 0$ on the coördinate planes.

The family of planes through this line is, by (202),

$$4x - 2y + 3z + 1 + k(5x + 3y + 2z - 3) = 0.$$

If we collect the coefficients of x, y, and z in this equation, we may write the equation in the form

$$(4 + 5k)x + (- 2 + 3k)y + (3 + 2k)z + 1 - 3k = 0. \quad (203)$$

The condition that a plane of this family is perpendicular to the xy-plane (that is, to the plane $z = 0$) is, by (188), that the coefficient of z in its equation is equal to zero.

If we put the coefficient of z in (203) equal to zero, we have $3 + 2k = 0$, from which $k = -\frac{3}{2}$. On substituting this value of k in (203) and simplifying, we obtain

$$7x + 13y - 11 = 0$$

which is the equation of the projecting plane of the line on the xy-plane.

The equations of the projecting planes of the line on the yz-plane and on the xz-plane are found similarly, by equating to zero the coefficients of x and of y in (203), to be

$$22y - 7z - 17 = 0 \quad \text{and} \quad 22x + 13z - 3 = 0,$$

respectively.

Example 2. Find the plane through the line in example 1 and the point $(1, 1, - 2)$.

Since the given point lies in the required plane, the value of k must be chosen so that the coördinates of this point satisfy equation (203). On substituting the coördinates of the point in (203) and solving, we obtain $k = 3$. If we now substitute this value of k in (203) and simplify, we have

$$19x + 7y + 9z - 8 = 0$$

as the equation of the required plane.

EXERCISES

1. Write the equations of the following lines and find their direction cosines, given that the positive direction on the line is chosen so that γ is acute.

(a) Through $(3, 1, 4)$; direction numbers $- 2, 2, 1$

(b) Through $(- 5, 2, 1)$; direction numbers $7, 6, 6$

(c) Through $(8, 0, - 3)$ and $(9, 4, 5)$

(d) Through $(4, - 1, 2)$ and $(1, 2, - 1)$

(e) Through $(5, 3, 7)$; parallel to the line through $(2, - 2, 5)$ and $(5, 0, - 1)$

(f) Through $(7, 1, 2)$; perpendicular to the plane $7x - 6y + 6z - 4 = 0$

(g) Through $(4, 2, - 6)$; perpendicular to the two lines whose direction numbers are $2, 1, 5$ and $3, - 2, 4$, respectively.

2. Show that the following points lie on a line and find the equations of the line.

(a) $(2, 5, - 3)$, $(12, 3, 1)$, $(- 3, 6, - 5)$

(b) $(3, 2, 5)$, $(1, 1, - 2)$, $(5, 3, 12)$.

3. Show that the following lines are parallel.

(a) $\dfrac{x - 5}{2} = \dfrac{y + 3}{- 4} = \dfrac{z - 1}{6}$ and $\dfrac{x + 1}{- 1} = \dfrac{y - 2}{2} = \dfrac{z - 5}{- 3}$

(b) $2x - y + 5z - 8 = 0$, $6x + 3y - 12z + 7 = 0$ and $4x - 2y + 10z + 5 = 0$, $2x + y - 4z + 8 = 0$.

4. Write the equations of the following lines in the two-point form and in the symmetric form

(a) $3x + 2y - 2z + 3 = 0$ $\quad 2x + y - 2z + 2 = 0$

(b) $x - 6y + 6z - 7 = 0$ $\quad 2x - 2y - 3z + 6 = 0$.

5. Find the acute angle between the two lines whose equations are given in Ex. 4.

6. Find the projecting planes on the coördinate planes of each of the lines in Ex. 4.

7. Write the equations of the line $2x - 3y + 3z + 1 = 0$, $4x - 3y + 4z - 5 = 0$ in the parametric form.

8. Determine the plane through the line defined in Ex. 7 and the point

  (a) $(3, 2, -1)$ (b) $(-5, -2, 4)$ (c) $(-10, 1, 2)$.

9. Determine the plane through the line defined in Ex. 7 that is perpendicular to the plane $4x - y - 5z + 5 = 0$.

TRANSFORMATION OF COÖRDINATES

In the following two articles, we shall derive the equations, analogous to those found in Chapter VI, for a translation or a rotation of axes in space.

★ **142. Translation of Axes.** Let the coördinates of a point P with respect to one set of axes OX, OY, OZ be (x, y, z) and,

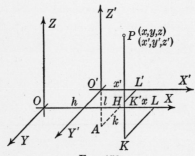

FIG. 159

with respect to a second set $O'X'$, $O'Y'$, $O'Z'$, having the same positive directions, respectively, as the first, be (x', y', z'). Let the coördinates of O' with respect to the first set of axes be (h, k, l).

We have, from Fig. 159,

$$x = \overline{OL} = \overline{OH} + \overline{HL} = \overline{OH} + \overline{O'L'} = h + x'.$$

In a similar way, we find that

$$y = k + y' \quad \text{and} \quad z = l + z'.$$

Hence the required equations for a translation of axes to the new origin $O'(h, k, l)$ are

$$x = x' + h, \quad y = y' + k, \quad z = z' + l. \tag{204}$$

Example. Transform the equation $x^2 + y^2 + z^2 - 2x + 6y - 10z + 26 = 0$ to parallel axes through the point $(1, -3, 5)$.

We first write the equation in the form

$$x^2 - 2x + 1 + y^2 + 6y + 9 + z^2 - 10z + 25 = 1 + 9 + 25 - 26$$

or $$(x - 1)^2 + (y + 3)^2 + (z - 5)^2 = 9.$$

If we now transform the origin to the given point according to the equations

$$x = x' + 1, \quad y = y' - 3, \quad z = z' + 5,$$

we obtain, as the required equation referred to the new axes,

$$x'^2 + y'^2 + z'^2 = 9.$$

★ **143. Rotation of Axes.** Let the coördinates of a point P with respect to one set of axes OX, OY, OZ be (x, y, z) and,

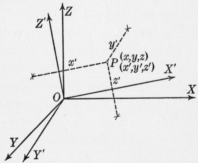

Fig. 160

with respect to a second set OX', OY', OZ', having the same origin, be (x', y', z'). Let the direction cosines of OX', OY', and OZ', referred to the first set of axes, be $\cos \alpha_1$, $\cos \beta_1$,

$\cos \gamma_1$; $\cos \alpha_2$, $\cos \beta_2$, $\cos \gamma_2$; and $\cos \alpha_3$, $\cos \beta_3$, $\cos \gamma_3$, respectively.

Since the $y'z'$-plane is perpendicular to OX', and passes through O (so that its distance, p, from the origin is zero), the normal form of its equation is, by Art. 129,

$$x \cos \alpha_1 + y \cos \beta_1 + z \cos \gamma_1 = 0.$$

Since this plane is the $y'z'$-plane, the distance of the point P from it is the x'-coördinate of P. Hence we have, by Art. 133,

$$x' = x \cos \alpha_1 + y \cos \beta_1 + z \cos \gamma_1.$$

Similarly, $\qquad y' = x \cos \alpha_2 + y \cos \beta_2 + z \cos \gamma_2$ $\qquad$ (205)

and $\qquad z' = x \cos \alpha_3 + y \cos \beta_3 + z \cos \gamma_3.$

The nine direction cosines in formulas (205) satisfy the following six equations.

Since the three cosines in the first, the second, and the third of equations (205) are the direction cosines of OX', OY', and OZ', respectively, we have, by (162),

$$\cos^2 \alpha_1 + \cos^2 \beta_1 + \cos^2 \gamma_1 = 1$$
$$\cos^2 \alpha_2 + \cos^2 \beta_2 + \cos^2 \gamma_2 = 1 \qquad (206)$$
$$\cos^2 \alpha_3 + \cos^2 \beta_3 + \cos^2 \gamma_3 = 1.$$

Moreover, since the three lines OX', OY', and OZ' are perpendicular to each other, we have, by (170)

$$\cos \alpha_1 \cos \alpha_2 + \cos \beta_1 \cos \beta_2 + \cos \gamma_1 \cos \gamma_2 = 0$$
$$\cos \alpha_2 \cos \alpha_3 + \cos \beta_2 \cos \beta_3 + \cos \gamma_2 \cos \gamma_3 = 0 \quad (207)$$
$$\cos \alpha_3 \cos \alpha_1 + \cos \beta_3 \cos \beta_1 + \cos \gamma_3 \cos \gamma_1 = 0.$$

From Fig. 160, it will be seen that the direction cosines of OX, OY, and OZ, referred to the second set of axes, are $\cos \alpha_1$, $\cos \alpha_2$, $\cos \alpha_3$; $\cos \beta_1$, $\cos \beta_2$, $\cos \beta_3$; and $\cos \gamma_1$, $\cos \gamma_2$, $\cos \gamma_3$, respectively. Hence, by the reasoning used in deriving equations (205), we obtain

$$x = x' \cos \alpha_1 + y' \cos \alpha_2 + z' \cos \alpha_3$$
$$y = x' \cos \beta_1 + y' \cos \beta_2 + z' \cos \beta_3 \qquad (208)$$
$$z = x' \cos \gamma_1 + y' \cos \gamma_2 + z' \cos \gamma_3.$$

These equations express x, y, and z in terms of x', y', and z'.

EXERCISES

1. Find the new coördinates of the following points when the origin is translated to the point $(1, 4, -3)$:

    (a) $(5, 1, 2)$ (b) $(-2, 3, 6)$ (c) $(2, 6, -5)$.

2. Find the equations of the following surfaces when the origin is translated to the point $(2, -1, 4)$:

    (a) $3x + 4y - 2z + 6 = 0$
    (b) $2x^2 + y^2 - 3z^2 - 8x + 2y + 24z - 55 = 0$.

3. By a translation of axes, remove the first degree terms from the equation

$$x^2 - 2y^2 + 6z^2 + 2x + 12y - 12z - 27 = 0.$$

4. Show that the lines $\dfrac{x}{6} = \dfrac{y}{2} = \dfrac{z}{-3}$; $\dfrac{x}{2} = \dfrac{y}{3} = \dfrac{z}{6}$; and $\dfrac{x}{3} = \dfrac{y}{-6}$ $= \dfrac{z}{2}$ are mutually perpendicular. Write the equations of a rotation of axes to these lines as x'-, y'-, and z'-axes, respectively.

5. Find the equation of the surface $11x^2 + 10y^2 + 6z^2 - 8yz + 4zx - 12xy - 12 = 0$ when the lines through the origin whose direction cosines are $\frac{1}{3}, \frac{2}{3}, \frac{2}{3}$; $\frac{2}{3}, \frac{1}{3}, -\frac{2}{3}$; $-\frac{2}{3}, \frac{2}{3}, -\frac{1}{3}$ are taken as x'-, y'-, and z'-axes, respectively.

6. Show that the equations of a rotation of axes in which the z-axis remains fixed may be written in the form

$$x = x' \cos \phi - y' \sin \phi \qquad y = x' \sin \phi + y' \cos \phi \qquad z = z'.$$

7. Show by means of equations (206) and (207) that the expression $x^2 + y^2 + z^2$ is transformed into $x'^2 + y'^2 + z'^2$ by a rotation of axes and interpret this result geometrically.

MISCELLANEOUS EXERCISES

1. Write the equations of the traces of the plane $6x + 3y - 2z - 12 = 0$ on the coördinate planes.

2. Write the equation of the plane in Ex. 1 in the normal form.

3. Find the equation of the plane through $(2, -5, 3)$ parallel to the plane $3x + 4y - z - 6 = 0$.

4. Find the equations of the line through $(1, 3, -4)$ parallel to the line

(a) $\dfrac{x+5}{4} = \dfrac{y-1}{3} = \dfrac{z-6}{-5}$

(b) $7x + 3y + 2z - 5 = 0, \quad 2x - 9y + 4z - 3 = 0.$

5. Find the distance from the plane $4x - 4y + 7z + 1 = 0$ to the point

(a) $(5, -2, 10)$ (b) $(2, 9, 0)$ (c) $(3, 1, 6)$.

6. Find the point of intersection of the planes $x - 3y + 2z - 14 = 0$, $2x + 5y + z - 5 = 0$, and $4x + 3y - 3z + 3 = 0$.

7. Find the point of intersection of the plane $4x - 5y + 3z - 3 = 0$ with the line $\dfrac{x-3}{2} = \dfrac{y-4}{3} = \dfrac{z-7}{4}$.

8. Show that the lines $x + y + z - 6 = 0$, $x - 2y + 3z - 4 = 0$ and $2x + y + 2z - 8 = 0$, $x - y + 2z - 3 = 0$ meet in a point.

9. Find the equation of a plane that is perpendicular to the xy-plane and passes through the points $(2, 1, 6)$ and $(8, 3, 4)$.

10. Find the equations of two planes that are perpendicular to the line $\dfrac{x-3}{1} = \dfrac{y-5}{-2} = \dfrac{z+2}{-2}$ and lie at a distance from the origin numerically equal to 2.

11. Find the points in which the line $4x + 3y - z + 10 = 0$, $2x - 2y - 3z - 10 = 0$ intersects the coördinate planes.

12. Find the equation of a plane through the point $(3, 8, -2)$ that is perpendicular to the line $5x + 2y - 3z = 0$, $2x - 9y - z + 11 = 0$.

13. Find the equation of a plane that contains the line $3x - 2y + 2z - 1 = 0$, $5x - 2y + 6z - 4 = 0$ and is perpendicular to the plane $4x + y + z - 1 = 0$.

14. Find the equation of a plane through the point $(2, 1, -4)$ that is parallel to the lines $\dfrac{x+1}{2} = \dfrac{y-5}{3} = \dfrac{z+4}{-6}$ and $\dfrac{x-4}{3} = \dfrac{y-3}{2} = \dfrac{z-7}{1}$.

15. Show that the line $\dfrac{x-3}{2} = \dfrac{y-1}{6} = \dfrac{z+5}{9}$ lies in the plane $6x - 5y + 2z - 3 = 0$.

16. Show geometrically that, if $x_2 = x_1$, the two-point form (199) of the equations of a line should be replaced by $x = x_1$, $\dfrac{y-y_1}{y_2-y_1} = \dfrac{z-z_1}{z_2-z_1}$. Find the corresponding forms if either $y_2 = y_1$ or $z_2 = z_1$.

17. Find the two-point form of the equation of a line if $x_2 = x_1$ and $y_2 = y_1$. Show that this line is parallel to the z-axis.

SELECTED EXERCISES

1. Derive the expression for the distance from the plane $A_1x + B_1y + C_1z + D_1 = 0$ to the point $P_1(x_1, y_1, z_1)$ by determining the coördinates of the foot of the perpendicular from P_1 to the plane and the distance of this point from P_1.

2. Find the point in which the plane through $P_1(x_1, y_1, z_1)$ perpendicular to the line $\dfrac{x-x_2}{a} = \dfrac{y-y_2}{b} = \dfrac{z-z_2}{c}$ meets this line. Hence derive an expression for the distance from this line to the point P_1.

3. Find the equations of the planes that bisect the pairs of vertical dihedral angles formed by the intersecting planes $A_1x + B_1y + C_1z + D_1 = 0$ and $A_2x + B_2y + C_2z + D_2 = 0$.

4. Let the equations of two non-parallel, non-intersecting lines be

$$\frac{x-x_1}{\cos \alpha_1} = \frac{y-y_1}{\cos \beta_1} = \frac{z-z_1}{\cos \gamma_1} \quad \text{and} \quad \frac{x-x_2}{\cos \alpha_2} = \frac{y-y_2}{\cos \beta_2} = \frac{z-z_2}{\cos \gamma_2}.$$

Write the equation of a plane through the first line parallel to the second and of a plane through the second parallel to the first.

5. Show that the distance between the planes found in Ex. 4 is the distance between the given lines, and find this distance.

6. Find the condition that four given planes meet in a point.

7. Find the equation of the plane through three given non-collinear points $P_1(x_1, y_1, z_1)$, $P_2(x_2, y_2, z_2)$, and $P_3(x_3, y_3, z_3)$ and express the result by equating to zero a fourth order determinant.

8. Find the length of the perpendicular from the point $P_4(x_4, y_4, z_4)$ to the plane found in Ex. 7.

9. Using the results of Ex. 8, and of Ex. 6, page 247, show that the volume of the tetrahedron having the points P_1, P_2, P_3, and P_4 as vertices is

$$\frac{1}{6} \begin{vmatrix} x_1 & y_1 & z_1 & 1 \\ x_2 & y_2 & z_2 & 1 \\ x_3 & y_3 & z_3 & 1 \\ x_4 & y_4 & z_4 & 1 \end{vmatrix}$$

CHAPTER XV

TYPES OF SURFACES AND CURVES

In this chapter, we shall discuss certain types of surfaces and of curves in space that are of especial importance in the applications of analytic geometry.

144. The Sphere. A sphere is the locus of a point in space that moves so that its distance from a fixed point, the center, is equal to a constant, the radius.

It follows at once from this definition that the equation of a sphere with center at the point (h, k, l) and radius a is

$$(x - h)^2 + (y - k)^2 + (z - l)^2 = a^2. \qquad (209)$$

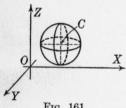

For, the left-hand member of this equation is the square of the distance of the point (x, y, z) on the locus from the center (h, k, l) and this is equal to the square of the radius.

In particular, if the center of the sphere is at the origin, equation (209) reduces to the simple form

Fig. 161

$$x^2 + y^2 + z^2 = a^2. \qquad (210)$$

The equation

$$x^2 + y^2 + z^2 + Gx + Hy + Iz + K = 0 \qquad (211)$$

is called the **general form** of the equation of the sphere.

To determine the center and radius of the sphere defined by equation (211), we complete the square of the terms in x, y, and z, separately, and write the equation in the form

$$\left(x + \frac{G}{2}\right)^2 + \left(y + \frac{H}{2}\right)^2 + \left(z + \frac{I}{2}\right)^2 = \frac{G^2 + H^2 + I^2 - 4K}{4}$$

By comparing this equation with (209), we find that its locus is a sphere with

center $$\left(-\frac{G}{2},\ -\frac{H}{2},\ -\frac{I}{2}\right)$$

and radius $\quad a = \frac{1}{2}\sqrt{G^2 + H^2 + I^2 - 4K}$

The sphere defined by equation (211) is thus a *real sphere*, a *point sphere*, or an *imaginary sphere*, according as

$$G^2 + H^2 + I^2 - 4K \gtreqless 0.$$

EXERCISES

1. Find the equations of the following spheres and their points of intersection with the coördinate axes

(a) Center $(6, 2, 3)$, $\quad a = 7$ $\quad$ (b) Center $(3, -4, 5)$, $a = 9$

(c) Center $(4, 1, -2)$, $a = 5$ $\quad$ (d) Center $(1, -1, 4)$, $a = 10$.

2. Determine the center and radius, and draw the sphere when it exists, given

(a) $x^2 + y^2 + z^2 + 8x - 4y + 6z + 4 = 0$

(b) $x^2 + y^2 + z^2 - 2x + 4y - 8z + 21 = 0$

(c) $x^2 + y^2 + z^2 + 10x + 4y - 6z - 11 = 0$

(d) $x^2 + y^2 + z^2 - 5x + 2y - 3z + 11 = 0$.

3. Find the equation of the sphere

(a) Having the points $(3, 9, 1)$ and $(-1, -3, -5)$ as ends of a diameter

(b) With center at $(3, 7, -5)$ and passing through the point $(5, 1, 4)$

(c) With center at $(4, 1, -7)$ and tangent to the plane $2x - y - 2z + 6 = 0$

(d) That lies in the first quadrant, is tangent to all the coördinate planes, and has its center in the plane $x - 3y + 4z - 6 = 0$

(e) That passes through the points $(0, 0, 0)$, $(3, 0, 0)$, $(1, 2, 1)$, and $(4, 3, 2)$

(f) That passes through the points $(1, -1, 1)$, $(-2, 0, 1)$, $(0, -4, 5)$, and $(1, -4, 4)$

(g) That passes through the points $(2, 1, 4)$ and $(1, 3, -5)$ and has its center on the line $x + y + 5z - 3 = 0$, $2x - 4y + 3z - 1 = 0$.

4. Write the equation, in cylindrical coördinates, of a sphere of radius a having its center at the point

    (a) $(0, 0, 0)$ (b) $(0, 0, a)$ (c) $(a, 0, 0)$.

5. Write the equations of the spheres in Ex. 4 in spherical coördinates.

6. Show that, for all values of θ and ϕ, the point

$$x = a \sin \phi \cos \theta, \quad y = a \sin \phi \sin \theta, \quad z = a \cos \phi$$

lies on the sphere $x^2 + y^2 + z^2 = a^2$.

Note. The above three equations are called the *parametric equations* of this sphere in terms of the parameters θ and ϕ.

145. Quadric Surfaces. The locus of an equation of the second degree in x, y, and z, that is, an equation of the form

$$Ax^2 + By^2 + Cz^2 + Dyz + Ezx + Fxy + Gx + Hy + Iz + K = 0,$$

wherein A, B, C, D, E, and F are not all zero, is called a *quadric surface*.

It is seen at once from equation (211) that a sphere is a quadric surface. In the following articles, we shall state the standard forms of the equations of the most important quadric surfaces other than the sphere, and point out a few of the outstanding properties of these surfaces.

146. The Ellipsoid. The locus of the equation

$$\frac{x^2}{a^2} + \frac{y^2}{b^2} + \frac{z^2}{c^2} = 1$$

is an *ellipsoid*.

This surface is symmetric with respect to each of the coördinate planes since, if we change the sign of any one of the coördinates, we do not change the equation. These planes are called the *principal planes* of the ellipsoid and their point of intersection, the origin, is its *center*.

The segments of the coördinate axes that lie inside the surface are the *axes* of the ellipsoid. By solving the equations of the axes as simultaneous with that of the surface, we find that the intercepts on the x-, y-, and z-axis are, respectively, $\pm a$, $\pm b$, and $\pm c$. If $a > b > c > 0$, these numbers are called the lengths of the *semi-major*, the *semi-mean*, and the *semi-minor axis*, respectively, of the ellipsoid.

The usual way to determine the form of a surface from its equation is to study the curves of section of the surface by a

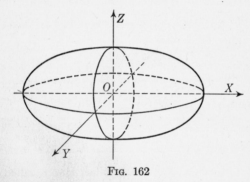

FIG. 162

family of parallel planes. For the ellipsoid, we shall use the sections by planes perpendicular to the z-axis.

The equations of the section of the given ellipsoid by a plane $z = k$ are found, by putting $z = k$ in the equation and simplifying, to be

$$\frac{x^2}{a^2} + \frac{y^2}{b^2} = 1 - \frac{k^2}{c^2}, \quad z = k,$$

or, if $k \neq \pm c$,

$$\frac{x^2}{\frac{a^2}{c^2}(c^2 - k^2)} + \frac{y^2}{\frac{b^2}{c^2}(c^2 - k^2)} = 1, \quad z = k.$$

If $k^2 < c^2$, these are the equations of an ellipse of semi-axes $\frac{a}{c}\sqrt{c^2 - k^2}$ and $\frac{b}{c}\sqrt{c^2 - k^2}$. The largest ellipse of section is thus in the plane $z = 0$. As k increases in numerical value, the ellipse of section becomes smaller and shrinks to a point when $k^2 = c^2$. If $k^2 > c^2$, the ellipse is imaginary; that is, there are no points on the surface in any plane defined by such a value of k.

If $a = b > c$, the ellipsoid is called an **oblate spheroid** and, if $a > b = c$, it is a **prolate spheroid**.

Exercise 1. Discuss the sections of the ellipsoid by the planes $x = k$.

Exercise 2. Given that the surface of the earth is an oblate spheroid with equatorial semi-axes of 3963 miles and polar semi-axis of 3950 miles, choose a suitable set of axes and write the equation of this spheroid.

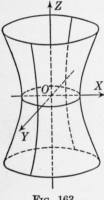

147. The Hyperboloid of One Sheet. The surface defined by the equation

$$\frac{x^2}{a^2} + \frac{y^2}{b^2} - \frac{z^2}{c^2} = 1$$

is a *hyperboloid of one sheet*.

This surface also has the coördinate planes as planes of symmetry (Why?), or *principal planes*, and the origin as *center*. It intersects the x-axis at $(\pm\, a, 0, 0)$ and

Fig. 163

the y-axis at $(0, \pm\, b, 0)$ but it has no point in common with the z-axis. (Why?)

The section of this hyperboloid by the plane $z = k$ is the ellipse defined by the equations

$$\frac{x^2}{a^2} + \frac{y^2}{b^2} = 1 + \frac{k^2}{c^2}, \quad z = k.$$

This ellipse is smallest for $k = 0$ and increases indefinitely in size as the numerical value of k increases. The surface thus extends indefinitely far from the origin.

Exercise 1. Show that the sections of the hyperboloid of one sheet by the planes $x = k$, when $k \neq \pm a$, are hyperbolas. Locate, and find the lengths of, the transverse and conjugate axes. What are the curves of section by the planes $x = \pm a$?

Exercise 2. Discuss, as in Ex. 1, the sections of the hyperboloid of one sheet by the planes $y = k$.

148. The Hyperboloid of Two Sheets. This name is given to the locus of the equation

$$\frac{x^2}{a^2} - \frac{y^2}{b^2} - \frac{z^2}{c^2} = 1.$$

This surface has the coördinate planes as *principal planes* and the origin as *center*. Its x-intercepts are $\pm a$ but it does not meet either of the other coördinate axes.

The equation of its curve of section by the plane $x = k$ are

$$\frac{y^2}{b^2} + \frac{z^2}{c^2} = \frac{k^2}{a^2} - 1, \qquad x = k.$$

If $k^2 < a^2$, this curve is an imaginary ellipse and has no points on it. If $k^2 = a^2$, the curve is a point ellipse and, if $k^2 > a^2$,

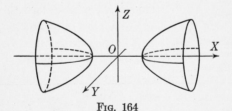

Fig. 164

the curve is a real ellipse which increases indefinitely in size as k^2 increases indefinitely. The surface thus consists of two distinct parts which extend indefinitely far away from the yz-plane.

Exercise. Discuss the sections of the hyperboloid of two sheets by the plane $y = k$ and by the plane $z = k$. Find the coördinates of the vertices and the foci and the equations of the asymptotes.

149. The Elliptic Paraboloid. The locus of the equation

$$\frac{x^2}{a^2} + \frac{y^2}{b^2} = z$$

is an *elliptic paraboloid*.

The surface is symmetric with respect to the xz- and yz-planes but not with respect to the xy-plane. It has no center.

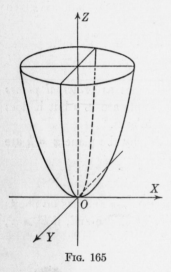

It touches the xy-plane at the origin but does not extend below it.

The section of this surface by the plane $z = k$, when $k > 0$, is an ellipse whose semi-axes are $a\sqrt{k}$ and $b\sqrt{k}$. This ellipse thus increases indefinitely in size as k increases. The sections of the surface by planes perpendicular to the x-axis, or to the y-axis, are parabolas.

Exercise. Show that the latera recta of the parabolas of section of the elliptic paraboloid by the family of planes $y = k$ are equal.

Fig. 165

150. The Hyperbolic Paraboloid. The surface

$$\frac{x^2}{a^2} - \frac{y^2}{b^2} = z$$

is a *hyperbolic paraboloid*.

It has the xz- and yz-planes as principal planes, passes through the origin, and has no other points in common with any of the coördinate axes. It has no center.

Its section by the xy-plane is composed of the two lines $y = \pm \dfrac{bx}{a}$, $z = 0$. The planes $z = k$ parallel to the xy-plane intersect it in hyperbolas that have their transverse axes parallel to the x-axis if $k > 0$ and parallel to the y-axis if $k < 0$. The planes $y = k$ intersect the surface in parabolas which are concave upward; the planes $x = k$, in parabolas which are concave downward.

If $a = b$, the surface is said to be a **rectangular hyperbolic paraboloid**. In this special case, the equation of the surface may be written in the form

$$x^2 - y^2 = a^2 z. \tag{212}$$

If we now rotate the x- and y-axes, in their own plane, through an angle of $- 45°$ by means of the equations (97) of a

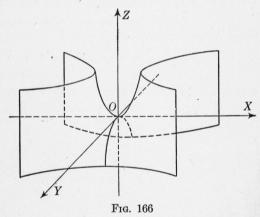

Fig. 166

rotation of axes; that is, if we apply to x and y the transformation

$$x = \frac{x'}{\sqrt{2}} + \frac{y'}{\sqrt{2}}, \quad y = \frac{- x'}{\sqrt{2}} + \frac{y'}{\sqrt{2}}$$

equation (212) reduces to

$$2x'y' = a^2 z'. \tag{213}$$

In the applications of solid analytic geometry, the equation of the rectangular hyperbolic paraboloid is frequently encountered in this form.

151. The Quadric Cone. The surface defined by the equation

$$\frac{x^2}{a^2} + \frac{y^2}{b^2} = \frac{z^2}{c^2}$$

is symmetric with respect to each of the coördinate planes. Its

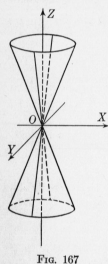

FIG. 167

trace in the yz-plane consists of the two lines $y = \pm \dfrac{bz}{c}$, $x = 0$ and, in the xz-plane, of the two lines $x = \pm \dfrac{az}{c}$, $y = 0$. Its intersection with the xy-plane is a single point, the origin. The section of the surface by any plane $z = k$, parallel to the xy-plane is an ellipse the lengths of whose semi-axes, $\dfrac{ak}{c}$ and $\dfrac{bk}{c}$, are proportional to the distance of the plane from the xy-plane. This surface is a cone with vertex at the origin and axis coinciding with the z-axis. It is called a **quadric cone**.

If $a \neq b$, the quadric cone is also called an *oblique circular cone* and if $a = b$, so that the sections perpendicular to the z-axis are circles, it is a *right circular cone*.

EXERCISES

Sketch the following surfaces and state, in each case, the name of the surface:

1. $\dfrac{x^2}{4} + \dfrac{y^2}{9} + \dfrac{z^2}{25} = 1$

2. $x^2 - \dfrac{y^2}{4} + \dfrac{z^2}{16} = 1$

3. $36x^2 - 9y^2 + 4z^2 = 144$

4. $5x^2 + 2y^2 + 15z^2 = 60$

5. $xy = z$

6. $4y^2 - 9z^2 = 36x$

7. $x^2 + y^2 = z$

8. $x^2 + y^2 = z^2$

9. $3x^2 - 6y^2 - 2z^2 = 12$

10. $x^2 - 4z^2 = y$

11. $x^2 - 2y^2 - z^2 = -1$

12. $4x^2 = 100z + 25y^2$

13. $2x^2 + 3y^2 - z^2 = -1$

14. $9x^2 + z^2 = 4y^2$

15. $9x^2 + 16z^2 = 144y$

16. $3x^2 = y - 5z^2$

17. Show that, if $P_1(x_1, y_1, z_1)$ is any point, other than the origin, on the quadric cone $\dfrac{x^2}{a^2} + \dfrac{y^2}{b^2} = \dfrac{z^2}{c^2}$, then every point on the line through P_1 and the origin also lies on this surface.

18. Show that, for any given value of k, the line of intersection of the planes (a) $\dfrac{x}{a} - \dfrac{y}{b} = k$, $z = k\left(\dfrac{x}{a} + \dfrac{y}{b}\right)$, (b) $\dfrac{x}{a} + \dfrac{y}{b} = k$, $z = k\left(\dfrac{x}{a} - \dfrac{y}{b}\right)$ lies on the hyperbolic paraboloid $\dfrac{x^2}{a^2} - \dfrac{y^2}{b^2} = z$.

19. Show that, for any given value of k, the line of intersection of the planes (a) $\dfrac{x}{a} - \dfrac{z}{c} = k\left(1 + \dfrac{y}{b}\right)$, $1 - \dfrac{y}{b} = k\left(\dfrac{x}{a} + \dfrac{z}{c}\right)$, (b) $\dfrac{x}{a} - \dfrac{z}{c} = k\left(1 - \dfrac{y}{b}\right)$, $1 + \dfrac{y}{b} = k\left(\dfrac{x}{a} + \dfrac{z}{c}\right)$ lies on the hyperboloid of one sheet $\dfrac{x^2}{a^2} + \dfrac{y^2}{b^2} - \dfrac{z^2}{c^2} = 1$.

Note. The family of lines defined by the two equations in Ex. 18a, 18b, 19a, or 19b is called a *regulus*.

152. Cylinders. A surface generated by a line which moves so that it is always parallel to a fixed line and always intersects a fixed curve is called a **cylinder**. Any position of the generating line is an *element* of the cylinder and the fixed curve which all of these elements intersect is the directrix curve.

In elementary solid geometry, special attention is given to the circular cylinders; that is, to cylinders that have circles as directrix curves. Although the circular cylinders are included among the surfaces we shall study, most of the cylinders that will be considered in this course are not circular cylinders.

Consider, for example, the locus in space defined by the equation

$$b^2x^2 + a^2y^2 = a^2b^2. \tag{214}$$

The trace of this surface on the xy-plane is the ellipse

$$b^2x^2 + a^2y^2 = a^2b^2, \qquad z = 0. \tag{215}$$

Let $P'(x, y, 0)$ be any point on this ellipse. Draw through P' a line parallel to the z-axis and let $P(x, y, z)$ be any point on this line. Then the x- and y-coördinates of P are equal,

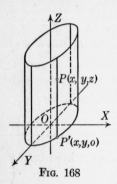

Fig. 168

respectively, to those of P'. (Why?) By hypothesis, the coördinates of P' satisfy equations (215) and, since z does not occur in the first of these equations at all, it follows that the coördinates of P will satisfy equation (214); that is, every point P on the line through P' parallel to the z-axis lies on the locus of equation (214).

If we now let P' describe the ellipse (215), the line $P'P$ will describe a cylinder which has the ellipse (215) as directrix curve and elements parallel to the z-axis. The coördinates of every point on this cylinder (and no others) satisfy equation (214). Hence, this cylinder is the required locus. It is called an **elliptic cylinder**.

If $a \neq b$, the elliptic cylinder is also called an *oblique circular cylinder*. If $a = b$, the sections perpendicular to the z-axis are circles and the surface is a *right circular cylinder*.

Let us now consider the locus in space defined by the equation

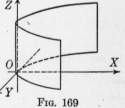

Fig. 169

$$y^2 = 2px. \qquad (216)$$

Using the same reasoning as before, we find that a point $P(x, y, z)$ will lie on this surface if, and only if, the line through it parallel to the z-axis intersects the xy-plane in a point $P'(x, y, 0)$ that lies on the parabola

$$y^2 = 2px, \qquad z = 0. \qquad (217)$$

The surface defined by equation (216) is thus a cylinder having its elements parallel to the z-axis and having the parab-

ola (217) as directrix curve. It is called a **parabolic cylinder**
(Fig. 169).

By extending the reasoning used in the preceding two examples, we are led to the following theorem: *If the equation of
a surface does not contain the variable z, then the surface is a
cylinder with elements parallel to the z-axis and having the curve of
section by the plane z = 0 as directrix curve.* Similarly, if *y*, or *x*,
is absent from the equation, then the surface is a cylinder with
elements parallel to the *y*-axis, or the *x*-axis, respectively.

EXERCISES

Sketch the cylinders defined by the following equations:

1. $x^2 + y^2 = 9$ **2.** $9x^2 - y^2 = 36$

3. $25x^2 + 16z^2 = 400$ **4.** $2xz = a^2$

5. $y^2 + z^2 = 4y$ **6.** $z = y^3$

7. $\pm x^{\frac{1}{2}} \pm y^{\frac{1}{2}} = a^{\frac{1}{2}}$ **8.** $x^2 = z^3$

9. $y = e^x$ **10.** $z = \sin x$

Sketch the surfaces whose equations in cylindrical coördinates
are:

11. $r = a \cos \theta$ **12.** $r^2 \cos 2\theta = a^2$

13. $r^2 = a^2 \cos 2\theta$ **14.** $r = a(1 - \cos \theta)$

153. Surfaces of Revolution. The surface generated by revolving a plane curve about a line in its plane is a **surface
of revolution**. The line about which this curve revolves is the
axis of revolution and any position of the revolving curve is a
meridian section.

Let us find, for example, the equation of the right circular
cone generated by revolving the line defined by the equations

$$x = cz, \qquad y = 0 \tag{218}$$

around the *z*-axis.

Let $P_1(x_1, 0, z_1)$ be any point on the given line and let
$N_1(0, 0, z_1)$ be the foot of the perpendicular from P_1 to the
z-axis. As the given line revolves around the *z*-axis, P_1 describes

a circle with center at N_1, radius N_1P_1, and lying in a plane perpendicular to the z-axis (Fig. 170).

Let $P(x, y, z)$ be any point on this circle. Since it lies in a

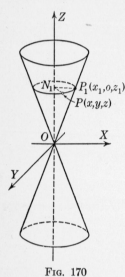

plane through P_1 parallel to the xy-plane, we have

$$z = z_1.$$

Since it also lies on a circle with center at N_1 and radius $N_1P = N_1P_1 = x_1$, we have further

$$\sqrt{x^2 + y^2} = x_1.$$

Since P_1 lies on the line (218), it follows that

$$x_1 = cz_1$$

and, on substituting in this equation the values already found for x_1 and z_1, we obtain

$$\sqrt{x^2 + y^2} = cz, \quad \text{or} \quad x^2 + y^2 = c^2z^2,$$

which is the required equation of the right circular cone. (Compare Art. 151.)

Fig. 170

As a second example of a surface of revolution, let us derive the equation of a sphere as the surface of revolution generated by revolving a circle about one of its diameters.

Consider the circle in the xy-plane

$$x^2 + y^2 = a^2, \qquad z = 0. \tag{219}$$

Let us find the equation of the sphere generated by revolving this circle about the y-axis.

Let $P_1(x_1, y_1, 0)$ be any point on the circle (219), let $M(0, y_1, 0)$ be the foot of the perpendicular from P_1 to the y-axis, and let $P(x, y, z)$ be any point on the circle described by P_1 as it revolves around the y-axis.

By the same reasoning that we used in the preceding example, we find that

$$y = y_1, \qquad \sqrt{x^2 + z^2} = x_1.$$

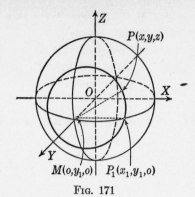

Fig. 171

Since P_1 lies on the circle (219), we have

$$x_1^2 + y_1^2 = a^2$$

and, after substituting the values of x_1 and y_1 from the preceding equations in this one, we have

$$(\sqrt{x^2 + z^2})^2 + y^2 = a^2,$$

or $$x^2 + y^2 + z^2 = a^2.$$

This is the equation of a sphere (Art. 144) with center at the origin and radius equal to a, the radius of the generating circle.

EXERCISES

Find the equation of the surface of revolution generated by revolving the given curve about the line indicated. Sketch the surface and, when possible, state its name.

1. $x^2 + z^2 = a^2,$ $y = 0,$ x-axis
2. $bz + ay = ab$ $x = 0,$ y-axis
3. $x^2 = 4z,$ $y = 0,$ z-axis
4. $x^2 = 4z,$ $y = 0,$ x-axis
5. $\dfrac{x^2}{a^2} + \dfrac{y^2}{b^2} = 1,$ $z = 0,$ y-axis
6. $\dfrac{x^2}{a^2} - \dfrac{z^2}{b^2} = 1,$ $y = 0,$ z-axis

7. $x = e^z$, $y = 0$, x-axis

8. $z^2 = x^3 - x$ $y = 0$, x-axis

9. $x^2 = z^3$, $y = 0$, z-axis

10. $y = \cos x$, $z = 0$, x-axis.

11. Write (a) in cylindrical coördinates, (b) in spherical coördinates, the equations of the surfaces in Ex. 3, 6, and 9.

154. Curves in Space. We have seen (Art. 136) that the position of a line in space is defined by considering simultaneously the equations of two planes that intersect in this line. Similarly, if a curve in space is the intersection of two surfaces, we take the equations of these two surfaces, considered simultaneously, as the equations defining this curve.

Thus, the first of the two equations

$$x^2 + y^2 + z^2 = 16, \qquad x + 2y + 3z = 6 \qquad (220)$$

is the equation of a sphere and the second, of a plane that intersects this sphere in a circle. The two equations taken simultaneously are, accordingly, the equations of this circle.

If, between the two equations of a curve, we eliminate successively x, y, and z, we obtain the equations of three cylinders (Art. 152) whose elements are perpendicular to the yz-, zx-, and xy-planes, respectively. These cylinders are called the **projecting cylinders** of the given curve on these three planes.

The projecting cylinders of the circle (220), for example, on the coördinate planes are found, by solving the second equation for x, y, and z successively and substituting in the first equation, to be

$$(6 - 2y - 3z)^2 + y^2 + z^2 = 16$$

$$x^2 + \left(3 - \frac{x}{2} - \frac{3z}{2}\right)^2 + z^2 = 16$$

$$x^2 + y^2 + \left(2 - \frac{x}{3} - \frac{2y}{3}\right)^2 = 16.$$

155. Parametric Equations of a Curve in Space. A second way of defining a curve in space, which is often more convenient than the one given in Art. 154, is to express the coördinates of the points on it in terms of a parameter. Thus

$$x = f_1(t), \qquad y = f_2(t), \qquad z = f_3(t)$$

are the parametric equations of a curve in space in terms of the parameter t.

For example, we have seen (Art. 139) that the equations

$$x = x_1 + ak, \qquad y = y_1 + bk, \qquad z = z_1 + ck$$

are parametric equations, in terms of the parameter k, of the line through the point (x_1, y_1, z_1) having the direction numbers a, b, c.

Similarly, the equations,

$$x = a (\sin \alpha \cos \phi - \cos \alpha \cos \beta \sin \phi)$$
$$y = a (\cos \alpha \cos \phi + \sin \alpha \cos \beta \sin \phi)$$
$$z = a \sin \beta \sin \phi,$$

wherein ϕ is the parameter, are parametric equations of a circle with center at the origin and radius a. For, by substituting the values of x, y, and z from the given equations in the following two equations, and simplifying, the student may readily verify that, for all values of ϕ, the points defined by the parametric equations lie in the plane

$$x \cos \alpha \sin \beta - y \sin \alpha \sin \beta + z \cos \beta = 0$$

and on the sphere

$$x^2 + y^2 + z^2 = a^2,$$

so that the locus of the given parametric equations is the circle of intersection of this plane with the sphere. Since the plane passes through the origin, which is the center of the sphere, the center of the circle is at the origin and its radius is a, the radius of the sphere.

The helix. As a third example, consider the curve defined by the parametric equations,

$$x = a \cos \phi \qquad y = a \sin \phi \qquad z = b\phi,$$

wherein ϕ is the parameter. This curve is called a **helix**. It winds around, and ascends, the right circular cylinder $x^2 + y^2 = a^2$ like the thread on a bolt, or the handrailing on a circular staircase.

EXERCISES

1. Draw the graph of the helix $x = 5 \cos \phi$, $y = 5 \sin \cdot \phi$, $z = \phi$ from $\phi = 0$ to $\phi = 6\pi$.

Sketch the following curves and find the equations of their projecting cylinders on the coördinate planes.

2. $x^2 + y^2 = a^2$, $\qquad z = y$

3. $x^2 + y^2 = z$, $\qquad z = 2y$

4. $x^2 + z^2 = a^2$, $\qquad y^2 + z^2 = a^2$

5. $x^2 + y^2 + z^2 = a^2$, $\quad x^2 + y^2 = a^2$

6. $x^2 + y^2 + z^2 = a^2$, $\quad x^2 + y^2 = 2ax$

7. $x^2 + y^2 + z^2 = 2a^2$, $\quad x^2 + y^2 = az$

Sketch the following curves and find, for each of them, the equations of two surfaces that contain the curve.

8. $x = 1 - 2t$, $\quad y = t$, $\qquad z = t^2$

9. $x = a \cos \phi$, $\quad y = a \sin \phi$, $\quad z = 2a \sin \phi$

10. $x = a \cos^2 \phi$, $\quad y = b \sin^2 \phi$, $\quad z = c \cos \phi$

11. $x = t$, $\qquad\quad y = t^2$, $\qquad z = t^3$

12. $x = a \cos \phi$, $\quad y = b \sin \phi$, $\quad z = c\phi$

13. $x = \phi \cos \phi$, $\quad y = \phi \sin \phi$, $\quad z = a\phi$

TABLES

TABLE I. FOUR–PLACE LOGARITHMS

N	0	1	2	3	4	5	6	7	8	9
10	0000	0043	0086	0128	0170	0212	0253	0294	0334	0374
11	0414	0453	0492	0531	0569	0607	0645	0682	0719	0755
12	0792	0828	0864	0899	0934	0969	1004	1038	1072	1106
13	1139	1173	1206	1239	1271	1303	1335	1367	1399	1430
14	1461	1492	1523	1553	1584	1614	1644	1673	1703	1732
15	1761	1790	1818	1847	1875	1903	1931	1959	1987	2014
16	2041	2068	2095	2122	2148	2175	2201	2227	2253	2279
17	2304	2330	2355	2380	2405	2430	2455	2480	2504	2529
18	2553	2577	2601	2625	2648	2672	2695	2718	2742	2765
19	2788	2810	2833	2856	2878	2900	2923	2945	2967	2989
20	3010	3032	3054	3075	3096	3118	3139	3160	3181	3201
21	3222	3243	3263	3284	3304	3324	3345	3365	3385	3404
22	3424	3444	3464	3483	3502	3522	3541	3560	3579	3598
23	3617	3636	3655	3674	3692	3711	3729	3747	3766	3784
24	3802	3820	3838	3856	3874	3892	3909	3927	3945	3962
25	3979	3997	4014	4031	4048	4065	4082	4099	4116	4133
26	4150	4166	4183	4200	4216	4232	4249	4265	4281	4298
27	4314	4330	4346	4362	4378	4393	4409	4425	4440	4456
28	4472	4487	4502	4518	4533	4548	4564	4579	4594	4609
29	4624	4639	4654	4669	4683	4698	4713	4728	4742	4757
30	4771	4786	4800	4814	4829	4843	4857	4871	4886	4900
31	4914	4928	4942	4955	4969	4983	4997	5011	5024	5038
32	5051	5065	5079	5092	5105	5119	5132	5145	5159	5172
33	5185	5198	5211	5224	5237	5250	5263	5276	5289	5302
34	5315	5328	5340	5353	5366	5378	5391	5403	5416	5428
35	5441	5453	5465	5478	5490	5502	5514	5527	5539	5551
36	5563	5575	5587	5599	5611	5623	5635	5647	5658	5670
37	5682	5694	5705	5717	5729	5740	5752	5763	5775	5786
38	5798	5809	5821	5832	5843	5855	5866	5877	5888	5899
39	5911	5922	5933	5944	5955	5966	5977	5988	5999	6010
40	6021	6031	6042	6053	6064	6075	6085	6096	6107	6117
41	6128	6138	6149	6160	6170	6180	6191	6201	6212	6222
42	6232	6243	6253	6263	6274	6284	6294	6304	6314	6325
43	6335	6345	6355	6365	6375	6385	6395	6405	6415	6425
44	6435	6444	6454	6464	6474	6484	6493	6503	6513	6522
45	6532	6542	6551	6561	6571	6580	6590	6599	6609	6618
46	6628	6637	6646	6656	6665	6675	6684	6693	6702	6712
47	6721	6730	6739	6749	6758	6767	6776	6785	6794	6803
48	6812	6821	6830	6839	6848	6857	6866	6875	6884	6893
49	6902	6911	6920	6928	6937	6946	6955	6964	6972	6981
50	6990	6998	7007	7016	7024	7033	7042	7050	7059	7067
51	7076	7084	7093	7101	7110	7118	7126	7135	7143	7152
52	7160	7168	7177	7185	7193	7202	7210	7218	7226	7235
53	7243	7251	7259	7267	7275	7284	7292	7300	7308	7316
54	7324	7332	7340	7348	7356	7364	7372	7380	7388	7396

TABLE I. FOUR–PLACE LOGARITHMS *Continued*

N	0	1	2	3	4	5	6	7	8	9
55	7404	7412	7419	7427	7435	7443	7451	7459	7466	7474
56	7482	7490	7497	7505	7513	7520	7528	7536	7543	7551
57	7559	7566	7574	7582	7589	7597	7604	7612	7619	7627
58	7634	7642	7649	7657	7664	7672	7679	7686	7694	7701
59	7709	7716	7723	7731	7738	7745	7752	7760	7767	7774
60	7782	7789	7796	7803	7810	7818	7825	7832	7839	7846
61	7853	7860	7868	7875	7882	7889	7896	7903	7910	7917
62	7924	7931	7938	7945	7952	7959	7966	7973	7980	7987
63	7993	8000	8007	8014	8021	8028	8035	8041	8048	8055
64	8062	8069	8075	8082	8089	8096	8102	8109	8116	8122
65	8129	8136	8142	8149	8156	8162	8169	8176	8182	8189
66	8195	8202	8209	8215	8222	8228	8235	8241	8248	8254
67	8261	8267	8274	8280	8287	8293	8299	8306	8312	8319
68	8325	8331	8338	8344	8351	8357	8363	8370	8376	8382
69	8388	8395	8401	8407	8414	8420	8426	8432	8439	8445
70	8451	8457	8463	8470	8476	8482	8488	8494	8500	8506
71	8513	8519	8525	8531	8537	8543	8549	8555	8561	8567
72	8573	8579	8585	8591	8597	8603	8609	8615	8621	8627
73	8633	8639	8645	8651	8657	8663	8669	8675	8681	8686
74	8692	8698	8704	8710	8716	8722	8727	8733	8739	8745
75	8751	8756	8762	8768	8774	8779	8785	8791	8797	8802
76	8808	8814	8820	8825	8831	8837	8842	8848	8854	8859
77	8865	8871	8876	8882	8887	8893	8899	8904	8910	8915
78	8921	8927	8932	8938	8943	8949	8954	8960	8965	8971
79	8976	8982	8987	8993	8998	9004	9009	9015	9020	9025
80	9031	9036	9042	9047	9053	9058	9063	9069	9074	9079
81	9085	9090	9096	9101	9106	9112	9117	9122	9128	9133
82	9138	9143	9149	9154	9159	9165	9170	9175	9180	9186
83	9191	9196	9201	9206	9212	9217	9222	9227	9232	9238
84	9243	9248	9253	9258	9263	9269	9274	9279	9284	9289
85	9294	9299	9304	9309	9315	9320	9325	9330	9335	9340
86	9345	9350	9355	9360	9365	9370	9375	9380	9385	9390
87	9395	9400	9405	9410	9415	9420	9425	9430	9435	9440
88	9445	9450	9455	9460	9465	9469	9474	9479	9484	9489
89	9494	9499	9504	9509	9513	9518	9523	9528	9533	9538
90	9542	9547	9552	9557	9562	9566	9571	9576	9581	9586
91	9590	9595	9600	9605	9609	9614	9619	9624	9628	9633
92	9638	9643	9647	9652	9657	9661	9666	9671	9675	9680
93	9685	9689	9694	9699	9703	9708	9713	9717	9722	9727
94	9731	9736	9741	9745	9750	9754	9759	9763	9768	9773
95	9777	9782	9786	9791	9795	9800	9805	9809	9814	9818
96	9823	9827	9832	9836	9841	9845	9850	9854	9859	9863
97	9868	9872	9877	9881	9886	9890	9894	9899	9903	9908
98	9912	9917	9921	9926	9930	9934	9939	9943	9948	9952
99	9956	9961	9965	9969	9974	9978	9983	9987	9991	9996

TABLE II. NATURAL TRIGONOMETRIC FUNCTIONS

Radians	Degrees	Sine	Tangent	Cotangent	Cosine		
.0000	0	.0000	.0000	——	1.0000	90	1.5708
.0175	1	.0175	.0175	57.290	.9998	89	1.5533
.0349	2	.0349	.0349	28.636	.9994	88	1.5359
.0524	3	.0523	.0524	19.081	.9986	87	1.5184
.0698	4	.0698	.0699	14.301	.9976	86	1.5010
.0873	5	.0872	.0875	11.430	.9962	85	1.4835
.1047	6	.1045	.1051	9.5144	.9945	84	1.4661
.1222	7	.1219	.1228	8.1443	.9925	83	1.4486
.1396	8	.1392	.1405	7.1154	.9903	82	1.4312
.1571	9	.1564	.1584	6.3138	.9877	81	1.4137
.1745	10	.1736	.1763	5.6713	.9848	80	1.3963
.1920	11	.1908	.1944	5.1446	.9816	79	1.3788
.2094	12	.2079	.2126	4.7046	.9781	78	1.3614
.2269	13	.2250	.2309	4.3315	.9744	77	1.3439
.2443	14	.2419	.2493	4.0108	.9703	76	1.3265
.2618	15	.2588	.2679	3.7321	.9659	75	1.3090
.2793	16	.2756	.2867	3.4874	.9613	74	1.2915
.2967	17	.2924	.3057	3.2709	.9563	73	1.2741
.3142	18	.3090	.3249	3.0777	.9511	72	1.2566
.3316	19	.3256	.3443	2.9042	.9455	71	1.2392
.3491	20	.3420	.3640	2.7475	.9397	70	1.2217
.3665	21	.3584	.3839	2.6051	.9336	69	1.2043
.3840	22	.3746	.4040	2.4751	.9272	68	1.1868
.4014	23	.3907	.4245	2.3559	.9205	67	1.1694
.4189	24	.4067	.4452	2.2460	.9135	66	1.1519
.4363	25	.4226	.4663	2.1445	.9063	65	1.1345
.4538	26	.4384	.4877	2.0503	.8988	64	1.1170
.4712	27	.4540	.5095	1.9626	.8910	63	1.0996
.4887	28	.4695	.5317	1.8807	.8829	62	1.0821
.5061	29	.4848	.5543	1.8040	.8746	61	1.0647
.5236	30	.5000	.5774	1.7321	.8660	60	1.0472
.5411	31	.5150	.6009	1.6643	.8572	59	1.0297
.5585	32	.5299	.6249	1.6003	.8480	58	1.0123
.5760	33	.5446	.6494	1.5399	.8387	57	.9948
.5934	34	.5592	.6745	1.4826	.8290	56	.9774
.6109	35	.5736	.7002	1.4281	.8192	55	.9599
.6283	36	.5878	.7265	1.3764	.8090	54	.9425
.6458	37	.6018	.7536	1.3270	.7986	53	.9250
.6632	38	.6157	.7813	1.2799	.7880	52	.9076
.6807	39	.6293	.8098	1.2349	.7771	51	.8901
.6981	40	.6428	.8391	1.1918	.7660	50	.8727
.7156	41	.6561	.8693	1.1504	.7547	49	.8552
.7330	42	.6691	.9004	1.1106	.7431	48	.8378
.7505	43	.6820	.9325	1.0724	.7314	47	.8203
.7679	44	.6947	.9657	1.0355	.7193	46	.8029
.7854	45	.7071	1.0000	1.0000	.7071	45	.7854
		Cosine	Cotangent	Tangent	Sine	Degrees	Radians

TABLE III. EXACT VALUES OF TRIGONOMETRIC FUNCTIONS OF CERTAIN ANGLES

Radians	Degrees	Sine	Cosine	Tangent	Cotangent	Secant	Cosecant
0	0	0	1	0	——	1	——
$\frac{1}{6}\pi$	30	$\frac{1}{2}$	$\frac{1}{2}\sqrt{3}$	$\frac{1}{3}\sqrt{3}$	$\sqrt{3}$	$\frac{2}{3}\sqrt{3}$	2
$\frac{1}{4}\pi$	45	$\frac{1}{2}\sqrt{2}$	$\frac{1}{2}\sqrt{2}$	1	1	$\sqrt{2}$	$\sqrt{2}$
$\frac{1}{3}\pi$	60	$\frac{1}{2}\sqrt{3}$	$\frac{1}{2}$	$\sqrt{3}$	$\frac{1}{3}\sqrt{3}$	2	$\frac{2}{3}\sqrt{3}$
$\frac{1}{2}\pi$	90	1	0	——	0	——	1
$\frac{2}{3}\pi$	120	$\frac{1}{2}\sqrt{3}$	$-\frac{1}{2}$	$-\sqrt{3}$	$-\frac{1}{3}\sqrt{3}$	-2	$\frac{2}{3}\sqrt{3}$
$\frac{3}{4}\pi$	135	$\frac{1}{2}\sqrt{2}$	$-\frac{1}{2}\sqrt{2}$	-1	-1	$-\sqrt{2}$	$\sqrt{2}$
$\frac{5}{6}\pi$	150	$\frac{1}{2}$	$-\frac{1}{2}\sqrt{3}$	$-\frac{1}{3}\sqrt{3}$	$-\sqrt{3}$	$-\frac{2}{3}\sqrt{3}$	2
π	180	0	-1	0	——	-1	——

TABLE IV. SQUARE ROOTS

N	0	1	2	3	4	5	6	7	8	9
0	0.00	1.00	1.41	1.73	2.00	2.24	2.45	2.65	2.83	3.00
1	3.16	3.32	3.46	3.61	3.74	3.87	4.00	4.12	4.24	4.36
2	4.47	4.58	4.69	4.80	4.90	5.00	5.10	5.20	5.29	5.39
3	5.48	5.57	5.66	5.74	5.83	5.92	6.00	6.08	6.16	6.24
4	6.32	6.40	6.48	6.56	6.63	6.71	6.78	6.86	6.93	7.00
5	7.07	7.14	7.21	7.28	7.35	7.42	7.48	7.55	7.62	7.68
6	7.75	7.81	7.87	7.94	8.00	8.06	8.12	8.19	8.25	8.31
7	8.37	8.43	8.49	8.54	8.60	8.66	8.72	8.77	8.83	8.89
8	8.94	9.00	9.06	9.11	9.17	9.22	9.27	9.33	9.38	9.43
9	9.49	9.54	9.59	9.64	9.70	9.75	9.80	9.85	9.90	9.95

ANSWERS

(The answers to many of the exercises are omitted to enable the student to acquire independence in his work and to afford him practice in checking his own results.)

Pages 5, 6

4. (a) 18; (b) $\frac{15}{2}$.   **6.** (3, 5).

7. $\sqrt{29}$.   **9.** (5, 5), $(-5, 5)$, $(-5, -5)$, $(5, -5)$.

15. $(1, \sqrt{3})$.

Page 13

1. (2, 1).   **3.** $(2, \frac{1}{2})$.

5. $\left(\dfrac{107}{76}, \dfrac{-13}{76}\right)$.   **7.** $(-4, -13)$, (3, 8).

9. $(-4, 2)$, (2, 4).   **11.** (1, 2), (2, 1), $(-1, -2)$, $(-2, -1)$.

15. $F = C = -40$.

Page 16

1. (a) 3; (c) 6; (e) -10.   **3.** (a) 3, -4; (c) -6, 5.

4. (a) 5; (b) 13.

Pages 17, 18

2. (a) 5; (b) 13.   **4.** (a) 10; (b) 17.

6. $\sqrt{5}$, $\sqrt{34}$, $\sqrt{53}$.   **8.** $4\sqrt{5}$, $\sqrt{58}$, $\sqrt{34}$.

18. $x = 4$.   **19.** $y = 6$, $y = -2$.

20. $x^2 + y^2 = 9$.   **22.** $x + y - 2 = 0$.

Page 20

1. $(-2, 3)$, $(1, -1)$.   **3.** (a) $(-2, 6)$; (b) $(6, -1)$.

4. (a) (6, 8); (b) $(-3, 4)$.

5. (a) $(1, -2)$, (3, 2), $(-4, -1)$; $\sqrt{34}$, $\sqrt{130}$, $2\sqrt{37}$.

6. (a) (6, 2).   **8.** $(-2, -6)$.   **9.** 3 : 2.   **10.** (3, 10).

Pages 23, 24

1. (a) 1; (c) 2.9042.   **3.** (a) 135°; (c) 150°.

4. (a) 20°; (c) 144°.   **6.** (a) 0.5794, 30°.

9. $\sqrt{3}$, $-\sqrt{3}$, 0.   **12.** $y - 5 = 2(x - 3)$.

Pages 26, 27

1. 27°.   **8.** (a) 4°; (b) 105°.   **9.** (a) -7.

10. 25°, 33°, 122°.   **12.** 156°, 10°, 15°.   **13.** $x = 9$.

Page 28

1. (a) 13; (b) 15.   **3.** (a) 16; (b) $\frac{1}{2}$.   **5.** $y = 9$, $y = -\frac{13}{3}$.   **8.** $h = 7$.

Page 35

3. $(\sqrt{3}, 1)$, $\left(\dfrac{5\sqrt{2}}{2}, \dfrac{5\sqrt{2}}{2}\right)$, $\left(\dfrac{5\sqrt{2}}{2}, -\dfrac{5\sqrt{2}}{2}\right)$, $(0, 4)$, $\left(\dfrac{-3\sqrt{2}}{2}, \dfrac{-3\sqrt{2}}{2}\right)$,
$(-3.825, 1.170)$, $(-1.545, -4.755)$.

4. $(4\sqrt{2}, 45°)$, $(2, 180°)$, $(4, 210°)$, $(5\sqrt{2}, 315°)$, $(\sqrt{73}, 339°)$.

7. (a) $r \cos \theta = 6$;   (c) $r - 2 \sin \theta = 0$.

8. (a) $x^2 + y^2 = 16$;   (c) $x - 8 = 0$.

Pages 36, 37 (Miscellaneous Exercises)

2. $(2, 16)$.   **3.** $(4\sqrt{2}, 0)$, $(0, 4\sqrt{2})$, $(-4\sqrt{2}, 0)$, $(0, -4\sqrt{2})$.

4. $72°$.   **7.** $39°, 51°$.   **9.** $(5\sqrt{3}, 5)$, $(10 + 5\sqrt{3}, 5)$.

13. $(4, 7)$, $(8, 9)$, $(0, 1)$.   **14.** $(10, 1)$, $(-6, 13)$.   **15.** $x^2 + y^2 = 16$.

Pages 41, 42

1. (a) $5x - 2y - 4 = 0$;   (c) $2x - y - 6 = 0$;   (e) $y - 9 = 0$.

2. (a) $y - 5 = 0$;   (c) $\sqrt{3}x + y - 5 + 2\sqrt{3} = 0$.   **4.** (a) $y = 2x + 1$.

5. (a) $x + 2y - 8 = 0$.   **11.** $(-\frac{5}{2}, \frac{3}{2})$, $3x - y + 9 = 0$.

Pages 44, 45

1. (a) $2x + y - 11 = 0$;   (c) $2x - 3y + 13 = 0$;   (e) $13x + 5y - 1 = 0$.

3. (a) $y = -\frac{3}{5}x + 3$.   **4.** 12.

6. (a) $3x - 5y - 7 = 0$, $3x - 5y + 11 = 0$, $3x + y + 5 = 0$, $3x + y - 13 = 0$;
(b) $3x - 2y - 1 = 0$, $y - 1 = 0$.

10. $4x + y = 0$, $x - 5y + 7 = 0$, $x + y - 1 = 0$.

11. $x + 3y - 13 = 0$, $2x - y - 6 = 0$, $3x - 5y + 1 = 0$.

Pages 47, 48

1. (a) $\frac{5}{4}$, -4, 5.   **2.** $58°$.

3. $x - \sqrt{3}y - 5 = 0$.   **10.** $A = 100 + 6n$.

17. (a) $4x + 7y - 25 = 0$, $7x - 4y + 5 = 0$.

Page 52

2. (a) $-\frac{4}{5}x + \frac{3}{5}y + 3 = 0$, $\omega = 143°$, $p = -3$;

(c) $\dfrac{2}{\sqrt{13}}x + \dfrac{3}{\sqrt{13}}y = 0$, $\omega = 56°$, $p = 0$;

(e) $x - 3 = 0$, $\omega = 0°$, $p = 3$.   **3.** (a) $x + y - 3 = 0$.

4. $7x - 24y + 625 = 0$.   **6.** $8x - 15y + 34 = 0$, $8x - 15y - 34 = 0$, 2, 6.

8. $4x + 3y - 25 = 0$, $3x - 4y + 25 = 0$.

Pages 55, 56

1. (a) $\frac{21}{5}$, above; (b) $-\frac{7}{13}$, below. **4.** $4x - 8y + 21 = 0$.

5. (a) $\frac{11}{10}$. **7.** (a) $7x + 24y + 55 = 0$.

8. $(-1, 4)$, $(3, 2)$. **9.** $\frac{10}{13}\sqrt{65}$, $\frac{5}{2}\sqrt{10}$, $2\sqrt{5}$. **11.** $27x + 21y - 149 = 0$.

12. $5x + 3y + 1 = 0$, $x + 4y - 1 = 0$, $11x - 7y + 7 = 0$, $(-\frac{7}{17}, \frac{6}{17})$.

Pages 59, 60

3. (a) $y = 5x + 8$. **4.** (a) $y = 3x + 12$.

5. $3x + y - 11 = 0$. **8.** $x + 3y + 12 = 0$.

10. $13x - 13y - 29 = 0$, $2x - 8y - 11 = 0$, $9x + 3y - 7 = 0$.

11. $3x - y - 5 = 0$.

Pages 62, 63

7. $r(\cos\theta + \sin\theta) - 6 = 0$. **11.** $\tan\theta = 1$.

14. $x - y + 5\sqrt{2} = 0$. **16.** (a) $r\cos\theta - 3 = 0$.

17. (a) $r\sin\theta - 5 = 0$. **18.** $r\cos\left(\theta - \frac{\pi}{6}\right) - 4 = 0$.

19. $r\cos(\theta - 60°) - 3 = 0$. **22.** $4\sqrt{3}$.

Pages 63, 64, 65 (Miscellaneous Exercises)

2. $x + y = 0$, $x + 2y = 0$. **3.** $(0, -5)$, $53°$.

5. $5x + 2y - 41 = 0$. **7.** $5x - 2y = 0$.

8. $(19, -28)$. **10.** $3x - 8y - 27 = 0$, $3x - 8y - 14 = 0$, $\frac{182}{73}$.

12. $(\frac{1}{4}, \frac{5}{8})$, $(-5, -2)$, $(-11, \frac{35}{2})$, $(-\frac{35}{16}, -\frac{1}{8})$. **16.** $x + 2y - 2 = 0$, $8x + y - 4 = 0$.

17. $x + y - a = 0$, $y = (2 + \sqrt{3})(x - a)$, $y = (2 - \sqrt{3})x + a$.

18. $5x + y + 7 = 0$, $5x + y - 21 = 0$.

19. $x - 3y + 1 = 0$, $3x + y - 17 = 0$. **26.** $(6, 30°)$.

Pages 70, 71

1. (a) $x^2 + y^2 + 2x - 6y + 6 = 0$; (c) $x^2 + y^2 + 6x + 8y = 0$;

(e) $x^2 + y^2 + 2x - 14y + 1 = 0$.

2. (a) $x^2 + y^2 + 8x - 4y = 0$; (c) $x^2 + y^2 - 12x + 10y + 36 = 0$;

(e) $x^2 + y^2 + 2ax - 2ay + a^2 = 0$.

3. (a) $(3, -5)$, 6; (c) $(-2, 6)$, $2\sqrt{10}$;

(e) $(-\frac{5}{2}, \frac{1}{2})$, $\frac{1}{2}\sqrt{-6}$; (g) $(-4, -\frac{5}{3})$, $\frac{13}{3}$.

4. $x^2 + y^2 - 4x - 10y + 11 = 0$. **7.** $(-1, 1)$, $(4, 2)$.

8. (a) $x^2 + y^2 = a^2$; (c) $x^2 + y^2 + Dx = 0$.

Pages 74, 75

1. (a) $x^2 + y^2 - 4x + 2y = 0$; (c) $x^2 + y^2 + 15x - 5y = 0$;

(e) $x^2 + y^2 - 6x - 2y + 5 = 0$; (g) $3x^2 + 3y^2 - 4x - 14y - 4 = 0$.

4. $x^2 + y^2 + 14x + 18y - 39 = 0$.

6. $x^2 + y^2 - 10y = 0$, $x^2 + y^2 - 2x + 4y - 20 = 0$.
8. $x^2 + y^2 - 8x - 4y + 11 = 0$.   **10.** $x^2 + y^2 + 4x + 4y - 2 = 0$.
12. $x^2 + y^2 + 2x - 2y + 1 = 0$, $x^2 + y^2 + 10x - 10y + 25 = 0$.
14. $x^2 + y^2 - 4x - 4y + 4 = 0$.
16. $x^2 + y^2 - 24x - 24y + 144 = 0$, $x^2 + y^2 - 12x + 12y + 36 = 0$,
    $x^2 + y^2 + 8x - 8y + 16 = 0$.

Pages 76, 77

3. $(0, 4)$, $(0, -4)$.   **4.** $(11 \pm 4\sqrt{6})(x^2 + y^2) - 10x + 11 \mp 4\sqrt{6} = 0$.
5. $x^2 + y^2 - 19x - 3y = 0$.   **6.** $7x^2 + 7y^2 - 6x + 25y - 23 = 0$.
7. $6x + 3y + 4 = 0$, None.   **15.** $(-2, -1)$.

Pages 80, 81

3. $2x^2 + 2y^2 = k - 2c^2$, $k = 2c^2$.   **5.** $7x + y = 0$.
7. $x^2 + y^2 - 18x - 12y + 30 = 0$.   **9.** $x^2 + (y + b)^2 = 4a^2$.

Pages 82, 83

1. (a) $r = 5$; (c) $r^2 - 16r \cos\left(\theta - \dfrac{\pi}{4}\right) + 48 = 0$;

   (e) $r^2 - 8r \cos\left(\theta - \dfrac{5\pi}{4}\right) + 12 = 0$; (g) $r + 2a \sin\theta = 0$.

2. (a) $\left(10, \dfrac{3\pi}{2}\right)$, 10; (c) $\left(3, \dfrac{\pi}{4}\right)$, 3; (e) $(4, 0)$, $\sqrt{11}$; (g) $\left(3, \dfrac{\pi}{6}\right)$, 2.

3. (b) $x^2 + y^2 - 7x = 0$; (d) $x^2 + y^2 + 2x + 2\sqrt{3}y = 0$;
   (f) $x^2 + y^2 - 4y - 5 = 0$; (h) $x^2 + y^2 + 5\sqrt{2}x + 5\sqrt{2}y - 11 = 0$.

5. (a) $r = 4$; (c) $r - 2\cos\theta = 0$; (e) $r^2 - 14r \cos\left(\theta - \dfrac{\pi}{6}\right) + 24 = 0$.

6. (a) $r^2 - 10r \cos\left(\theta - \tan^{-1}\tfrac{4}{3}\right) + 5^2 = 5^2$, $(5, \tan^{-1}\tfrac{4}{3})$, 5.

Pages 83, 84 (Miscellaneous Exercises)

1. (a) $x^2 + y^2 + 4x + 4y - 26 = 0$; (c) $x^2 + y^2 - 10x - 8y + 31 = 0$;
   (e) $x^2 + y^2 + 2x + 8y - 8 = 0$; (g) $x^2 + y^2 + 8x + 2y - 68 = 0$.
4. $\sqrt{68}$.   **5.** $2\sqrt{26}$.
7. $x^2 + y^2 - 52x + 4y + 55 = 0$, $x^2 + y^2 + 44x - 24y + 3 = 0$.
13. (b) $4x + 3y - 25 = 0$, $3x - 4y + 25 = 0$.
14. (a) $(6, 60°)$, $(6, -60°)$.

Pages 93, 94

1. (a) $V(0, 0)$, $F(\tfrac{3}{2}, 0)$, l. r. 6, axis $y = 0$, directrix $x + \tfrac{3}{2} = 0$;
   (c) $V(0, 0)$, $F(0, -\tfrac{5}{2})$, l. r. 10, axis $x = 0$, directrix $y - \tfrac{5}{2} = 0$;
   (e) $V(0, 0)$, $F(-\tfrac{5}{4}, 0)$, l. r. 5, axis $y = 0$, directrix $x - \tfrac{5}{4} = 0$;
   (g) $V(0, 0)$, $F(0, \tfrac{9}{8})$, l. r. $\tfrac{9}{2}$, axis $x = 0$, directrix $y + \tfrac{9}{8} = 0$.
2. (a) $y^2 = 12x$; (c) $2y^2 = 25x$; (e) $y^2 = 4ax$; (g) $y^2 = 20x$, $y^2 = -20x$.
3. (a) $(0, 0)$, $(5, 5)$.   **8.** (a) 6; (c) 3, 15.
12. $y^2 = 12x$.   **14.** $7x^2 = 32,000y$.

15. (a) $x^2 - 6x - 2y + 10 = 0$; (c) $y^2 - 12x - 2y + 25 = 0$.
16. (a) $4x^2 - 4xy + y^2 + 10x + 20y - 25 = 0$;
   (c) $x^2 - 2xy + y^2 - 2ax - 2ay + a^2 = 0$.

Pages 99, 100

1. (a) $V(\pm 5, 0)$, $F(\pm 3, 0)$, $e = \frac{3}{5}$, $a = 5$, $b = 4$, $x = \pm \frac{25}{3}$;

   (c) $V(\pm 2, 0)$, $F(\pm \sqrt{3}, 0)$, $e = \dfrac{\sqrt{3}}{2}$, $a = 2$, $b = 1$, $x = \pm \frac{4}{3}\sqrt{3}$;

   (e) $V(\pm 5, 0)$, $F(\pm \frac{5}{2}\sqrt{2}, 0)$, $e = \dfrac{\sqrt{2}}{2}$, $a = 5$, $b = \frac{5}{2}\sqrt{2}$, $x = \pm 5\sqrt{2}$;

   (g) $V(0, \pm \sqrt{3})$, $F(0, \pm 1)$, $e = \dfrac{\sqrt{3}}{3}$, $a = \sqrt{3}$, $b = \sqrt{2}$, $y = \pm 3$.

2. (a) $\dfrac{x^2}{169} + \dfrac{y^2}{105} = 1$; (c) $\dfrac{x^2}{21} + \dfrac{y^2}{25} = 1$; (e) $\dfrac{x^2}{9} + \dfrac{y^2}{36} = 1$.

3. (a) $\dfrac{x^2}{2} + \dfrac{y^2}{3} = 1$.   **4.** $(-6, 3)$, $(2, 9)$.   **7.** $\dfrac{x^2}{169} + \dfrac{y^2}{144} = 1$.

8. $x^2 + y^2 = 73$.   **10.** $x^2 + 4y^2 = a^2$.

12. $a^2\sqrt{a^2 - b^2y^2} = b^4x$.   **13.** 94.5 and 91.3 million miles.

Pages 103, 104, 105

1. (a) $\dfrac{x^2}{36} + \dfrac{y^2}{27} = 1$; (c) $\dfrac{x^2}{16} + \dfrac{y^2}{12} = 1$; (e) $\dfrac{x^2}{64} + \dfrac{y^2}{100} = 1$.

3. $\dfrac{x^2}{16} + \dfrac{y^2}{64} = 1$.   **4.** 12, 4.5, 2.6, 2, 2.6, 4.5, 12.   **8.** (a) $\frac{3}{2}$, $\frac{5}{2}$.

9. (a) $24x^2 + 25y^2 + 48x - 100y - 476 = 0$.

10. (a) $x^2 + 4y^2 - 26x - 8y + 125 = 0$;
   (c) $7x^2 - 4xy + 7y^2 - 76x + 14y + 151 = 0$.

Pages 110, 111

1. (a) $V(\pm 5, 0)$, $F(\pm \sqrt{41}, 0)$, $e = \dfrac{\sqrt{41}}{5}$, l. r. $\frac{32}{5}$, $5y = \pm 4x$;

   (c) $V(\pm 6, 0)$, $F(\pm 2\sqrt{34}, 0)$, $e = \dfrac{\sqrt{34}}{3}$, l. r. $\frac{100}{3}$, $3y = \pm 5x$;

   (e) $V(0, \pm 2\sqrt{2})$, $F(0, \pm 2\sqrt{7})$, $e = \dfrac{\sqrt{14}}{2}$, l. r. $10\sqrt{2}$, $\sqrt{5}y = \pm \sqrt{2}x$;

   (g) $V(0, \pm 2)$, $F(0, \pm 2\sqrt{10})$, $e = \sqrt{10}$, l. r. 36, $3y = \pm x$.

2. (a) $\dfrac{x^2}{36} - \dfrac{y^2}{81} = 1$; (c) $\dfrac{25x^2}{16} - \dfrac{25y^2}{48} = 1$; (e) $\dfrac{x^2}{36} - \dfrac{y^2}{4} = 1$.

3. (a) $x^2 - \dfrac{y^2}{3} = 1$; (c) $\dfrac{x^2}{3} - \dfrac{y^2}{2} = 1$.   **4.** (a) $\dfrac{x^2}{9} - \dfrac{y^2}{16} = 1$.

5. $\dfrac{x^2}{20} + \dfrac{y^2}{15} = 1$.   **7.** $\left(\pm \dfrac{3\sqrt{65}}{13}, \pm \dfrac{4\sqrt{26}}{13} \right)$.

Pages 114, 115, 116

1. (a) $\dfrac{x^2}{9} - \dfrac{y^2}{27} = 1$; (c) $\dfrac{y^2}{36} - \dfrac{x^2}{45} = 1$; (e) $\dfrac{y^2}{16} - \dfrac{x^2}{48} = 1$.

2. (a) $4y^2 - 9x^2 = 36$, $2y = \pm 3x$, $(\pm 2, 0)$, $(0, \pm 3)$, $(\pm \sqrt{13}, 0)$,

$(0, \pm \sqrt{13})$, $x = \pm \dfrac{4\sqrt{13}}{13}$, $y = \pm \dfrac{9\sqrt{13}}{13}$;

(c) $4y^2 - x^2 = 4$, $2y = \pm x$, $(\pm 2, 0)$, $(0, \pm 1)$, $(\pm \sqrt{5}, 0)$,

$(0, \pm \sqrt{5})$, $x = \pm \tfrac{4}{5}\sqrt{5}$, $y = \pm \dfrac{\sqrt{5}}{5}$;

(e) $9y^2 - 4x^2 = 20$, $3y = \pm 2x$, $(\pm \sqrt{5}, 0)$, $(0, \pm \tfrac{2}{3}\sqrt{5})$,

$\left(\pm \dfrac{\sqrt{65}}{3}, 0\right)$, $\left(0, \pm \dfrac{\sqrt{65}}{3}\right)$, $x = \pm \dfrac{3\sqrt{65}}{13}$, $y = \pm \dfrac{4\sqrt{65}}{39}$.

6. (a) $5\sqrt{5} + 4$, $5\sqrt{5} - 4$.

7. (a) $16x^2 - 9y^2 - 192x + 54y + 351 = 0$; (c) $4xy + 3y^2 - 4 = 0$.

8. (a) $x^2 - 2y^2 - 4x + 24y - 62 = 0$;

(c) $7x^2 - 6xy - y^2 + 50x - 26y + 23 = 0$.

Page 119

1. (a) $e = \tfrac{1}{3}$, l. r. 14, $V(\tfrac{21}{2}, 0)$, $V'(\tfrac{21}{4}, \pi)$; (c) $e = 1$, l. r. 8, $V(2, \pi)$;

(e) $e = \tfrac{2}{3}$, l. r. 10, $V(3, 0)$, $V'(15, \pi)$;

(g) $e = 2$, l. r. 16, $V(-8, 0)$, $V'(\tfrac{8}{3}, \pi)$.

2. (a) $r \cos \theta + 21 = 0$; (c) $r \cos \theta + 4 = 0$; (e) $2r \cos \theta - 15 = 0$;

(g) $r \cos \theta + 4 = 0$.

9. $(e^2 - 1)x^2 - y^2 + 2e^2 px + e^2 p^2 = 0$, $(e^2 - 1)x^2 - y^2 - 2e^2 px + e^2 p^2 = 0$.

Page 120 (Miscellaneous Exercises)

2. $4x^2 + 3y^2 = 48$. **3.** $4x^2 - y^2 = 180$.

4. $(22, 4\sqrt{11})$, $(22, -4\sqrt{11})$. **6.** $4x^2 - 5y^2 = 20$.

7. $2x - 5y + 16 = 0$.

Pages 126, 127

1. (a) $(6, 2)$; (c) $(0, -6)$; (e) $(8, 0)$. **3.** $x' - 3y' = 0$.

5. $x'^2 + 4y'^2 = 16$. **8.** $x'^2 + 4y'^2 = 36$

10. $2x'^2 - 3y'^2 = 6$. **12.** (a) $3y' = 2x'^2$. **13.** 78.

15. $F(h \pm \sqrt{a^2 - b^2}, k)$, $V(h \pm a, k)$, $x = h \pm \dfrac{a^2}{\sqrt{a^2 - b^2}}$.

18. $25x^2 + 9y^2 - 250x + 54y + 481 = 0$, $25x'^2 + 9y'^2 = 225$.

20. $x^2 + 2x + 10y - 4 = 0$, $x'^2 + 10y' = 0$.

22. $x^2 - 3y^2 + 10x - 14y + 30 = 0$, $9y'^2 - 3x'^2 = 64$.

Page 131

1. (a) $(4\sqrt{3} + 3, -4 + 3\sqrt{3})$; (c) $\left(\dfrac{-\sqrt{3} - 3}{2}, \dfrac{1 - 3\sqrt{3}}{2}\right)$.

2. (a) $(7\sqrt{2}, -\sqrt{2})$; (c) $(-2\sqrt{2}, -\sqrt{2})$.   5. $y' - 2 = 0$.

7. $4x'^2 + 16y'^2 = 1$.   9. $5x^2 - 4xy + 8y^2 = 36$, $4x'^2 + 9y'^2 = 36$.

11. $x^2 - 6xy + 9y^2 + 12x + 4y - 4 = 0$, $10y'^2 + 4\sqrt{10}x' - 4 = 0$.

Pages 134, 135

1. $2x'^2 + 8y'^2 = 7$.   3. $2x'^2 + 10y'^2 + 7 = 0$.

5. $x'^2 - 4y'^2 = 0$.   7. $3x'^2 - 3y'^2 + 17 = 0$.

Page 137

1. $6x'^2 - 4y'^2 = 3$.   3. $34y'^2 = 5$.

5. $9x'^2 + y'^2 = 25$.   7. $8x'^2 - 9y'^2 = 35$.

Pages 139, 140

1. $4y''^2 - 6x''^2 + 29 = 0$.   3. $5y''^2 - 2x'' = 0$.

5. $2x''^2 + y''^2 = 4$.   7. $y''^2 - 2 = 0$.

9. $12y''^2 - 13x''^2 - 5 = 0$.   11. $5x''^2 + 9y''^2 + \frac{13}{2} = 0$.

13. $17x''^2 - 8y''^2 + 6 = 0$.

15. $x^2 + 4xy + y^2 - 4ax - 4ay + 2a^2 = 0$, $9x''^2 - 3y''^2 - 2a^2 = 0$.

17. $x^2 + 2xy - y^2 - ax - ay = 0$, $4\sqrt{2}(x''^2 - y''^2) = a^2$.

19. $9x^2 - 8xy + 3y^2 + 2x + 26y + 8 = 0$, $x''^2 + 11y''^2 = 140$.

Pages 170, 171

1. $x + 3y - 12 = 0$.   3. $xy = 4$.

5. $b^2x^2 + a^2y^2 = a^2b^2$.   7. $y^2 = 2px$.

9. $25(x - 2)^2 + 9(y + 3)^2 = 225$. 11. $a^2y = x^3$.

13. $\pm x^{\frac{1}{2}} \pm y^{\frac{1}{2}} = a^{\frac{1}{2}}$.   15. $dx - by + bc - ad = 0$, $\dfrac{d}{b}$.

17. $x = \dfrac{a(m^2 - 1)}{m^2 + 1}$, $y = \dfrac{am(m^2 - 1)}{m^2 + 1}$.   21. $x = \dfrac{m - 2}{m}$, $y = 2 - m$.

Pages 172, 173

2. $2\pi a$, $(\pi a, 2a)$.   4. $x = a(\theta - \pi - \sin \theta)$, $y = -a(1 + \cos \theta)$.

9. $x = abt - ct \sin bt$, $y = a - ct \cos bt$.

Pages 187, 188

15. Witch, $r^3 \cos^2 \theta \sin \theta + a^2 r \sin \theta - a^3 = 0$;
    Trisectrix of Maclaurin, $r \cos \theta + a(\cos^2 \theta - 3 \sin^2 \theta) = 0$.

16. Lemniscate, $(x^2 + y^2)^2 = a^2(x^2 - y^2)$;
    Limaçon, $(x^2 + y^2 + bx)^2 = a^2(x^2 + y^2)$.

Pages 189, 190

1. $(8, 30°)$, $(8, 150°)$. **3.** $(2, 0°)$, $(-1, 120°)$, $(-1, 240°)$, and origin.

5. $(\sqrt{2}, 45°)$, $(\sqrt{2}, -45°)$, and origin.

7. $\left(\dfrac{\sqrt{2}}{2}, 30°\right)$, $\left(\dfrac{\sqrt{2}}{2}, -30°\right)$, and origin.

9. $(1, 1)$, $(-1, 1)$.

Pages 196, 197

1. $x - 3y + 18 = 0$, $3x + y - 66 = 0$.
3. $8x - 9y - 5 = 0$, $9x + 8y - 60 = 0$.
5. $5x - 4y - 9 = 0$, $4x + 5y - 40 = 0$.
7. $5x - 6y + 21 = 0$, $6x + 5y - 48 = 0$.
9. $12x - y - 16 = 0$, $x + 12y - 98 = 0$.
11. $5x - y - 3 = 0$, $x + 5y - 11 = 0$.
14. $(2Ax_1 + By_1 + D)x + (Bx_1 + 2Cy_1 + E)y + Dx_1 + Ey_1 + 2F = 0$.
  $(Bx_1 + 2Cy_1 + E)(x - x_1) - (2Ax_1 + By_1 + D)(y - y_1) = 0$.
18. (a) $65°$; (c) $74°$. **20.** $DD' + EE' - 2F - 2F' = 0$.
21. (b) $\left| \dfrac{y_1\sqrt{a^4y_1^2 + b^4x_1^2}}{b^2x_1} \right|$, $\left| \dfrac{\sqrt{b^4x_1^2 + a^4y_1^2}}{a^2} \right|$, $\left| \dfrac{a^2y_1^2}{b^2x_1} \right|$, $\left| \dfrac{b^2x_1}{a^2} \right|$.

Page 200

2. (a) $y = 4x \pm 10$; (b) $x + 4y = \pm\sqrt{70}$. **3.** $y = x - 1$, $y = 2x - 5$.

6. $y = mx - pm - \dfrac{p}{2}m^3$.

9. $x^3 + xy^2 + \dfrac{p}{2}y^2 = 0$. **11.** (b) $y - k = m(x - h) \pm \sqrt{a^2m^2 + b^2}$.

Page 204

1. (a) $y = 2$. **3.** $y = 6x$. **5.** $y = 2x$, $4x - 3y = 0$.

Page 206

1. $y = x - 2$. **3.** $3x - 10y = 25$ (Tangent). **5.** $2x - 3y = 6$.
7. $2y = 3x + 6$ (Tangent). **11.** $(2, -8)$.
9. $x + 3y + 6 = 0$ (Tangent). **13.** $(\frac{3}{2}, 2)$.

Pages 214, 215

1. (a) $y = -2.52x - 1.29$; (b) $y = -2.64x - 1.29$.
3. (a) $y = 2.56x + 9.07$; (b) $y = 2.60x + 8.60$.
5. (a) $l = 0.12w + 7.16$; (b) $l = 0.12w + 7.16$.
7. (a) $R = 0.017C + 5.52$; (b) $R = 0.017C + 5.53$.
9. (a) $P = 0.20C + 54.34$; (b) $P = 0.19C + 54.49$.
11. (a) $l = 0.000013C + 1.00$; (b) $l = 0.000013C + 1.00$.

Pages 218, 219

1. $y = 449x^{-1.92}$.   **3.** $C = 0.0022v^2$.

5. $H = 11.5h^{1.50}$.   **7.** $p = 742v^{-1.41}$.   **9.** $T = a^{1.50}$.

Pages 221, 222

1. $y = 0.00092(10^{0.11x})$.   **3.** $I = 0.41(10^{0.4x})$.   **5.** $P = 0.65(10^{0.021C})$.

7. $N = 61.1(10^{0.084t})$.   **9.** $R = 1540(10^{-0.045t})$.

Pages 225, 226

1. $y = 0.56 + 2x - 0.33x^2$.   **3.** $C = 335.69 - 3.25x + 0.0125x^2$.

5. $F = 53.90 + 1.050h - 0.0055h^2$.   **7.** $v = 2.813 + 0.349x - 0.595x^2$.

9. $y = -3.64 + 6.09x - 1.95x^2 + 0.18x^3$ (Averages).

$y = -3.51 + 5.87x - 1.93x^2 + 0.18x^3$ (Least squares).

11. $x = 0.083xy + 0.48y$ (Averages), $x = 0.089xy + 0.46y$ (Least squares).

Page 231

3. (a) $(x, y, 0)$, $(x, 0, z)$, $(0, y, z)$.   **5.** $\sqrt{y^2 + z^2}$, $\sqrt{x^2 + z^2}$, $\sqrt{x^2 + y^2}$.

6. $\sqrt{x^2 + y^2 + z^2}$.   **14.** $(x, y, -z)$, $(x, -y, z)$, $(-x, y, z)$.

Pages 232, 233

1. (a) 11; (c) 7; (e) $\sqrt{42}$.   **6.** $(x - 2)^2 + (y - 5)^2 + (z + 1)^2 = 9$.

7. $4x + 2y - 4z - 7 = 0$.

Pages 236, 237

1. (a) $\dfrac{4}{9}, -\dfrac{8}{9}, \dfrac{1}{9}$;   (c) $\dfrac{3}{13}, \dfrac{4}{13}, -\dfrac{12}{13}$;   (e) $-\dfrac{3}{\sqrt{14}}, \dfrac{1}{\sqrt{14}}, \dfrac{2}{\sqrt{14}}$.

2. (a) $\frac{3}{7}, \frac{2}{7}, -\frac{6}{7}$;   (b) $\frac{8}{17}, -\frac{12}{17}, \frac{9}{17}$;   (c) $\frac{14}{15}, -\frac{5}{15}, -\frac{2}{15}$.

3. (a) $\dfrac{\sqrt{2}}{2}, \dfrac{1}{2}, \dfrac{1}{2}$;   (c) $-\dfrac{1}{2}, \dfrac{\sqrt{2}}{2}, \dfrac{1}{2}$.   **6.** $\dfrac{\sqrt{3}}{3}, \dfrac{\sqrt{3}}{3}, \dfrac{\sqrt{3}}{3}$.

Pages 240, 241

1. (a) 0; (c) $\dfrac{27}{143}$.   **2.** (a) $\dfrac{20}{33}$; (c) $\dfrac{5\sqrt{38}}{38}$.

4. 79°.   **9.** (a) 1, 2, -2.

Page 242

1. $(-1, 1, 7)$, $(-3, 4, 3)$.   **3.** 2 : 5.   **4.** $9\sqrt{2}, 3, 3\sqrt{19}$.

Pages 244, 245

1. (a) $(2\sqrt{2}, 2\sqrt{2}, 3)$;   (c) $(0, -1, 2)$.

2. (a) $(2\sqrt{2}, 45°, 5)$;   (c) $(2, 60°, 4)$.

3. (a) $(\sqrt{2}, \sqrt{2}, 2\sqrt{3})$;   (c) $(2\sqrt{3}, 6, -4)$.

4. (a) $(3, 180°, 90°)$;   (c) $(6, 45°, 71°)$.

5. (a) $x^2 + y^2 = 4$;   (c) $x^2 + y^2 - 3x = 0$.

6. (a) $x^2 + y^2 + z^2 = 4$;   (c) $x = 6$.

7. (a) $r^2 + z^2 = 9$, $\rho = 3$; (c) $4r^2 + 9z^2 = 36$, $4\rho^2 \sin^2\theta + 9\rho^2 \cos^2\theta = 36$.

Page 246 (Miscellaneous Exercises)

3. $\sqrt{30}$, $\sqrt{26}$.   **5.** $(5, -7, 0)$.

10. $102°$, $64°$, $14°$.   **11.** $\pm\dfrac{2\sqrt{65}}{65}$, $\mp\dfrac{6\sqrt{65}}{65}$, $\mp\dfrac{\sqrt{65}}{13}$.

Pages 251, 252

1. (a) $x + \sqrt{2}y + z - 6 = 0$; (c) $x - y - \sqrt{2}z - 10 = 0$.

2. (a) $2x + 6y + 3z \pm 7 = 0$; (c) $6x - 3y - 2z \pm 21 = 0$;

  (e) $2x - y + 6z \pm 4\sqrt{41} = 0$.

3. (a) $2x + y - 2z - 27 = 0$; (c) $9x + 2y + 6z - 121 = 0$.

4. (a) $-\frac{6}{7}x + \frac{2}{7}y + \frac{3}{7}z - 2 = 0$; $-\frac{6}{7}, \frac{2}{7}, \frac{3}{7}$; 2;]

  (c) $\frac{9}{11}x - \frac{6}{11}y + \frac{2}{11}z - \frac{12}{11} = 0$; $\frac{9}{11}, -\frac{6}{11}, \frac{2}{11}$; $\frac{12}{11}$.   **7.** $(-3, 3, 5)$.

Pages 254, 255

1. (a) $\dfrac{2}{3}$; (b) $-\dfrac{5}{9}$.   **2.** (a) $-\dfrac{16}{3}, -\dfrac{32}{9}$; (b) $\dfrac{16\sqrt{3}}{9}, -\dfrac{8\sqrt{3}}{3}$.

3. (a) $2x - y - 2z - 11 = 0$, $4x - 8y - z - 4 = 0$.

5. (a) $7x + 6y - 6z + 2 = 0$; (c) $4x + y - z - 11 = 0$.

6. $x - y - 2z + 13 = 0$.   **9.** (a) 2.

Page 258

1. (a) $2, 3, 6$; $\dfrac{x}{2} + \dfrac{y}{3} + \dfrac{z}{6} = 1$.

2. (a) $\dfrac{x}{5} + \dfrac{y}{2} + \dfrac{z}{-3} = 1$; (c) $8x - 3y - z - 23 = 0$.

3. $2x + 4y + z - 9 = 0$.   **4.** (a) $3x + 8y + 2z - 33 = 0$.

5. (a) $x - 6y - z + 7 = 0$.   **6.** $3x + 2y - 5z - 6 = 0$.

7. $3x - 2y + z - 3 = 0$. **8.** $x + 2y - 2z + 3 = 0$, $2x - 2y - z + 6 = 0$.

Pages 264, 265

1. (a) $\dfrac{x-3}{-2} = \dfrac{y-1}{2} = \dfrac{z-4}{1}$; $-\dfrac{2}{3}, \dfrac{2}{3}, \dfrac{1}{3}$;

  (c) $\dfrac{x-8}{1} = \dfrac{y}{4} = \dfrac{z+3}{8}$; $\dfrac{1}{9}, \dfrac{4}{9}, \dfrac{8}{9}$;

  (e) $\dfrac{x-5}{3} = \dfrac{y-3}{2} = \dfrac{z-7}{-6}$; $\dfrac{3}{7}, \dfrac{2}{7}, -\dfrac{6}{7}$;

  (g) $\dfrac{x-4}{2} = \dfrac{y-2}{1} = \dfrac{z+6}{-1}$; $\dfrac{\sqrt{6}}{3}, \dfrac{\sqrt{6}}{6}, -\dfrac{\sqrt{6}}{6}$.

2. (a) $\dfrac{x-2}{5} = \dfrac{y-5}{-1} = \dfrac{z+3}{2}.$ **5.** $68°.$

6. (a) $y + 2z = 0,\ x - 2z + 1 = 0,\ x + y + 1 = 0.$

8. (a) $2x + 3y - z - 13 = 0.$ **9.** $14x - 9y + 13z - 21 = 0.$

Page 268

1. (a) $(4, -3, 5).$ **2.** (a) $3x + 4y - 2z = 0.$

4. $x = \tfrac{6}{7}x' + \tfrac{2}{7}y' + \tfrac{3}{7}z',\ y = \tfrac{2}{7}x' + \tfrac{3}{7}y' - \tfrac{6}{7}z',\ z = -\tfrac{3}{7}x' + \tfrac{6}{7}y' + \tfrac{2}{7}z'.$

5. $x'^2 + 2y'^2 + 6z'^2 - 4 = 0.$

Pages 268, 269, 270 (Miscellaneous Exercises)

1. $2x + y - 4 = 0,\ z = 0;\ 3x - z - 6 = 0,\ y = 0;\ 3y - 2z - 12 = 0,\ x = 0.$

5. (a) $11.$ **7.** $(-1, -2, -1).$ **9.** $x - 3y + 1 = 0.$

11. $(\tfrac{5}{7}, -\tfrac{30}{7}, 0),\ (-4, 0, -6),\ (0, -\tfrac{40}{11}, -\tfrac{10}{11}).$ **12.** $29x + y + 49z + 3 = 0.$

13. $x - 2y - 2z + 2 = 0.$ **14.** $3x - 4y - z - 6 = 0.$

Pages 273, 274

1. (a) $x^2 + y^2 + z^2 - 12x - 4y - 6z = 0,\ (0, 0, 0),\ (12, 0, 0),\ (0, 4, 0),\ (0, 0, 6);$

(c) $x^2 + y^2 + z^2 - 8x - 2y + 4z - 4 = 0,\ (4 \pm 2\sqrt{5}, 0, 0),\ (0, 1 \pm \sqrt{5}, 0),$
$(0, 0, 2 \pm 2\sqrt{2}).$

2. (a) $(-4, 2, -3),\ 5;$ (c) $(-5, -2, 3),\ 7.$

3. (a) $x^2 + y^2 + z^2 - 2x - 6y + 4z - 35 = 0;$

(c) $x^2 + y^2 + z^2 - 8x - 2y + 14z - 15 = 0;$

(e) $x^2 + y^2 + z^2 - 3x + 11y - 25z = 0.$

4. (a) $r^2 + z^2 = a^2.$ **5.** (b) $\rho - 2a \cos \phi = 0.$

Pages 285, 286

3. $x^2 + y^2 = 4z.$ **5.** $\dfrac{x^2}{a^2} + \dfrac{y^2}{b^2} + \dfrac{z^2}{a^2} = 1.$

7. $x = e^{\sqrt{y^2 + z^2}}$ **9.** $x^2 + y^2 = z^3.$

Page 288

2. $x^2 + y^2 = a^2,\ x^2 + z^2 = a^2,\ z = y.$ **4.** $x^2 - y^2 = 0,\ x^2 + z^2 = a^2,\ y^2 + z^2 = a^2.$

6. $x^2 + y^2 = 2ax,\ 2ax + z^2 = a^2,\ (a^2 - z^2)^2 + 4a^2y^2 + 4a^2z^2 = 4a^4.$

INDEX

307

$Ax^2 + Bxy + Cy^2 + Dx + Ey + F = 0$ Conic

if $\Delta = \begin{vmatrix} A & B & D \\ B & C & E \\ D & E & F \end{vmatrix} = 0$, 2 st. lines

If $\Delta \neq 0$ & $B = 0$

if $\Delta \neq 0$, and $B^2 - 4ac < 0$ ellipse
$\qquad\qquad\qquad = 0$ parabola
$\qquad\qquad\qquad > 0$ hyperbola

any equation that has no constant term

where x is in the equation are $b^2 - 4ac$

if $\neq 0$, $B = 0$

1 - if
2 - if
3 - if
4 - if

10 - 11